DESCRIPTIVE
PALAEOCLIMATOLOGY

DESCRIPTIVE PALAEOCLIMATOLOGY

EDITED BY

A. E. M. NAIRN

Turner and Newall Fellow

University of Durham

King's College, Newcastle-upon-Tyne

1961

INTERSCIENCE PUBLISHERS INC., NEW YORK

Interscience Publishers Ltd., London

First published 1961 by Interscience Publishers Inc.

All Rights Reserved

Library of Congress Catalog Card Number 61–9063

Interscience Publishers Inc., 250 Fifth Avenue, New York 1, New York

For Great Britain and Northern Ireland:
Interscience Publishers Ltd., 88–90 Chancery Lane, London, W.C.2

Made and Printed in Great Britain by Richard Clay and Company Limited,
Bungay, Suffolk

AUTHORS

G. Y. CRAIG, Department of Geology, University of Edinburgh, Scotland

R. F. FLINT, Department of Geology, Yale University, New Haven, U.S.A.

E. D. GILL, National Museum of Victoria, Melbourne, Australia

ROBERT GREEN, Geology Division, Research Council of Alberta, Edmonton, Canada

L. C. KING, Department of Geology, University of Natal, Durban, S. Africa

T. KOBAYASHI, Department of Geology, University of Tokyo, Japan

R. KRAUSEL, Forschungs-Institut und Natur-Museum Senckenberg, Frankfurt-am-Main, Germany

H. H. LAMB, Meteorological Office, London

A. E. M. NAIRN, Department of Physics, King's College, University of Durham, Newcastle-upon-Tyne

N. D. OPDYKE, Department of Geology, The Rice Institute, Houston, U.S.A.

A. S. ROMER, Museum of Comparative Zoology, Harvard University, Cambridge, U.S.A.

M. SCHWARZBACH, Geological Institute, University of Cologne, Germany

T. SHIKAMA, Geological Institute, Yokohama National University, Japan

N. THORLEY, Department of Physics, King's College, University of Durham, Newcastle-upon-Tyne

F. B. VAN HOUTEN, Department of Geology, Princeton University, New Jersey, U.S.A.

PREFACE

Climate affects all living organisms and so has always, and always will have, an influence on human affairs. The awareness of the importance of climate is apparent in all peoples from the most primitive, where it is cloaked with magic and ritual, to the scientific aura surrounding the weather prophets of the more advanced. One of the main achievements of material civilization has been to insulate mankind from some of the worst effects of climatic variation and engender a feeling, however false, of independence.

It was only natural, therefore, when geology revealed the vast expanse of time, and unearthed bizarre animal forms, and a vastly different geography, to speculate on the climatic conditions of those ages. The harnessing of this intellectual curiosity to detailed observation and investigation has produced the sciences of palaeogeography and palaeoclimatology.

The climates of the past, because of their great general interest, have suffered more than most sciences from preconceived ideas, and the tendency to be used as an adjunct to other work. The biggest steps forward were the recognition that current climate cannot be regarded as 'normal', and the need to consider geographical position as a possible variable. The latter possibility is the centre of the geological controversy over Continental Drift. It is therefore difficult to strike a balance between the amount to which climatic variation can be attributed to latitudinal variation, and to actual climatic fluctuation due primarily to variations in the earth's heat budget.

In this volume, the pooled knowledge of many scientists has gone into the probing of the generally accepted evidence of climate, with results which show the need for caution. These follow a series of outline essays on the climatic histories of large areas. The paucity of information from many parts of the world as well as the size of the areas involved precludes any more detailed examination and prevents any rigid conclusions being drawn.

In assembling this symposium, it is a pleasant duty to acknowledge the full and friendly co-operation given by all the authors, the publishers and Dr. P. Rosbaud, with especial thanks to Mrs. A. Hide for her careful translations of Chapters X and XI. The help and interest of Professor S. K Runcorn in the preparation of this volume is also gratefully acknowledged. Faults there must inevitably be, and for such shortcomings the editor accepts full responsibility. Permission to reproduce various figures, freely granted by the Controller H.M.S.O. (Ch. II, Figs. 1, 4, 9, 10, 11 and 12), by Dr. C. Emiliani (Ch. VII, Figs. 1 and 2), by the Council of the Geological Society of London (Ch. XIII, Figs. 1, 2, 3 and 4) and by Professor Axelrod (Ch. XI, Fig. 6), is gratefully acknowledged.

A. E. M. NAIRN

King's College,
Newcastle-upon-Tyne.
December, 1959.

CONTENTS

I

The Scope of Palaeoclimatology

A. E. M. Nairn

The foundations of the scientific study of the earth's history were laid towards the end of the eighteenth and the beginning of the nineteenth century by Hutton and Smith. Palaeoclimatology, the study of climate through geological time, is therefore a nineteenth century science. The basic material is drawn from geology, but the interpretation of the significance of this material depends on many diverse sciences.

The early history of palaeoclimatology can be divided into two separate phases, the turning point being the appearance of Wegener's theory.[59] Each phase has been characterized by the concentration of attention upon particular problems, with the application of palaeoclimatological data where it could support or oppose a particular theory. With this volume it is hoped that a third phase will be entered, where the study of climate can be divorced from controversial issues until a better understanding of the climates of the past has been attained.

The earlier workers had only a knowledge of the geology of Europe and North America on which to base their climatic theories. Since Pre-Cambrian glaciation in North America had not been recognized, the general view was one of genial climates throughout geological time [35] until the Tertiary when the gradual refrigeration, culminating in the Pleistocene glaciation, began. The occurrence of reef corals, desert sandstones, evaporite and coal deposits in high latitudes was merely evidence that subtropical climates reached to near the poles. The second phase was introduced when climatic information from the southern hemisphere became available.[19, 22] The revelation that glaciation was not uniquely Pleistocene, but was a recurrent phenomenon, necessitated drastic revision of older ideas. It meant that the evidence of warm climates in high latitudes became anomalous, an anomaly for which there were two possible explanations. The first, a simple modification of earlier ideas, supposed that global warm climates existed during certain geological periods only. The second alternative upset implicit assumptions about world geography by invoking large scale relative movements of continental blocks with respect to each other and to the poles. Only relative continental shift was in fact new, for shift of position relative to the poles had previously been proposed.[24, 46] This second alternative formed the basis of the Wegener hypothesis, on which hypothesis Köppen and Wegener's classic work [37] was based (see also Richarz [51]). The controversy over these two diverse interpretations is the characteristic of the second phase of palaeoclimatological history. Köppen and Wegener have been followed in their treatment of world climates by Schwarzbach [54] in Germany, Brooks [7] and

1

Edwards[23] in Britain, Coleman,[12-14] Huntington and Visher[31] and others[5, 53] in America, Kobayashi[36] in Japan and King[34] in South Africa, some supporting one view some the other.

The third phase of palaeoclimatology must therefore be free from prior assumptions about land–sea distribution. A meteorologically acceptable framework is needed to which inferences about past climates can be referred. This information in turn must be acquired by methods whose reliability and whose limitations have been established by the critical examination of the criteria involved. When world cross-sections of the climatic sequences of different areas can be assembled it may prove possible to piece together climatic zones and in so doing palaeoclimatologists will have made a significant contribution to the history of the earth's crust. The first attempts in this direction have already been made.[27, 52, 57] It is with the descriptive part of this scheme, the meteorological framework, the climatic criteria and the regional climatic histories, that this volume is concerned.

Palaeoclimatology, climate in space and time, is four-dimensional. Present climate by eliminating the time dimension leaves a section of climate which can be studied by direct measurement. It is because direct measurement is possible that present climate is important to the palaeoclimatologist in deriving a meteorological basis for the study of past climates. This obvious application of Lyell's *Principle of Uniformity* is not without dangers. Climate is the result of the interplay of many different factors which themselves are subject to, or the result of, other processes, and attention is, therefore, necessarily confined to those factors which are believed to be constant.

Fundamentally, the climate of the earth depends upon the amount of heat received from the sun,[21] or rather upon the balance between the heat received and that radiated back into space. Since the earth is nearly spherical a temperature gradient must exist from the equator to the poles. The existence of a temperature gradient, by producing variations in density, gives rise to a general air and water circulation. The net effect at the surface is an air flow towards the equator and a polewards drift of warm equatorial waters, the return flows being at higher and lower levels respectively. The directions of movement are controlled by the earth's rotation, although modified by the land–sea distribution. This is the basic framework which must persist whatever the fluctuations in the earth's supply of heat.

The variables affecting climate can be divided according to their origin, as either terrestrial or extra-terrestrial. The extra-terrestrial influences can only affect the intensity of solar radiation, the most obvious being a fluctuation in the intensity of solar radiation from the sun itself. Minor climatic changes associated with the sun-spot cycle are known, and climatic cycles of the order of several hundreds of years which have been suggested may be likewise related to solar activity, although the evidence is inconclusive. The small diminution in heat radiation needed to cause a glacial period makes this theory attractive.[2, 3, 31, 60] With present knowledge, nothing definite can be said about possible causes of climatic variation in space, although several have been suggested, ranging from clouds of cosmic dust[45] or nebulosity[55] to gas-filled areas in space.[17] The effect of the varying distance between the earth and the sun from perihelion to aphelion, the basis of Croll's theory of the origin of ice ages,[15,16] is not now thought to be a significant factor in climate.

Turning now to terrestrial influences on climate, the heat balance between the heat received and that radiated back into space depends in part on the albedo of the surface, and in part on the amount and constitution of the atmosphere and the wavelength of the radiation. The albedo in turn is related to the position and extent of the land masses. More heat is reflected from a white, snow-covered surface than from a green-clad area of similar size. Although Harlé and Harlé[28] were led to suggest a much denser atmosphere from a consideration of certain flying reptiles and insects, there is no other evidence that this might have been the case, and their view is not generally accepted. From the point of view of heat retention the constitution of the atmosphere is much more important. This resolves into the question of the amounts of water vapour and carbon dioxide in the atmosphere, and much attention has focused on possible variations in the content of the latter gas;[4,8,30] Chamberlin[9] and Arrhenius[4] in particular assembled many facts and figures in support of their contention that there has been a steady diminution of the amount of carbon dioxide in the atmosphere as more and more carbon has become locked up in limestone and coal deposits at a rate faster than it has become available, and consequently the ability of the atmosphere to retain heat has been diminished. The presence in the atmosphere of large quantities of volcanic dust has not been overlooked as a possible cause of climatic change.

From the climatic point of view the amount of heat supplied through the earth's surface, whether derived from the cooling of the earth, or as a by-product of radio-activity, is regarded as insignificant. Some early theories considered this heat as an important factor in climate.[26,32,44]

The recurrence of glaciations and of tropical climates throughout the geological column suggests that the range of variation was never very great. If, as a reasonable assumption, it can be accepted that the temperature tolerance of organisms in the past has always been similar to that of present-day organisms, the same conclusion will be reached. In this context it must be remembered that the low intensity of illumination, by inhibiting photosynthesis during the long polar night, is an important additional factor in restricting the number of plants capable of growth in high latitudes. For over five hundred million years, covering most of the period of interest to the palaeoclimatologist, it has never been too hot at the poles nor too cold at the equator for life to exist. These are the extremes of the temperature range, as the widespread occurrence of fossils would suggest. The actual distribution of sea-water temperatures may eventually result if it becomes possible to extend ^{18}O isotope studies [38,58] to sedentary fossils.

The remaining variables which affect climate can be classified under the general heading of changes in land–sea distribution. Simpson[56] has shown that although the mean temperature of any climatic zone is almost entirely unaltered by the land–sea distribution, local departures rarely being greater than 5°C, the range of temperature is radically altered. A study of the climatic maps of Eurasia or North America along any line of latitude adequately illustrates this point, and by showing the differences between the western and eastern sides of continents, and monsoon developments, makes clear how, to a certain extent, a large land mass 'generates its own climate'. It is scarcely surprising, therefore, that a group of theories including those of Ramsay[48] and Deeley[20] sought to explain climatic change solely in terms of elevation and depression, while Hull[29] and Chamberlin[10] looked particularly at the possible effects of changes in oceanic circulation. Certainly, there is no lack of evidence of considerable climatic change in the Tertiary floras of North America[11] and Europe,[49] where the predominant changes in land–sea distribution are associated with orogenic movement. The chief merit of the Köppen–Wegener theory,[37] so acceptable to South African geologists,[22,34] is that it avoids the meteorological absurdity of a near equatorial Permo-Carboniferous ice-cap, at a time when subtropical conditions existed in the latitude of Spitzbergen.

The briefest of references to the geological record is sufficient to make it abundantly clear that since land–sea distribution has altered almost continuously throughout geological time, there can be no reason for assuming climatic zones were always as well defined as at the present day. Consequently, there is no reason to assume ice-caps were the normal polar cover, while on the other hand unqualified statements about generally warmer climates are also unjustified.

The climatic framework is, therefore, one of broad latitudinal temperature zonation exercising a general control over wind and water circulation. On the basis of the assumptions made, it is accepted, provisionally, that the ranges of temperatures experienced were not significantly different from the present day[47] and that the amount and constitution of the atmosphere has remained much the same, although it is possible that the carbon dioxide content may have been higher. As no assumption can be made about land–sea distribution the framework bears little resemblance to actual climate. It may be possible to remedy this situation, however, when palaeomagnetic results for the different continents become generally available.

The criteria from which it is possible to infer past climate may be as numerous as Köppen and Wegener[37] suggested: 'Die Zahl der Zeugnisse für das vorzeitliche Klima ist Legion. Im Grunde genommen trägt jedes Gestein jede fossile Flora und Fauna den Stempel des Klimas, zur Entstehungszeit', but those which are unambiguous are comparatively few. Thus the familiar grey-white sandstone may result from cool temperate weathering or be due to decolourization of a bright sediment deposited in a reducing environment[8] or it could represent a second cycle deposit in almost any environment.[7] Even the reduction of the possibilities by petrological examination may still not result in a clear picture of climatic conditions at the time of formation (see in particular Barrell[7]). The recognition of an aeolian sandstone, aided by the wind artifacts such as dreikanters, gives no indication whether the original desert was hot or cold. However, the association of one or more criteria, such as evaporite deposits representing hot desiccating conditions with the dune bedded sandstone, may remove the ambiguity. Advances in the science of pedology will make it possible to obtain more information of climatic importance than the usual range of conclusions drawn from lateritic and bauxitic palaeosols, calcretes and ferricretes. The occurrence of thick limestones for physico-chemical reasons[50] is more likely to be the product of warm rather than cold seas. The ambiguity may sometimes be due to uncertainty about the mode of formation of a certain deposit, and there is no better example of this than the question of the origin of red beds (see Chapter V).

The evidence from rocks may be quite diverse, sun-cracks, rain pittings, salt pseudomorphs, all tend to be associated with warm climates. Tillites and associated varved clays are unequivocal evidence of cold climates, although varved clays by themselves only indicate 'seasonal' variation.

When the habitats of plants and animals are known it is natural to infer similar conditions for their fossilized remains. Where specific identification with living species is possible the inference seems reasonable (see however Mitchell in reference 56), and it probably also holds for closely related species in similar ecological conditions. Interest obviously centres around those plants and animals which live in a restricted environment where climate is the dominant control. Tropical plants and the coral reefs of warm seas are good examples. Many creatures are however tolerant to wide ranges of temperature[56,57] and from these and migratory animals not a great deal is to be learned. Dangerous ground is reached when assumptions are made about groups without living representatives. The rugose corals are commonly considered to have required tropical waters because of the requirements of living hexacoralids. Whether or not this assumption is correct, it is an assumption and as it is by such means that palaeontologists extend the time range over which they can contribute to palaeoclimatology, it is essential to realize this limitation.

For a species which exists within a limited envrionment, it is intuitively accepted that stunted growth is likely under marginal conditions, in contrast to the form under optimum conditions, the outstanding, much-quoted example being the Mesozoic rudistids.[18] Seaonal growth is valuable evidence of climatic variation, of which tree rings[1,33] form the best known example. They also illustrate the dangers of too sweeping generalizations, for Antevs[1] has stated that because sensitivity of climatic periodicity tends to be specific, the absence of rings may indicate lack of response to climatic conditions rather than being an indication of an equatorial climate. The presence of rings is, however, indicative of seasonal variation. Growth variation, described as seasonal, has also been found in corals[25,39-42] and has been used with quite startling effect.[43] In all studies of living organisms the importance of ecology is being increasingly realized, and should be of the greatest help in drawing correct inferences from fossil floras and faunas.

To these criteria modern geophysics adds information on actual temperature, for instance the temperature variation between successive layers of a belemite shell has been interpreted as seasonal growth,[38,58] and on position. The latitude and orientation of land masses in the past can be derived from the study of the permanent magnetism of rocks, a method enhanced by its applicability to unfossiliferous rocks and igneous rocks which may never have been exposed at the surface until long after emplacement (see Chapter VII).

A truer palaeoclimatological synthesis will result from the combination of several lines of evidence. When the floral, faunal, lithological and geophysical evidence all point to the same climate for a given region at a given time, the conclusion is inescapable and the climate of the past becomes a reality. The examination of the geological record everywhere reveals changes of climate on a scale far beyond minor fluctuations, regions now equatorial bear traces of large-scale glaciation and arctic regions show every sign of having been much warmer. Thus palaeoclimatology, by revealing the distribution in space and time of the climates of the past, has an important part to play in the elucidation of the history of the earth's surface, to which end the following pages are dedicated.

References

1. Antevs, E. *Amer. J. Sci.*, **9**, 296 (1925)
2. Arctowski, H. *Amer. J. Sci.*, **37**, 305 (1914)
3. Arctowski, H. *C.R. Acad. Sci., Paris*, **163**, 665 (1916)
4. Arrhenius, S. *Phil. Mag.*, **41**, 237 (1896)
5. Bain, G. W. *Yale sci. Mag.*, **27**, 5 (1953)
6. Barrell, J. *J. Geol.*, **16**, 159, 255, 363 (1908)
7. Brooks, C. E. P. *Climate through the Ages*. 1926. London: Benn
8. Cartwright, L. D. *Bull. Amer. Ass. Petrol. Geol.*, **12**, 85 (1928)
9. Chamberlin, T. C. *J. Geol.*, **7**, 545, 667, 757 (1899)
10. Chamberlin, T. C. *J. Geol.*, **14**, 363 (1906)
11. Chaney, R. W. *Bull. geol. Soc. Amer.*, **51**, 469 (1940)
12. Coleman, A. P. *Amer. J. Sci.*, **1**, 315 (1921)
13. Coleman, A. P. *Amer. J. Sci.*, **9**, 195 (1925)
14. Coleman, A. P. *Ice Ages Recent and Ancient*. 1926. New York: Macmillan
15. Croll, J. *Phil. Mag.*, **28**, 121 (1864)
16. Croll, J. *Climate and Time in their Geological Relations: A Theory of Secular Changes of the Earth's Climate*. 1878. London: Daldy Isbister
17. Culverwell, E. P. *Geol. Mag.*, **32**, 55 (1895)
18. Dacqué, E. *Grundlagen und Methoden der Paläogeographie*. 1915. Jena: Fisher
19. David, T. W. E. *Quart. J. geol. Soc. Lond.*, **52**, 289 (1896)
20. Deeley, R. M. *Geol. Mag.*, **2**, 450 (1915)
21. Dines, W. H. *Quart. J. R. met. Soc.*, **43**, 151 (1917)
22. Du Toit, A. L. *Our Wandering Continents*. 1937. Edinburgh and London: Oliver and Boyd
23. Edwards, W. N. *Advanc. Sci., Lond.*, **12**, 165 (1955)
24. Evans, J. *Geol. Mag.*, **3**, 171 (1866)

25. Faul, H. *Amer. J. Sci.*, **241**, 579 (1943)
26. Faye, C. R. *Acad. Sci., Paris*, **100**, 926 (1885)
27. Gerth, H. *Geol. Rdsch.*, **40**, 84 (1952)
28. Harlé, E. and Harlé, A. *Bull. Soc. géol. Fr.*, **11**, 118 (1911)
29. Hull, E. *Quart. J. geol. Soc. Lond.*, **53**, 107 (1897)
30. Hunt, T. W. *Phil. Mag.*, **26**, 323 (1863)
31. Huntington, E. and Visher, S. S. *Climatic Changes, Their Nature and Causes*. 1922. New Haven: Yale University Press
32. Hutton, F. W. *Phil. Mag.*, **44**, 401 (1872)
33. Hylander, C. J. *Amer. J. Sci.*, **4**, 315 (1922)
34. King, L. C. *Quart. J. geol. Soc. Lond.*, **114**, 47 (1958)
35. Knowlton, F. H. *Bull. geol. Soc. Amer.*, **30**, 499 (1919)
36. Kobayashi, T. *Jap. J. Geol. Geogr.*, **18**, 157 (1942)
37. Köppen, W. and Wegener, A. *Die Klimate der Geologischen Vorzeit*. 1924. Berlin: Borntraeger
38. Lowenstam, H. A. and Epstein, S. *J. Geol.*, **62**, 207 (1954)
39. Ma, T. Y. H. *Proc. imp. Acad. Japan*, **8**, 407 (1933)
40. Ma, T. Y. H., *J. geol. Soc. Japan*, **44**, 931 (1937)
41. Ma, T. Y. H. *Bull. geol. Soc. China*, **17**, 177 (1937)
42. Ma, T. Y. H. *Palaeont. sinica*, **16**, 1 (1937)
43. Ma, T. Y. H. *Research on Past Climate and Continental Drift*, 1–5. 1952. Tawian: Ma
44. Manson, M. *The Evolution of Climate*, [*Amer. Geologist*] (1903)
45. Noelke, F. *Das Problem der Entwicklungsgeschichte unseres Planetensystems*. 1908. Berlin: C. E. P. Brooks: *Climate Through the Ages*. 1926. London: Benn
46. Oldham, R. D. *Geol. Mag.*, **3**, 300 (1886)
47. Ramsay, A. C. *Nature, Lond.*, **22**, 383 (1880)
48. Ramsay, W. *Geol. Mag.*, **61**, 152 (1924)
49. Reid, E. M. and Chandler, M. E. J. *The London Clay Flora*. 1933. British Museum (N.H.)
50. Revelle, R. *J. sediment. Petrol.*, **4**, 103 (1934)
51. Richarz, S. *Z. Dtsch. geol. Ges.*, **74**, 180 (1922)
52. Schove, D. J., Nairn, A. E. M. and Opdyke, N. D. *Geogr. Ann., Stockh.*, **40**, 216 (1958)
53. Schuchert, C. *Amer. J. Sci.*, **1**, 320 (1921)
54. Schwarzbach, M. *Das Klima der Vorzeit*. 1950. Stuttgart: Enke
55. Shapley, H. *J. Geol.*, **29**, 502 (1921)
56. Simpson, G. C. *Proc. roy. Soc.*, B **106**, 299 (1930)
57. Stehli, F. G. *Amer. J. Sci.*, **255**, 607 (1957)
58. Urey, H. C., Lowenstam, H. A., Epstein, S. and McKinney, C. R. *Bull. Geol. Soc. Am.*, **62**, 399 (1951)
59. Wegener, A. *Die Entstehung der Kontinente und Ozeane*, 3rd edn. 1922. Braunschweig: Vieweg
60. Wood, S. V. *Geol. Mag.*, **3**, 385, 442 (1876)

II

Fundamentals of Climate

H. H. Lamb

I. Introductory Survey

I.1 *Prime Importance of Solar Radiation and its Distribution According to Latitude*

The general circulation of the atmosphere and oceans is the mechanism of climate. The heat and energy of the system is supplied by the sun in quantities graded according to latitude and season. It may be surmised that the sun is to some extent a variable star, though it has not been possible to establish any measurable variation of solar energy over the few decades since pyrheliometric measurements at mountain observatories began.[41, 73] The rôle of geography is to modify—within limits—the distribution of heat input, through the different responses of land, sea and ice to incoming radiation and through the mobile reserves of heat stored in the oceans, as well as to channel and constrain the free flow of the winds. The actual braking effect upon the atmosphere is most important at great mountain barriers, especially those arrayed north and south across the mainstreams of the atmospheric circulation.

In considering the climatology of past geological epochs, major differences of geographical setting must be contemplated and certain astronomical 'constants' must be treated as variables.[11,44] Thus, the tilt of the earth's axis relative to its orbit round the sun (the obliquity of the ecliptic), which affects the range of the seasons, is believed to vary at least between 22° and 24½° with a periodicity of the order of 40 000 years—the last maximum having been about 10 000 years ago. The eccentricity of the earth's elliptical orbit also varies between about 0 and 0·07 with a period of some 92 000 years. When the eccentricity is greatest, the intensity of the solar beam reaching the earth must undergo a seasonal range of over 30 per cent. At the present epoch a range of about 7 per cent is experienced, the least solar distance (earth in perihelion) occurring about the December solstice—an arrangement which makes the seasonal range of incoming radiation intensity greater in the southern than in the northern hemisphere. The season in which perihelion falls undergoes a cyclic variation with period 21 000 years (due to precession of the equinoxes and rotation of the elliptical orbit), so that some 10 000 years ago the northern hemisphere had the greater seasonal range.

Variable transmissivity of the earth's atmosphere, due to changes of moisture content, cloudiness, the slight carbon dioxide concentration and volcanic dust, is also thought to affect the intensity of the radiation reaching the earth's surface by several per cent. None of these things, however, seriously affect the permanently greater heating of the earth's equatorial zone than the polar caps, owing to the obliquity of the incident beam in high latitudes: the equator at present receives about 2·5 times as much heat in the course of a year as the poles. This is a near-constant which must be presumed to give the stamp of permanency to a general arrangement of climatic zones more or less parallel with the latitude circles and it is not surprising to find that the most fundamental features of the atmospheric circulation bear an obvious correspondence to this latitudinal arrangement of the energy drive.

It will be seen later (Sections II.1 and 4) that the most prominent feature of the atmospheric circulation considered in depth is the great circumpolar whirl of upper westerly winds, strongest in middle latitudes in either hemisphere (see Figs. 4a and b). These westerlies dominate the scene over extratropical latitudes (and at times even nearer the equator also) from a height of little more than 1 km up to great altitudes in the stratosphere and carry most of the momentum in the atmosphere. They are the mainstream of the atmospheric circulation and play a more fundamental rôle than the depressions and anticyclones familiar on the surface weather map; indeed, the development and maintenance of these surface features largely depend upon the upper westerlies, whose circumpolar form is witness to the planetary basis of the system.

The southern hemisphere, over 80 per cent of whose surface is water, presents us with the nearest observable approach to the conditions of a uniform globe and it is there that the observed pattern of the upper westerlies approximates most closely to the ideal circumpolar ring, though centred

B

rather about the middle of the Antarctic ice region near 82°S, 60°E than at the pole itself (Fig. 4b). In the northern hemisphere the circumpolar ring of planetary westerlies is deformed by strong geographical influences (Fig. 4a): the annual mean pattern is dominated by the winter situation, when gradients are strongest, and shows marked 'cold troughs' towards the down-stream ends of the great continents, attributable to continental winter cooling. The relative warmth of the northern Atlantic and Pacific Oceans produces marked bulges of the isotherms over them and distinct warm ridges in the upper atmospheric circulation with their crests over Alaska and near Spitzbergen; but the ridges and troughs by no means destroy the general circumpolar form of the circulation.

I.2 *The Heat Budget*

The earth's surface receives virtually all its heat from the sun, either directly or after diffusion in the atmosphere. The flow of geothermal heat from the earth's interior is by comparison negligible, and is generally supposed to have been negligible for at least the last 500 million years.

At the present epoch it is estimated that on a world-wide average 43 per cent of the incoming solar radiation reaches the earth's surface—about half of this as a direct beam, the rest after reflections and scattering during passage through the atmosphere—and is absorbed at the surface or partly transmitted to appreciable depths in the oceans.[28, 75] Another 42 per cent is lost by reflection to outer space, especially from cloud-tops, from the ocean surface and from ice and snow: the proportion reflected is a characteristic, known as the albedo, of each type of surface. Only the remaining 15 per cent is directly absorbed in the atmosphere, nearly half of this by ozone in the upper stratosphere and the rest chiefly by the water vapour distributed throughout the lower atmosphere.

By far the greatest portion of the heat absorbed by the atmosphere comes from the earth's surface. Some of the terrestrial radiation is reflected and re-radiated back to the earth, particularly under cloudy skies, but on balance an amount equivalent to about 15 to 20 per cent of the intensity of the incoming solar radiation passes from the earth to the atmosphere. The balance is completed by radiation escaping to space from the earth's surface and from the atmosphere.

An amount of heat estimated at about 20 per cent of the total incident solar radiation is involved in exchanges between earth and atmosphere in the evaporation–condensation cycle. In this way latent heat is converted into sensible heat in the atmosphere sometimes at places far from where the evaporation occurred and even well outside the same latitude zone.[13, 67]

The proportion of the incident solar radiation which is actually used for heating the earth's surface and the atmosphere is greatly affected by events in the atmosphere and by the nature of the surface. The albedo of different kinds of surface varies from about 7 to 20 per cent in the case of black soil, yellow sand or dry bushes to 90 per cent or more in the case of hard frozen snow or ice.[29] Dry land surfaces also heat and cool much more readily than oceans because of the great specific heat of water and the transmission and conduction of heat below the ocean surface, especially in the layers stirred by surface waves.[10, 11]

Losses during transmission tend to be greatest in high latitudes, where the path of the oblique rays through the atmosphere is longest, and wherever

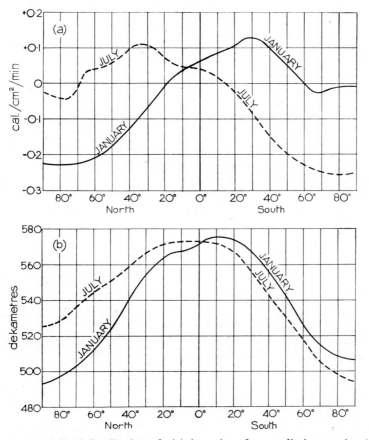

Fig. 1. Latitudinal distribution of: (a) intensity of net radiation receipt (after Simpson); (b) thickness of the layer between the 1000 and 500 mb pressure levels (brief name—1000–500 mb thickness or relative topography)

(*Reproduced by courtesy of the Controller of Her Majesty's Stationery Office, London*)

cloudiness is most extensive, as over the subpolar oceans and in the belt of equatorial rains. The albedo of completely overcast skies is 70 to 80 per cent.[3, 29]

These factors have a general tendency to increase thermal gradients over the earth in middle latitudes, and especially near the limits of the main

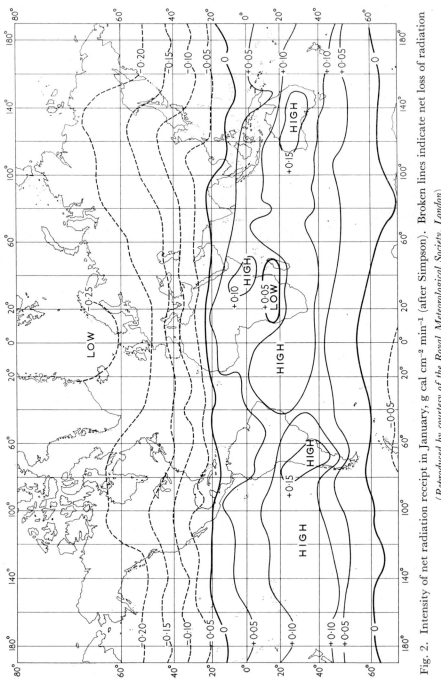

Fig. 2. Intensity of net radiation receipt in January, g cal cm⁻² min⁻¹ (after Simpson). Broken lines indicate net loss of radiation

(Reproduced by courtesy of the Royal Meteorological Society, London)

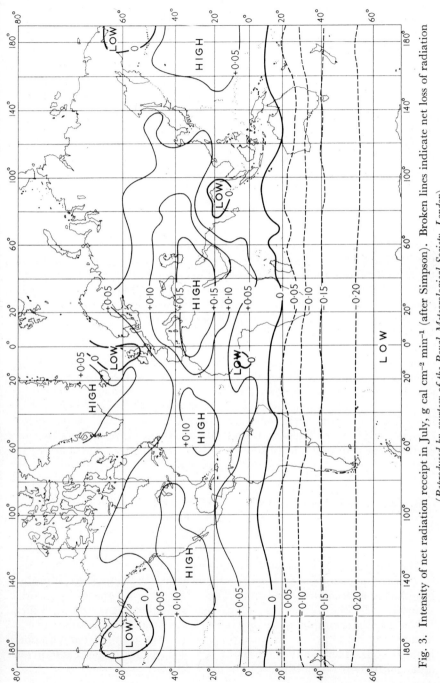

Fig. 3. Intensity of net radiation receipt in July, g cal cm^{-2} min^{-1} (after Simpson). Broken lines indicate net loss of radiation

(Reproduced by courtesy of the Royal Meteorological Society, London)

snow and ice-fields and at the ocean margins, whereas the poleward gradient should be reduced or reversed near the equatorial belt on account of the great cloudiness there.

Curves (Fig. 1a) of the balance between incoming and outgoing radiation at each latitude, following computations by Simpson,[62] show the main gradient in middle latitudes and a particularly strong gradient in the northern summer over a narrow zone near 70°N, where the heated land masses of Asia and America abut upon the Arctic ice. The over-all gradients from equator to pole are, however, very much weaker in summer than in winter in both hemispheres.

In the 24-hour day about the solstice the poles may for a time, under suitably clear skies, receive more radiation *per diem* than anywhere else. The net radiation used for heating the surface is however reduced by the high reflectivity (albedo) of the ice and snow. The January radiation curve (Fig. 1a) should in fact dip rather lower than it does in the Antarctic, since Simpson underestimated the albedo of the ice-cap in summer.

Fig. 1b presents curves of the mean height difference ('thickness') between the 1 000 and 500 mb pressure levels for each latitude. This is a measure of the mean temperature of the lower half of the atmosphere. These curves are complicated by the effect of moisture content on atmospheric density, which is appreciable in the lower latitudes, but they display the expected corre-spondence with the cardinal features of the radiation heating curves in Fig. 1a. Some general smoothing of the thermal gradients in Fig. 1b as against 1a may probably be attributed to the effect of heat transport by the atmosphere.

The world maps of net radiation receipt (incoming *minus* outgoing) in January and July, reproduced in Figs. 2 and 3, are based on Simpson's calculations. They demonstrate a basically zonal distribution, especially in the southern hemisphere, and show that the strongest general gradient lies in middle latitudes, being especially strong in the winter hemisphere. Geography produces important gradients more locally near the coasts of north Africa and southern Australia and Chile in summer. There are local reversals of gradient in the equatorial rainbelt.

II. The Atmosphere in Motion: Surface and Upper Circulations and their Perturbations

II.1 *Establishment of the Basic Current: the Upper Westerlies*

The unequal heating of different portions of the earth's surface creates inequalities of density in the horizontal field in the atmosphere, thereby introducing a circulation tendency. The colder air sinks and spreads hori-zontally under the warmer air, which rises and spreads over the cold air. In this way the atmosphere may be regarded as a heat engine, which conveys heat from warm source to cold sink, performing work against ground friction in the process. The energy of the system is constantly fed by the heat sources, although friction would bring it to rest in a few days.

To understand how the observed circulation pattern arises, suppose the atmosphere momentarily at rest on the surface of the earth with no inequalities of pressure, no geographical complications and uniform heating in each latitude zone.

Owing to the relatively low density of the warmest air, there should be less of the atmosphere below any given altitude and more of the atmosphere at greater heights over the tropics than nearer the poles. This must result in a pressure gradient in the upper air from the warm zone to the cold zone, and this pressure gradient should increase up to the greatest height to which the density gradient continues in the same sense. Similarly, with regard to differences of temperature within any latitude zone, warm areas will appear in the upper atmosphere as ridges of high pressure extending polewards from the tropical zone and cold areas as troughs extending from the polar zone.

These pressure gradients do in fact hold sway above surface levels, as seen from Figs. 4a and b, which present the mean height (topography) of the 500 mb pressure level over the northern and southern hemispheres respectively.

The stronger the pressure gradient, the greater the accelerating force to which the air is subjected. The air does not, however, move directly from high to low pressures. As the earth rotates underneath it, moving air is deflected to the right in the northern and to the left in the southern hemisphere. This leads to an anticlockwise circulation around centres of low pressure in the northern, clockwise in the southern hemisphere. A centrifugal force arises and eventually an equilibrium is achieved with the air moving along the isobars (lines of equal pressure) with a balance between the pressure gradient and other forces acting in opposite directions. This equilibrium is expressed by the gradient wind equation:

$$\frac{1}{\rho}\frac{\partial p}{\partial s} = 2\omega \, . \, V \, . \, \sin \phi \pm \frac{V^2}{r} + A \qquad (1)$$

where ρ = air density, $\partial p/\partial s$ = the pressure gradient measured at right angles to the air's path, ω = angular velocity of the earth's rotation about its axis, ϕ = latitude, V = wind velocity, measured along its path, r = radius of curvature of the air's path, and A stands for other forces, represented chiefly by friction at the ground or due to turbulence.

The term $2\omega \, . \, V \, . \, \sin \phi$ represents the deflection due to earth rotation, the so-called geostrophic or Coriolis acceleration. The term V^2/r represents the centrifugal acceleration which operates against the pressure gradient (positive sign taken) when the air's path is cyclonically curved (about a low pressure region), but is in the same sense as the pressure gradient (negative sign taken) in the case of anticyclonic curvature.

The chief points to note at this stage are that under equilibrium conditions on a reasonably straight path, the V^2/r term being small, the wind moves (along the lines of equal pressure or contours of equal height of the given pressure level as in Figs. 4a and b) at a speed proportional to the pressure gradient; secondly, the equilibrium wind speed for a given pressure

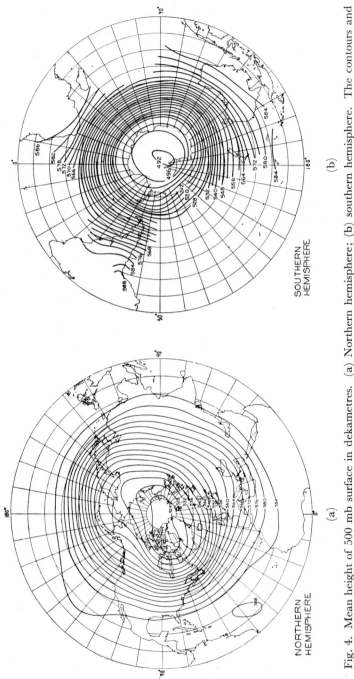

(b)

SOUTHERN
HEMISPHERE

(a)

NORTHERN
HEMISPHERE

Fig. 4. Mean height of 500 mb surface in dekametres. (a) Northern hemisphere; (b) southern hemisphere. The contours and gradients of the 500 mb surface have nearly the same significance as isobars and pressure gradients at about the 5 to 6 km level. Under equilibrium conditions the wind blows along the contours anti-clockwise about the North Polar 'low' and clockwise about the South Polar 'low'.

(Reproduced by courtesy of the Controller of Her Majesty's Stationery Office, London)

gradient is greater the lower the latitude. Hence, if we suppose a uniform gradient from equator to poles the wind should be stronger in lower latitudes, increasing in proportion to cosec ϕ.

Thus the principal observed features of the upper wind circulation follow the pattern of the basic thermal distribution.

The observed form of the general circulation is very far from being the simple overturning of warm air rising in the tropics and spreading to the polar regions aloft, whilst its place is taken at the surface by airstreams spreading equatorwards all the way from the Pole. Nevertheless, the elements of this gravitational circulation (overturning) may be recognized in the broad-scale vertical circulation in the Trade Wind zone and the average circulation over the polar caps (see Fig. 5), as well as in the air motion on either side of strongly developed fronts between unlike airstreams, in coastal sea breezes and in the katabatic drainage of cold air off ice-caps and mountain regions exposed to radiation cooling.

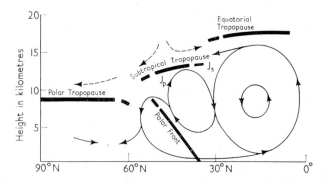

Fig. 5. Mean vertical, meridional circulation. J_p indicates position of the (westerly) polar front jet stream, and J_s indicates position of the (westerly) subtropical jet stream. Note: both jet streams blow approximately at right angles to the meridional plane represented by the paper.

(Reproduced by courtesy of the Royal Meteorological Society, London)

Fig. 5, adapted from Palmén,[49] presents the best picture at present available of the mean circulation in the vertical between the equator and the North Pole. Relative to the westerlies, this is a very slow circulation; it results from wind components occurring where the principal horizontal airstreams are out of equilibrium with the forces acting upon them (i.e. from 'ageostrophic' wind components). The simple 'direct' (or gravitational) circulation originally proposed by Hadley[27] takes place over the tropical zone and on a smaller scale over the polar regions; over middle latitudes the vertical circulation is rather in the 'indirect' (warm air sinking) sense. J_p and J_s mark the positions at which maxima of the west winds in the horizontal field are normally found; J_p (the 'polar front jet stream', normally at 9–10 km) is associated with confluence of rising air in the troposphere below and subsiding air in the stratosphere above, J_s (the 'subtropical jet stream', normally at about 12 km) is associated with confluence between air from north and south. The upper westerlies generally reach a maximum just below the tropopause (the discontinuity of vertical lapse rate of temperature which divides the lower atmosphere, or troposphere, from the stratosphere). Winds exceeding 100 kt are common in both polar front and subtropical jet streams; in the latter, extremes of 200–300 kt are occasionally observed. The stratosphere exists because of the entirely separate source of atmospheric heating (by direct absorption of solar radiation) in the ozone layer higher up. This gives rise to a very different horizontal temperature distribution and the westerlies are in most cases weakened in the stratosphere. Nevertheless, disequilibrium in the westerlies in the layer of maximum wind sets up vertical motion in which the lower stratosphere becomes involved. This vertical motion modifies the sharpness of the discontinuity at the tropopause.

II.2 *The Form and Intensity of the Upper Westerlies: Rossby Waves*

The winter cold troughs over north-east Asia and Quebec–Labrador, which are intense enough to impress themselves on the annual mean pressure distribution (Fig. 4a), are readily understood as a consequence of the maximum cooling of the air towards the downstream end of its passage over the continents.

Orographic disturbance of the flow of the upper west winds past the Rocky mountains and the mountains of Asia should also produce troughs in the regions downstream. The trough over north-eastern Canada is present to some extent throughout the year and the trough near north-east Siberia has its axis over the north-west Pacific in summer.[12] Maintenance of the troughs in the warm season may be largely due to the orographic braking of the circulation, although it happens that the cold waters of Hudsons Bay and the Canadian Arctic and of the Behring Sea and Okhotsk Sea should also tend to induce troughs in the observed regions. Furthermore, the extensive high plateaux of Tibet and Mongolia act as a specially effective heat source in summer, since the ground is strongly heated by solar radiation which has passed through materially less of the earth's atmosphere than elsewhere. These regions are covered by a high-level anticyclone in summer,[1] necessarily marked off by lower pressure over the sea to the east.

Rossby[56-59] assumed that the winds tend to maintain constant absolute vorticity as they move over the rotating earth. This appears to explain the long waves observed in the flow pattern of the upper westerlies. These waves move (generally eastwards) at a speed c which is less than that of the west winds themselves U, defined by the formula

$$c = U - \frac{\beta\lambda^2}{4\pi^2} \qquad (2)$$

where λ is the wavelength and β stands for $d\,(2\omega \cdot \sin \phi)/d\phi$. The wave pattern becomes stationary ($c = 0$) when $U = \beta\lambda^2/4\pi^2$. This expression defines a stationary wavelength which increases with the square root of the general speed of the westerlies: the wavelength is also greater in high latitudes.

Since orography and thermal inequalities in the zone of westerlies repeatedly generate ridges and troughs in certain longitudes, the atmospheric circulation has a tendency to settle down in a persistent pattern whenever the stationary wavelength harmonizes with these preferred wave positions. The régimes thus occurring always break down when the circulation intensity changes with the changing seasons; nevertheless the preferred wavelengths show up in the seasonal and yearly averages.

These Rossby waves are thought to account for the position of a secondary maximum of trough frequency seen on Fig. 4a as a minor trough with NE: SW axis from the Arctic coast of Siberia to the eastern Mediterranean; this is at about the appropriate wavelength downstream from the Canadian cold trough and itself induces a trough in the isotherms over eastern Europe and western Siberia.

Corresponding to circulation intensities prevailing at the present epoch, spacings of four or five troughs in the zone of westerlies around the hemisphere are commonest,[47, 48] with often as few as three troughs in the stronger westerlies of the southern hemisphere; six or even seven troughs may appear at times of weak circulation in the northern hemisphere, especially in the lower latitudes and in summer.

The troughs observed in the mean circulation are therefore of mixed origin, partly thermal, partly orographic and partly produced by preferred wavelengths in the general upper westerly flow. The effect of the passing depressions and anticyclones of the surface weather map, advecting warm and cold air in turn, is to produce a moving train of warm ridges and cold troughs. More or less 'anchored' troughs are likely to appear downstream from the main mountain blocks, and the travelling depressions and anticyclones are steered around these bigger troughs by the mainstream of the upper westerlies. Investigations by Lamb[38] have shown that snow and ice surfaces introduce a stabilizing factor north of about 45°N in winter on account of radiation losses and the great quantities of latent heat required to thaw them. A snow or ice surface of more than about 1 500 miles west–east extent in winter apparently guarantees the existence of a more or less fixed cold trough in the higher latitudes.

The eccentric arrangement of the remarkably circular mean flow around the southern hemisphere, effectively a broad trough in the Indian Ocean sector, is also apparently related to the broadest part of the Antarctic cooling surface and the principal drainage of cold air off the ice-cap in this sector.[40]

Sverdrup[70] pointed out that the great ocean currents of the North Atlantic and North Pacific make an appreciable contribution to the poleward transport of heat in the northern hemisphere which exceeds anything in the southern hemisphere and is without parallel south of 40°S (see Lamb[39]). This weakens the thermal gradients (and hence the circulation intensity) in the atmosphere over the northern hemisphere. For this reason, and because surface friction is much less over water than land, the atmospheric circulation is much stronger over the southern than over the northern hemisphere in the present epoch (*cf.* Figs. 4a and b). The ratio of net westerly momentum (southern to northern hemisphere) averages 1·5. Whether as a consequence of the centrifugal forces associated with these respective circulations or because of the greater heating in the northern hemisphere, the meteorological equator does not precisely coincide with the geographical equator but has an over-all mean position about 4°N. The southern climatic zones are accordingly several degrees nearer the equator than their northern counterparts. This disparity may be subject to minor variations even from century to century.

Variations in the strong southern circulation must have important repercussions on the northern hemisphere.[9, 39, 40, 46] Moreover, as long as the northernmost Atlantic offers the main outlet for Arctic ice drifting south, any general shift of the northern climatic zones towards or away from the equator is likely to be considerably amplified in the Atlantic sector and regions bordering upon it, including most of Europe and eastern North America.

II.3 *Perturbations of the Upper Westerlies and Development of Surface Pressure Systems*

A uniformly zonal circulation could not conceivably persist for any length of time without suffering perturbation, e.g. at mountain ranges, on passing coastlines (due to change of friction), or owing to the unequal heating and cooling of land and sea within each latitude zone.

A purely zonal circulation would be bound to break down at more or less frequent intervals even in the absence of these external disturbing factors, since it would transport no heat away from the tropics towards the polar

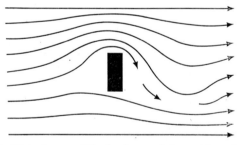

Fig. 6. Disturbance of the basic zonal current by a barrier
(Northern hemisphere)

regions. The temperature difference would go on building up and the circumpolar westerlies would get ever stronger until dynamical effects of the enormous anticyclonic shear at the warm side of the jet stream brought about a breakdown.

Fig. 6 illustrates an idealized case of perturbation due to a physical barrier

B such as a mountain range. There is accelerated flow in the higher latitudes before the barrier and in the lower latitudes downstream. Examples on the grand scale occur at the Rocky Mountains, the Andes and the mountainous plateaux of Asia. The winter cold troughs over the northern continents and warm ridges over the oceans affect the flow similarly.

Each region of strengthened westerly flow means that the air entering this part of the pattern has to be accelerated and, for the time being, moves too slowly for equilibrium: here the pressure gradient force $\partial p/\partial s$ in equation (1) is able to produce a movement of the air across the isobars towards lower pressure, as at *P* in Fig. 7. Where the air emerges, as at *Q*, into regions of weaker pressure gradient it moves too fast for equilibrium with the pressure gradient and develops a component across the isobars towards the higher pressure side. Since the air farther out on either flank of the stream undergoes less acceleration and retardation, with smaller departures from equilibrium, convergence occurs to the left of the confluence and to the right of the exit (delta) from the strongest part of the stream. These effects could build up formidable differences of surface pressure, were it not that at the surface friction ensures that the lower air always moves too slowly for

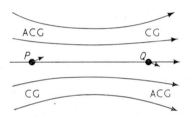

Fig. 7. Regions of convergence and divergence in the mainstream of the upper westerlies associated with surface pressure rise or anticyclogenesis (marked ACG) and surface pressure fall or cyclogenesis (marked CG). The main flow is represented by stream lines corresponding to air passing, under conditions of geostrophic balance, along the isobars. Small arrows at *P* and *Q* show the characteristic departures of flow direction observed in the confluences and diffluences of the mainstream.

equilibrium and has a component across the isobars from high to low pressure, tending to even out the pressure differences.

Attention has long been directed to a degree of unbalance between frictionally produced convergence at the surface and divergence at the level of strongest upper winds as the dynamic explanation of cyclonic development at the surface.[8, 20, 60, 66] More recent work has emphasized how much detail of surface pressure changes can be derived from the main atmospheric thermal pattern and the flow patterns of the upper troposphere;[50, 58, 68] indeed, this is the ultimate basis of most current approaches to numerical weather forecasting using electronic computers.[15, 31, 51]

Various causes combine to prolong the zone of strong winds downstream and give the greater weight to anticyclogenetic effects at the warm side of the stream and cyclogenetic effects at the cold side—i.e. to the developments expected at the exit from the strong stream. The warm side of the jet stream is marked by a belt of generally high pressure (subtropical anticyclones), interrupted more locally by low pressure (cell divisions) corresponding to the confluences in the upper circulation. At the cold side of the jet stream is the subpolar low pressure belt, interrupted at certain longtitudes by anticyclones or ridges associated with the confluences in the upper westerlies.

Factors which determine this preferred arrangement probably include:

(a) Frictional drag from the surrounding air, greatest where decreasing thermal gradients in the lower latitudes give rise to an important shear at the warm side of the jet stream.

(b) Radiation cooling at the cloud tops, which must be greatest at the warm side of the jet stream (emission being proportional to the fourth power of the temperature in °K and moisture content being generally greater the warmer the air). This produces a tendency for sinking and disturbs equilibrium in the horizontal field.

These, and probably other factors, combine to produce a net component of flow across the isobars towards the warm side of the jet stream at the level of maximum wind, compensated by a general poleward component at and near the surface in the same latitude zone. In middle latitudes, therefore, the upper westerlies correspond to prevailing SW or WSW winds at the surface in the northern hemisphere.

A good deal nearer the equator, the extreme fringe of the upper westerly winds is subjected to additional braking from vertical convection cells developing to great heights in the moister unstable air of the equatorial zone. At its maximum development, near the intertropical convergence, this vertical convection is forced up so high that adiabatic cooling of the rising (expanding) air and radiation cooling from the cloud masses formed in it introduce a cold equatorial zone in the high troposphere, with reversed thermal gradients and easterly wind components. Thus highest pressure occurs at some distance north and south of the meteorological equator at all levels up to nearly 20 km.

II.4 *Definition of the Main Zonal Arrangement of the Atmospheric Circulation*

The observed surface pressure and wind distributions are related to the thermally driven upper westerlies.

A. *Surface Pressure Systems and Average Pressure Distributions*

Surface pressure is illustrated by annual mean maps for the northern and southern hemispheres (Figs. 8a and b) and by profiles of mean pressure for January and July (Fig. 9). The latitude scale of the profiles is proportional to sin ϕ to indicate the lesser area of the high latitude zones and thereby the distribution of atmospheric mass. Notice the greater intensity of the southern circulation and the corresponding equatorward shift of the southern subtropical high-pressure belt.

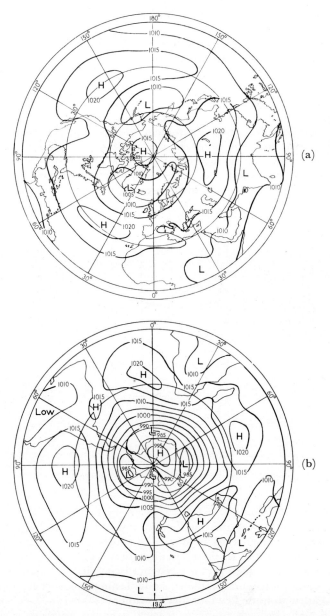

Fig. 8 (a). Annual mean pressure in millibars at sea level (northern hemisphere) for 1900–1940 approx.

(b) Annual mean pressure in millibars at sea level (southern hemisphere) for 1900–1950s approx.

(*Reproduced by courtesy of the Controller of Her Majesty's Stationery Office, London*)

The following zones may be distinguished:

(1) *Relatively High Pressure over the Polar Caps.* This is partly a consequence of the dynamic development of lowest pressure *close to* the cold side of the main upper westerlies. Also the ready accumulation of a dense mass of air in the lowest 1 to 2 km due to very low surface temperatures produces high pressure.

Occasionally, when dynamic anticyclogenesis takes place in association with the jet stream over the northern polar regions or over parts of the northern continents where intensely cold air can collect at the surface, extreme high pressures occur in the anticyclone centres. Computation readily shows that, at the winter temperatures (−25 to −30°C) commonly prevailing in the lowest 2 to 3 km over Siberia, this layer (capped by a temperature inversion which discourages penetration or disturbance by the

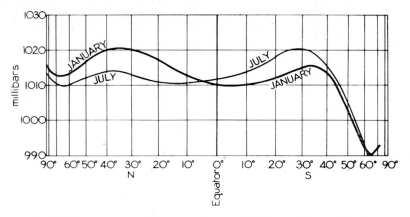

Fig. 9. Mean pressure of the atmosphere at M.S.L. in different latitudes; January and July.
(*Reproduced by courtesy of the Controller of Her Majesty's Stationery Office*)

dynamical processes of the middle and upper troposphere) may contribute by its density as much as 30 mb more to the surface pressure than at temperatures of 0 to +5°C. In these circumstances M.S.L. pressure may rise to over 1 070 mb in a high pressure system surrounded by extensive, and often strong, outblowing winds, capable of establishing a snow cover and persistent cold weather to quite low latitudes in winter.

Such high pressures are never reached over the Antarctic, there being a general deficit of mass south of the strong upper westerlies over the Southern Ocean (Fig. 9): this deficit exceeds 2 per cent (20 mb) when the zone 60–70°S is compared with 60–70°N.

Average pressure is not very high over either polar region, partly because of occasional invasions by travelling depressions developing their energy from the thermal contrast around the polar fringe.

(2) *The Subpolar Low Pressure Belts.* These belts are a feature of the cold side of the jet stream. At the surface they mark the meeting point of prevailing winds of polar origin with the Brave West Winds moving generally polewards in middle latitudes. The individual depressions may develop central pressures as much as 50 to 60 mb below the average for the region, which is characterized by frequent strong winds and gales from various directions. The convergence of airstreams of unlike density gives rise to extensive cloud sheets and frontal rains associated with overrunning by the uplifted warmer air.

The northern hemisphere circulation in this zone is liable to greater persistent anomalies from time to time than the southern, and anticyclones persisting for some weeks in parts of the zone 50–70°N are quite common. These are called *blocking anticyclones*, because they block or reverse for a time the prevailing west winds in middle latitudes; they are particularly common over north-east Siberia, Alaska, northern Greenland and Scandinavia, where their development may often be explained as a dynamical consequence of curvature of the thermal boundary between warm ocean water pushing far to the north and an established snow cover over the continent to the east and south-east.

The apparent weakness of the Iceland depression in Fig. 8a by comparison with the sub-Antarctic system is partly produced by this variability of pattern in the northern hemisphere. Moreover, the lowest pressure in the sub-Arctic zone tends to be transferred to positions over the continents in summer.

(3) *The Subtropical High Pressure Belts.* These are a feature of both hemispheres, principally related to the warm side of the broad belt of upper westerlies, though other factors (Section II.3) require a pressure maximum in subtropical or tropical latitudes at all heights up to nearly 20 km. In consequence, the belt of high pressure is quasi-permanent, producing the steadiness of the Trade Winds. Apart from regions of lower pressure in the cell divisions between the subtropical anticyclones, interruptions of the anticyclone belt do occur when the flow of the main upper westerlies is extremely contorted by large amplitude waves such as lead to blocking anticyclones in the higher latitudes. At such times, persistent low pressure systems (*cold lows*) occur in the subtropical zone south of the blocking anticyclones and the Trade Winds are liable to be disrupted in the sectors affected for periods lasting up to several weeks. Such cold lows are commonest in the Azores–Madeira region and near Hawaii; there is no obvious counterpart in the southern hemisphere, where persistent blocking anticyclones are almost unknown in the belt of westerlies over the ocean. Summer monsoon lows (see Section V) also intrude into the subtropical zone.

The geographical distribution of anticyclones, including the important erratic systems known as blocking anticyclones, is brought out by Figs. 10a,

C

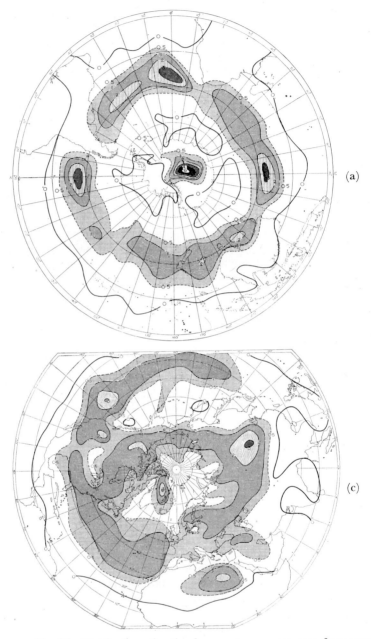

(a)

(c)

Fig. 10. Distribution of anticyclone centres: percentage frequency of
(a) Northern hemisphere, summer; (b) northern hemisphere, winter;
(Reproduced by courtesy of the Controller of

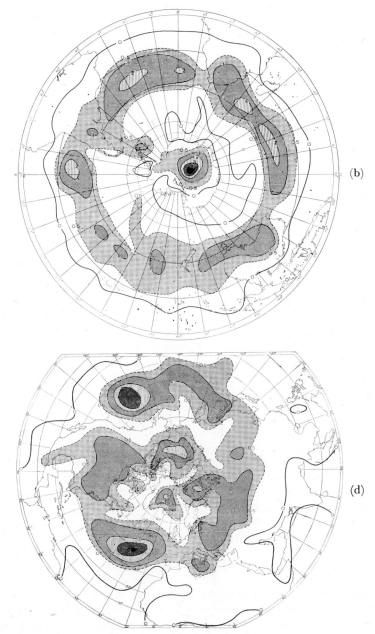

occurrence of a centre within an area of 100 000 km² about any point.
(c) southern hemisphere, summer; (d) southern hemisphere, winter.

Her Majesty's Stationery Office, London)

b, c, d, showing summer and winter frequencies for both hemispheres. Over the southern hemisphere there is a good approach to the ideal arrangement in polar and subtropical zones. The much more complicated pattern over the northern hemisphere leaves no doubt that the rather frequent occurrence of persistent blocking anticyclones is related to the geography of land and sea contrasts.

(4) *The Intertropical Zone or Meteorological Equator.* Between the subtropical anticyclone belts the Trade Winds, mainly from NE and SE in the northern and southern hemispheres respectively, meet in a zone of rather lower pressure. Convergence in this zone is associated with large scale ascent of air giving rise to great cloudiness (through adiabatic expansion leading to temperature fall and condensation) and equatorial rains. The rainfall is characteristically heavier than in the frontal rains of the subpolar depressions because of the greater water content of warm equatorial air and because of the strong vertical lapse rate of temperature which encourages vertical motion.

The intensity of the Trade Winds and of the equatorial rains seems to be related to the intensity of the subtropical anticyclones; hence they ultimately depend upon the prevailing strength of the circumpolar westerlies and the main poleward temperature gradient in either hemisphere.

Riehl[54] has pointed out that the intensity of the Trade Winds probably reacts upon the over-all intensity of the general circulation. The prevailing strength of the Trades is close to the critical speed for smooth or rough sea surface: so small changes in the average strength of the Trades might make a big difference to the amount of evaporation; and, since moisture in the atmosphere represents potential energy (through the latent heat of condensation), this might materially increase or decrease the vigour of the entire atmospheric circulation.

Tropical cyclones (hurricanes, typhoons) are a class of short-lived (3–10 days) disturbances of great violence which develop occasionally in the tropics when special conditions are satisfied.[7] They only form over the oceans and where the zone of intertropical convergence has become far enough displaced from the geographical equator for the Coriolis acceleration (the $2\,\omega\,.\,V\sin\,.\,\phi$ term in equation (1)) to be significant, so that horizontal air movements near the surface feeding the most violent and extensive vertical convection currents are sufficiently deflected over the spinning earth to acquire a cyclonic rotation in approaching the centre. Sea surface temperature must also be high enough (over 27°C) to promote high moisture content in the air. These storms have probably never been appreciably more frequent than now. The warm geological epochs may have had insufficient horizontal temperature contrasts to produce the required degree of vertical instability in the air masses moving equatorwards over the sea, and during the ice ages the zone of great convection (intertropical convergence) probably had too little freedom to wander far from the geographical equator except, perhaps, in the Pacific.

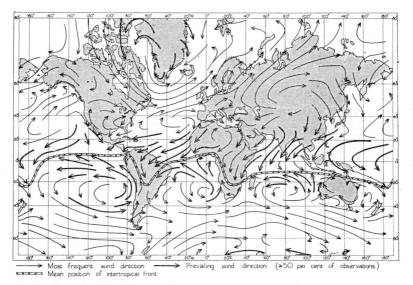

Fig. 11. Prevailing surface winds in January, present epoch.
(Reproduced by courtesy of the Controller of Her Majesty's Stationery Office, London)

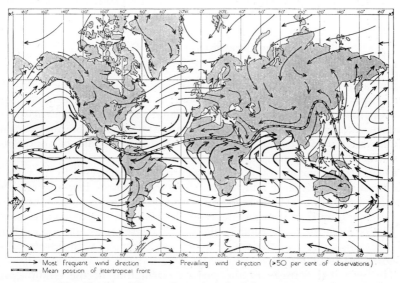

Fig. 12. Prevailing surface winds in July, present epoch.
(Reproduced by courtesy of the Controller of Her Majesty's Stationery Office, London)

B. *Surface Winds*

The prevailing surface winds shown in Figs. 11 and 12 result from the sea-level pressure distribution whose origins have been described; they are: (1) the rather variable *polar easterlies*, (2) the prevailing westerlies in middle latitudes (*Brave West Winds*), and (3) *the Trade Winds* (tropical easterlies).

Between (1) and (2) is a zone of variable winds affected by the centres of the subpolar depressions. Between (2) and (3) is the zone of light winds in the central regions of the subtropical anticyclones (Horse Latitudes). The Trade Winds meet in the Doldrums belt, where directions are again variable and the winds mainly light.

Conservation of total angular momentum in the earth and its atmosphere imposes certain restrictions upon the general atmospheric circulation.[65] As much angular momentum must be restored to the earth by friction in the zones of westerly surface winds as the atmosphere takes from the earth by friction upon the surface easterlies. This condition suggests that, assuming similar average speeds of the easterlies and westerlies, the total areas of surface east-wind and surface west-wind zones should be roughly equal (*cf.* reference 45). The condition is satisfied when the subtropical high pressure belt, dividing the Trade Winds from the westerlies of middle latitudes, has its axis on average just far enough on the equatorward side of latitude 30° to correspond to the additional area of prevailing east winds in the polar zones.

The persistence of the Trades and of the katabatic winds draining cold air off the ice-caps of Antarctica and Greenland is unmatched by other wind systems.

III. The Circulation of the Oceans

The ocean surface is set in motion by the wind stress upon it. To what extent accelerations due to horizontal density gradients in the water also play a part in the circulation is not sure; it appears to be a minor part, though there must be appreciable horizontal motion (lateral drift) of the surface water feeding the vertical overturning at boundaries of water currents of unlike temperature and salinity.[11, 18, 69] Horizontal eddies of appreciable size also occur along such boundaries.

Owing to the earth's rotation, water currents are deflected to the right in the northern hemisphere and to the left in the southern hemisphere. This causes a head of water to be built up in the central regions of the subtropical anticyclones, until an outward force due to this head of water balances the deflecting force due to the earth's rotation. In consequence, the mainstreams of the ocean surface circulation are in general alignment with the prevailing winds.

The principal features of the surface circulation in the Atlantic and Pacific Oceans are gyrals in which the water circulates anticyclonically around centres in the high pressure belts both north and south of the equator. The strongest flow is concentrated in relatively narrow streams moving polewards near the western margins of the oceans.[21, 69]

The general shape of the coastline at the western limit of the Atlantic helps to guide the surface water towards higher latitudes. The nose of South America in 5°S is so shaped and placed as to guide into the northern hemisphere much of the water of the Equatorial Current which should otherwise recurve towards the south: this water helps to feed the Gulf Stream and maintain a general slow meridional overturning of the Atlantic Ocean— surface water moves north from the Sub-Antarctic and, after rounding the respective gyrals in the South and North Atlantic several times, reaches the Arctic by way of the Norwegian Sea and sinks beneath the ice-bearing currents of lesser salinity. There is a return current towards the south in the deeper layers of the ocean. It has been calculated that the water involved in this circulation has an average sojourn of 600 years in the deep Atlantic.

A different geography, particularly in the neighbourhood of the Brazilian coast, would make a great difference to the transport of heat from south to north by the Gulf Stream. The importance of the northernmost arm of this current entering the Norwegian Sea also evidently depends upon the depth of water over the submarine ridge between Iceland, the Faroes and Scotland.

A slight southward shift of the climatic zones in the North and South Atlantic or a weakening of the subtropical anticyclones, such as might occur if the southern circumpolar westerlies were to weaken temporarily, might well shift and weaken the ocean surface currents including the Equatorial Current, more of which would be deflected south along the Brazilian coast from 5°S. Both aspects should weaken the supply of equatorial warm water to the Gulf Stream. The net effects would appear to reinforce the postulated southward expansion of the polar zone in the North Atlantic and contraction of the Antarctic zone—an example of a self-maintaining mechanism of which there are many in the circulation of the atmosphere and oceans.

By contrast with the arrangement of the ocean surface circulation in gyrals favouring meridional transport of heat in the Atlantic and Pacific Oceans, the water currents in the Antarctic Ocean, which completely rings the earth in 60°S, are predominantly circumpolar. This again conforms with the prevailing winds.

IV. Oceanic and Continental Climates

The oceans exert less friction upon the wind than land surfaces and are the main source of the atmospheric water supply. Gales are most prevalent over and near the oceans, and rainfall is heaviest where moisture-bearing winds from the sea are forced up over the first mountain ranges or have vertical convection currents induced in them over the first strongly heated ground. Atmospheric moisture also energizes the circulation wherever horizontal convergence leads to ascent and condensation, liberating latent heat.

In important respects, however, the oceans exercise a moderating influence.

Poleward transport of heat in the ocean water reduces the over-all thermal gradients from which the energy supply of the atmospheric circulation is derived.

The diurnal and seasonal ranges of temperature of the ocean surfaces are also much less than those of dry land at the same latitude. Swampy ground has an intermediate behaviour. The great specific heat of water, partial penetration of solar radiation to some depth, and conduction and convection within the oceans all enter into this.[10] Consequently, the climates of islands are noted for their moderate ranges of temperature and the same applies in only gradually lessening degree as one goes inland from the windward coasts of the continents.

Mountain ranges barring the progress of oceanic winds have the effect of an abrupt wall between maritime and continental climates, the latter having greater extremes of temperature and low rainfall.

Table I. Extent of Snow and Ice Surface

	Area in km²	Equivalent[a] latitude of limit
Southern hemisphere		
Summer minimum	19·6 × 10⁶	68°S
Winter maximum	35 × 10⁶ approx.	60°S
Northern hemisphere		
Summer minimum	12·4 × 10⁶	72°N
Winter maximum[b]	55 to 65 × 10⁶	50°N

[a] i.e. the latitude the limit would have if it were a circular area, centred at the pole.

[b] The winter maximum extent of snow and ice surface over the northern hemisphere is far from being a circular area but bulges far south over the continents occasionally beyond 30°N in Asia. The part south of 45°N is generally impermanent, much of it thin snow easily removed by sunshine or rain accompanying incursions of warm air. A better estimate for the winter maximum of *persistent* snow cover would be about 55°N—equivalent to an area of 46 × 10⁶ km².

The greatest extremes of temperature and, on the whole, the slightest rainfalls in each latitude zone are encountered well towards the downstream end of the great land masses in the sense of the prevailing wind, often surprisingly near the leeward coast. The rainfall gradient is much sharpened across the mountain barriers.

Another aspect of the moderating influence of oceans is seen when we compare the (present) normal seasonal range of extent of snow and ice surface in the northern and southern hemispheres. The figures are given in Table I.

V. Seasonal Effects: Monsoons

The zones of the atmospheric circulation (see Section II.4) move north and south with the seasons. The movement is, however, much less than the seasonal shift of latitude of the zenith sun at noon. The seasonal shift of the sub-Antarctic low pressure belt, the southern subtropical high pressure belt and the southern upper westerlies is about the same as that of the ice limit: 8° of latitude (*cf.* Table I). In the northern hemisphere considerable differences between continental and oceanic sectors complicate the picture: the over-all seasonal range of the subtropical anticyclones is again about 8° of latitude; the prevailing depression tracks move north and south more or less with the general position of the ice limit in each sector. This association emphasizes how the latitudinal position of the strongest thermal gradient is largely controlled by the ice limit at the present epoch.

The intertropical convergence (meteorological equator) has a bigger seasonal movement, between about 5°S and 15°N, a range of 20°. Here the controlling factor is presumably the greater strength of the Trade Winds from the winter hemisphere, in which they also extend over the continental areas.[16,17]

In the summer hemisphere the subtropical high pressure belt and the Trade Wind zone are extensively disturbed by the monsoon depressions over land. '*Monsoon*' is in origin an Arabic word, meaning 'season' and in meteorology usually describes wind and pressure régimes which reverse with the seasons.

The common 'explanation' that continental summer heating produces low pressure by reducing the air density is inadequate, since it ignores dynamical processes; though it has been seen that, in winter, the extreme density of the very cold air in the bottom 1 to 3 km in moderate to high northern latitudes probably does explain the extremity of the highest pressures occurring. Over most of the southern hemisphere the present normal seasonal pressure changes are contrary to the conventional monsoon model: pressure is highest over most of the oceans in the southern hemisphere in winter and over the Antarctic ice it is highest in summer.

Monsoonal low pressure appears to develop over the heated continents in the early part of the warm season in association with waves in the planetary westerlies (*cf.* references 23, 26, 52). In spring the circulation in the upper troposphere over southern North America, over the Sahara and over southwest Asia is confluent in the western part owing to the heating (warm ridges) thrusting north over Mexico, Ethiopia and India respectively. Cyclogenesis (pressure fall) is thereby induced at the warm side of the confluence (*cf.* Fig. 7), i.e. *over the south-western sectors of each of the continents in 20 to 40°N*. The distribution of heated land tends to anchor the low pressure over these sectors of North America, Africa and Asia. A weaker but similar development pattern also becomes active over Indo-China later in the season.

Analogous patterns in the upper circulation at the equatorial fringe of the westerlies are found in the southern spring, and may be held responsible for the development of the lowest pressures near 20°S over South America, South Africa and western Australia.

The onset of the monsoons can be advanced or held back in a given year by favourable or unfavourable phase relationship with the Rossby waves in the westerlies of higher latitudes. The monsoon is therefore affected by deep persistent snow on the plateaux of Asia.[6, 52, 53]

It seems that the lowest pressure in summer monsoon circulations, initially associated with the equatorial fringe of the upper westerlies, should always be found rather towards the western side of any extensive land masses in the strongly heated zone. In accordance with Fig. 7, there should be another area of low average surface pressure in high latitudes in the eastern sector of great continents—as found over North America, Asia, and to some extent over and near the extreme south-east of Australia: the latter low pressure regions are produced by travelling depressions in the subpolar zone commonly deepening or becoming slow-moving in the given sector.

At the height of the northern summer in July and August the upper circulation over South Asia consists of a great easterly airstream from the China Sea to North Africa along the southern fringe of an elongated upper anticyclone, whose centre is associated with the intense heating of the high Tibetan plateau. At times the easterly jet stream over India reaches speeds of over 100 kt. A weaker, but generally easterly, airstream develops in the upper levels over other parts of the tropical zone (e.g. Caribbean and Gulf of Mexico). Waves travel forwards in the upper easterly stream similarly to the waves in the upper westerlies.[33, 55] This arrangement favours cyclonic development according to the same principles operating in the case of the upper westerlies. In extreme cases tropical cyclones are induced over the seas, and in general a sequence of lesser disturbances travels westwards and ultimately feeds into the surface low pressure centres maintained towards the western limits of the principal land masses in the zone.

A special feature which changes the character of the Indian monsoon low is that, in spite of being centred near 30°N, it becomes intense enough to draw in the intertropical convergence and equatorial rains. The equatorial rain system at times also gets drawn into some of the smaller monsoon lows nearer the equator—e.g. over Africa, Australia and the Amazon basin, but not over Arizona and California which are too far north (the North American continent having too little longitudinal extent in the lower latitudes). The rainfall distribution is strongly influenced by orography.

Two factors which may influence the great northward bulge of the meteorological equator over Asia in the northern summer are:

(1) The great mountain land of Tibet and Mongolia which, partly mechanically and partly through its strong heating in summer, diverts the mainstream of the northern westerlies far to the north.

(2) The continual outflow of cold air off the Antarctic ice-cap which produces the main trough and most intense part of the southern hemisphere winter circulation in rather low latitudes in the Indian Ocean sector.

The amplitude of waves introduced into the circumpolar westerlies by direct heating and cooling of the land surfaces is greatest at times when the planetary westerlies are on the whole weak. It has been widely suggested that monsoonal circulations are most strongly developed at such times.

VI. Climatic Variations

VI.1 *Controlling Circumstances and the Lessons of Known Changes in Recent Times*

Changes in the *intensity of insolation*, whether due to possible changes of solar output or to variations in the transparency of the earth's atmosphere or interplanetary space, must alter the mean temperature of the atmosphere. The intensity of the thermal gradients between equator and pole and hence the over-all intensity of the atmospheric circulation would also be changed proportionately.

Increased insolation should, other things being equal, intensify the atmospheric circulation and decreased insolation should weaken it. Changes of this nature corresponding to variations in the prevailing amount of volcanic dust in the atmosphere during the last four or five centuries are strongly suggested by observation. Certainly the intensity of the atmospheric circulation seems to have undergone a general increase from 1800 to about 1930,[72] and there were more frequent great volcanic eruptions in the eighteenth and nineteenth centuries than since—though, of course, actual measurements of the dust in the atmosphere over the requisite period are lacking (see, however, references 19, 30, 72, 73).

Various hints have been found [61, 74, 76] of 11-year, 22-year, 80-year and 400-year cyclic variations of weather phenomena associated with variations of the general circulation of the atmosphere and presumably related to sun-spot cycles. It has been suggested that variations in the ultra-violet intensity in the solar beam and in corpuscular radiation channelled to high latitudes by the earth's magnetic field may be responsible.

The intensity of the solar beam is, however, far from being the only thing controlling the amount of energy which drives the atmospheric circulation. Other factors affect the efficiency with which the incident radiation is used. The most important of these other factors are probably:

(1) *Ice and snow cover.* It has been seen that at the present time the mean seasonal *position of the ice and snow margin* appears to exercise the main control over the strongest thermal gradients (Section V). On account of the high albedo of snow and ice, the intensity as well as the position of the thermal gradient is affected. An increase of incoming solar heat sufficient to melt the polar ice-caps entirely would, therefore, reach a point where the thermal gradients abruptly decreased because of the more uniform albedo of the surface, and the atmospheric circulation should slacken. Brooks[11] has suggested that at the post-glacial climatic optimum about 2000–4000 B.C. there was no permanent ice on the northern polar seas and that an abrupt chilling of the climate and increase of storminess in Europe about 500 B.C. corresponded to the re-establishment of quasipermanent Arctic ice: it can be accepted as certain that there was a marked southward shift of the ice margin and of the depression tracks about the latter date, probably accompanied by general intensification.

(2) Possible *changes in the extent of land and water and in the relief of the land* (*and submarine ridges*) are chiefly important for their likely effects upon the existence, distribution and extent of ice and snow surfaces, secondly for their effect upon the pattern of maximum heating in the lower latitudes, and thirdly for their control of the preferred positions and intensities of waves in the upper westerlies.

(3) *Changes in the main ocean currents* must affect the extent to which oceanic heat transport can introduce thermal ridges and troughs which distort the planetary circulation of the atmosphere and strengthen or weaken it in certain sectors. It is doubtful, however, whether the influence of ocean currents can ever have been much greater than it is at present in the Atlantic sector. In warm epochs with no polar ice, the thermal gradients in the ocean surface would be much weakened, and on account of more uniform salinity a greater proportion of the transport of cold water equatorwards would take place at levels below the surface.

(4) *Changes in the moisture content of the atmosphere and of the prevailing cloudiness* affect the intensity of the atmospheric circulation in ways already referred to, but are hardly likely to affect the main zonal arrangement.

Changes in moisture content and cloudiness are themselves consequences of the general atmospheric circulation[4, 5] and of the available solar energy which drives it. This is one of many delicate internal mechanisms in the earth–atmosphere system, which induce persistence for a time of various atmospheric circulation patterns (self-maintaining mechanisms) or build up long-period oscillations in the atmospheric response to external controls.

Simpson[63, 64] has put forward the theory that a small increase in solar radiation at a time when there was no extensive polar ice might actually initiate an ice age by intensifying the atmospheric circulation and moisture transport and increasing the winter snowfall in high latitudes (especially on mountains and plateaux) more than could be melted in summer. Further increase of solar radiation might suffice to melt even the greatest ice-caps. In colder epochs on the other hand precipitation might be insufficient to sustain an ice-cap against the summer melting. Hence Simpson envisages a cycle in which we should distinguish not only ice ages but both warm and cold types of interglacial epoch, corresponding to the maxima and minima of the supposed solar variation.

VI.2 *Extreme Types of Atmospheric Circulation: Ice Age Type and Warm Epoch Type*

A. *General*

All the various atmospheric responses to changing circumstances discussed in the last section are but variations superimposed upon a single theme, the planetary circulation of the atmosphere and its wave patterns. Observational evidence of the circulation changes over the past 50 to 200 years has been published by Kraus[34–37] and Lamb.[39, 40, 77] Ahlmann[2] and Taulis[71] also provide useful data.

Fanciful constructions which purport to explain the ice age of the Carboniferous epoch as a result of extraordinary elevation of the present equatorial lands (where the evidence of glaciation is found) and extreme distortion of the climatic zones by special guidance of the main ocean currents cannot be accepted without much firmer evidence than has so far been put forward.

Expansion of the polar ice and of the ring of circumpolar westerlies may take place simultaneously in both hemispheres, leading to narrowing of the equatorial (Trade Wind) zone. At other times there may be an equatorward shift in one hemisphere and poleward in the other. Both cases are believed to cause greater changes in the Atlantic than in other sectors, as long as the northern Atlantic provides the sole effective outlet for the Arctic ice (see Figs. 13–16).

It seems likely that at the present epoch a small increase in the available solar radiation would increase the melting of the world's greatest ice-cap in the Antarctic, spreading cold melt-water of low salinity over a wider zone of the Southern Ocean and cooling the sub-Antarctic regions. This would tend to carry the belt of southern westerlies a degree or two nearer the equator and intensify the atmospheric circulation, pushing the meteorological equator a little farther north and increasing the supply of warm equatorial water to the Gulf Stream. In the northern hemisphere, and especially in the North Atlantic, this would reinforce the warming and northward shift of the climatic zones to be expected from milder winters and melting of the ice on the Arctic Ocean.[39] This is probably a fair description of the changes from the culmination of the 'Little Ice Age' around 1800 to 1940. In these 140 years world temperatures rose by between 1 and 2°C. A greater increase of the available solar radiation might ultimately redress the balance somewhat —by warming the sub-Antarctic zone also and allowing the meteorological equator to move nearer the geographical equator again.

The postulated secular shifts of the ice limit on the Southern Ocean and of the mean latitude of the southern westerlies are quite small. A change of one degree of latitude in the present average ice limit would mean a change of about 15 per cent in the total amount of ice on the Southern Ocean. The northward shift since 1800 may amount to rather over 1° in the Southern Ocean, but probably amounts to 2 or 3° in the North Atlantic.[32]

The present geography of the southern hemisphere, with a polar continent and surrounding ocean occupying most of the hemisphere apart from some strongly heated lands in the equatorial and desert zones, is about as favourable as it could be for developing a strong circulation. Hence if the existing displacement of the meteorological equator to 4°N is rightly attributed to the preponderant strength of the southern circulation, this displacement is unlikely to have been greatly exceeded in any other epoch.

Times of weak circulation are accompanied by increased wave number (shorter spacing between successive ridges and troughs) in the upper westerlies. The wave number decreases, however, the higher the latitude in which the westerlies are located. The amplitude of purely thermal ridges and

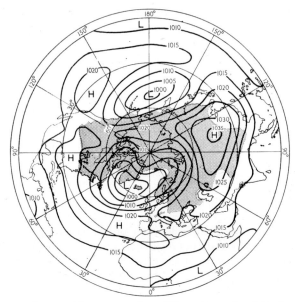

Fig. 13. Average barometric pressure in millibars at sea level in January, present
epoch (1900–39). Ice and snow cover shaded.

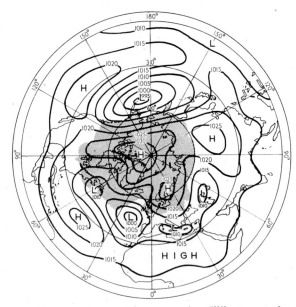

Fig. 14. Supposed average barometric pressure in millibars at sea level in January,
maximum Quaternary glaciation. Ice sheet shaded; winter snow cover would
extend beyond the ice over land especially when northerly wind components prevailed.

troughs associated with land–sea contrasts should also be increased when the general planetary circulation is weak.

Reconstruction of the atmospheric circulation patterns of the remote past is unavoidably speculative, but the maximum phases of the Quaternary ice age were in essence merely an extension of the circumstances of the present day. The pattern of events may with reasonable assurance be outlined as follows.

B. *Ice Age Circulation*

Figs. 13–16 give a tentative reconstruction of the mean surface pressure distribution over the northern hemisphere about the maximum of the Quaternary ice age and show the comparison with the present day.

The main features are the intensified circulation during the ice age, especially in summer, both in the belt of westerlies and in the Trades, and a general displacement of the zonal circulation towards lower latitudes. It is likely that in winter in the higher latitudes over the ice the circulation was weaker than now. The equatorward shift and the expansion of the ice sheet were greatest in the Atlantic sector, there being very little change from present positions in the Pacific.

Rainfall was presumably increased for some time in the lower middle latitudes and subtropics, which were affected by most travelling depressions associated with the upper westerlies. Intensified upper westerlies would cause greater mobility in the subtropical anticyclones, which presumably moved east in an endless sequence punctuated by 'intercellular' fronts and occasional frontal rains—as in the southern hemisphere today. There was less possibility than now of persistent anomalies in the subtropical zone associated with cold lows and less room for development of monsoon depressions, except over Asia. Probably the intense general circulation ensured that persistent anomalies were a rarity in all latitudes except over the ice. The northern part of the extensive summer low-pressure area over Asia (Fig 16) during glacial times would represent a sequence of low pressure systems travelling from west to east near the ice margin, as in winter. There was presumably less change of character of the general circulation from winter to summer than now: in this and other respects the situation probably bore more resemblance to that over the southern hemisphere today.

Flohn's estimates [24, 25] of surface temperatures about the maximum of the Quaternary ice age, partly based on geological and palaeobiological evidence, are more generally accepted than Simpson's suggestion [63, 64] of a general rise of temperature over the rest of the world. According to Flohn the air and ocean temperatures in the tropical zone were about 4°C lower than now, the upper westerlies were 10–15° nearer the equator, and there was an over-all reduction of the amount of moisture in the atmosphere, and hence of precipitation, by about 20 per cent. The principal decrease of precipitation would be in the higher latitudes over the ice, where depression activity would be diminished. With more frequent calms and temperature inversions, the mean annual temperature over central Europe was probably 8–12°C lower

H. H. LAMB

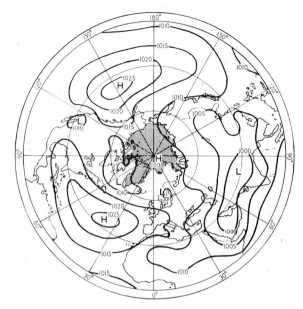

Fig. 15. Average barometric pressure in millibars at sea level in July, present epoch (1900–39). Ice and snow cover shaded.

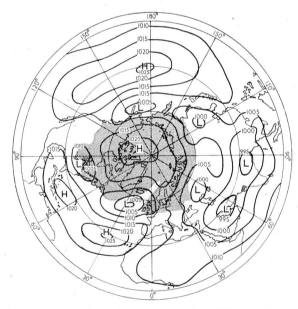

Fig. 16. Supposed average barometric pressure in millibars at sea level in July, maximum Quaternary glaciation. Ice and snow cover shaded.

than today. Over the Arctic Ocean the change would be much smaller than elsewhere. The snow line underwent an appropriate lowering on mountain ranges in the temperate and tropical zones.

The discrepancy between Flohn's evidence and Simpson's suggestions may perhaps be resolved if we accept Flohn's figures as applying to the Atlantic and adjacent sectors north of the equator, where the ice spread farthest. The southern hemisphere generally and most of the Pacific may well have been warmer than now, as required by Simpson, especially during the earlier phases of the ice age. This would increase the atmospheric moisture content and precipitation above present averages and would be consistent with greater snowfall over the ice-caps (cf. Meinardus[43]). It is uncertain how wide the ice-belt would be on the Southern Ocean, since greater outflow from Antarctica would be offset by greater melting especially in the sub-Antarctic zone.[42]

Butzer[14] adduces evidence that the climatic régime associated with the onset of each wave of the Quaternary ice age was chiefly characterized by world-wide increase of precipitation very much as required by Simpson's theory. At the maxima of the ice age the climate appears, however, to have been relatively dry even in the subtropical lands of the Mediterranean and Near East, perhaps because the spread of the ice ultimately lowered the temperature of the world's oceans and of the atmosphere in general.

The distribution of ice in the Quaternary ice age (Figs. 14 and 16) suggests a representation of the form of the ring of upper westerlies which is in reasonable agreement with the proposed surface isobars. Clearly there were broad cold troughs over eastern North America and over Europe which were possibly more pronounced than the one over east Asia. The amplitude of the troughs and ridges was evidently less than now except over the Pacific.

The northern hemisphere circulation at the ice age maximum seems likely to have been centred near 80°N 50°W (cf. ice-covered area on Figs. 14 and 16). The existing circulation over the southern hemisphere has a similar order of eccentricity. The circulation would be strongest in the lower latitudes of the Atlantic sector. Both westerlies and Trade Winds would be confined to narrower zones and nearer the equator than at present, the Trades scarcely extending north of 20–25°N even in summer.

C. Circulation During the Warm (Ice-Free) Epochs of Geological Time

Reconstruction of the general circulation in ice-free epochs is much more speculative than for the ice age. We have no observational evidence to guide us as to the form of the circulation over a hemisphere in the absence of the maximum thermal gradient near the ice margin and without the inertia of ice which the play of the atmospheric circulation cannot readily remove.

A thermal gradient would still exist from equator to pole, and if the available solar radiation were stronger than now the poleward thermal gradient should be stronger than at present, except as regards the zone within 10–15° of latitude on either side of the ice margin.

D

As the ice margin shrank towards the pole, with the depression track and belt of upper westerlies accompanying it, another concentration of thermally driven upper westerly winds accompanied by another depression sequence might be expected to come to prominence in rather low latitudes. Two belts of westerlies, near 25 and 75°N, and an extra zone of middle latitude easterlies, in addition to narrow zones of polar easterlies and Trade Winds, are occasionally observed today over the North Atlantic and North Pacific. Analogous sequences are also suspected over the South Pacific at times when the main depression track moves into very high latitudes.

If the ice were to disappear, the depression sequence in the warmer latitudes would become the main one and would probably be transferred to rather higher latitudes, producing a hemispheric pressure distribution and prevailing winds not greatly different from now (cf. Fleagle's result [22] that the strongest thermal gradient on a uniform earth should be in middle latitudes).

It is possible, however, that the over-all thermal gradient from equator to pole would remain weaker than today after the albedo contrast at the ice margin had disappeared or because of increased moisture content, cloudiness and albedo in low latitudes. In this case, the weakened upper westerlies might be deformed by many ridges and troughs corresponding to differences of surface within each latitude zone; chaotic circulations with generally light and variable surface winds would result. Even the monsoons would probably develop only weak and complex circulations, since a fairly strong planetary circulation or an improbably simple geography appear to be prerequisites of orderly circulation patterns. Convection rains would probably be localized and sporadic, but violent. The total amount of moisture in the atmosphere would be greater than today (because of the warmer ocean surfaces); total precipitation would also be greater and, in spite of haphazard distribution in time, much more uniformly distributed over the world. Great rainfall would be offset by greater evaporation; deserts would occur as now, though possibly in less extreme form.

The seasonal shift north and south of the wind belts would probably be rather greater than at present though hardly exceeding 10–15° of latitude.

VII. Acknowledgment

The author wishes to thank the Director-General of the Meteorological Office, London, for permission to write this contribution to the book.

References

1. *Academia Sinica*, Staff Members of the Meteorological Institute, Peking: *Tellus*, **9**, 432 (1957); **10**, 58 (1958)
2. Ahlmann, H. W. *Geogr. J.*, **112**, 165 (1948)
3. Aldrich, L. B. *Smithson. misc. Coll.*, **69**, No. 10 (1919)
4. Ångström, A. *Geogr. Ann., Stockh.*, **17**, 242 (1935)

5. Arakawa, H. *Tokyo Met. Research Inst. Papers in Met. and Geophys.*, **7**, 1 (1956)
6. Banerji, S. K. *Indian J. Met. Geophys.*, **1**, 4 (1950)
7. Bergeron, T. *Quart. J. R. Met. Soc.*, **80**, 131 (1954)
8. Bjerknes, J. *U.G.G.I.*, *Assoc. Mét.*, *Procès Verb.*, *Edinburgh* 1936, **2**, 106 (1939)
9. Bliss, E. W. *Mem. R. Met. Soc.*, **1**, No. 6, 87 (1926)
10. Brooks, C. E. P. *Met. Mag.*, *Lond.*, **72**, 153 (1937)
11. Brooks, C. E. P. *Climate through the ages*, 2nd edn. 1949. London: Ernest Benn
12. Brooks, C. E. P., Durst, C. S., Carruthers, N., Dewar, D. and Sawyer, J. S. *Met. Off. Lond.*, *Geophys. Mem.*, No. 85 (1950)
13. Budyko, M. I. *Atlas of heat balance.* 1955. Leningrad: Central Geophysical Observatory
14. Butzer, K. W. *Geogr. Ann.*, *Stockh.* **39**, 48 (1957)
15. Charney, J. G. and Eliassen, A. *Tellus*, **1**, 38 (1949)
16. Crowe, P. R. *Trans. Inst. Brit. Geogr.*, **1949**, No. 15, 37 (1951)
17. Crowe, P. R. *Trans. Inst. Brit. Geogr.*, **1950**, No. 16, 23 (1952)
18. Deacon, G. E. R. *Quart. J. R. Met. Soc.*, **71**, 11 (1945)
19. Defant, A. *Geogr. Ann.*, *Stockh.*, **6**, 13 (1924)
20. Dines, W. H. *J. Scot. met. Soc.*, **16**, 304 (1914)
21. Eady, E. T. 'Circulation of the atmosphere and oceans' in *The Planet Earth.* 1957. London and New York: Pergamon Press
22. Fleagle, R. G. *Quart. J. R. Met. Soc.*, **83**, 1 (1957)
23. Flohn, H. *Ber. dtsch Wetterdienstes U.S. Zone*, **18** (1950)
24. Flohn, H. *Geol. Rdsch.*, **40**, 153 (1952)
25. Flohn, H. *Erdkunde*, **7**, 266 (1953)
26. Flohn, H. *Ber. dtsch. Wetterdienstes U.S. Zone*, **22** (1955)
27. Hadley, G. *Phil. Trans.*, **39**, 58 (1735)
28. Haurwitz, B. and Austin, J. M. *Climatology.* 1944. New York: McGraw-Hill
29. Houghton, H. G. *J. Met.*, **11**, 1 (1954)
30. Humphreys, W. J. *Physics of the air*, 3rd edn. 1940. New York: McGraw-Hill
31. Knighting, E. *Met. Mag.*, **85**, 176 (1956)
32. Koch, L. *Medd. om Grønland*, **130**, No. 3 (1945)
33. Koteswaram, P. and George, C. A. *Indian J. Met. Geophys.*, **9**, 9 (1958)
34. Kraus, E. B. *Quart. J. R. Met. Soc.*, **80**, 591 (1954)
35. Kraus, E. B. *Quart. J. R. Met. Soc.*, **81**, 198 (1955)
36. Kraus, E. B. *Quart. J. R. Met. Soc.*, **81**, 430 (1955)
37. Kraus, E. B. *Quart. J. R. Met. Soc.*, **82**, 289 (1956)
38. Lamb, H. H. *Quart. J. R. Met. Soc.*, **81**, 172 (1955)
39. Lamb, H. H. *Met. Mag.*, **87**, 364 (1958)
40. Lamb, H. H. *Quart. J. R. Met. Soc.*, **85**, 1 (1959)
41. MacPherson, H. G. *Mon. Weath. Rev.*, Supplt. No. 39, 98 (1940)
42. Manley, G. *Quart. J. R. Met. Soc.*, **72**, 307 (1946)
43. Meinardus, W. *Nachr. Ges. Wiss. Göttingen*, 137 (1928)
44. Milankovitch, M. 'Mathematische Klimalehre und astronomische Theorie der Klimaschwankungen' in Köppen & Geiger's *Handbuch der Klimatologie*, I. A., 1930. Berlin: Borntraeger
45. Mintz, Y. *Univ. Calif.*, *Dept. Met.*, *Sci. Rep. No.* 3 (1953)
46. Montgomery, R. B. *Mon. Weath. Rev.*, Supplt. No. 39, 1 (1940)
47. Namias, J. *J. Met.*, **7**, 130 (1950)
48. Namias, J. *Mon. Weath. Rev.*, *Wash.*, **83**, 155 (1955)
49. Palmén, E. *Quart. J. R. Met. Soc.*, **77**, 337 (1951)
50. Petterssen, Sv. *Cent. Proc. R. met. Soc.*, 120 (1950)

51. Phillips, N. A. *Quart. J. R. Met. Soc.*, **82**, 123 (1956)
52. Ramage, C. S. *J. Met.*, **9**, 403 (1952)
53. Ramaswamy, C. *Tellus*, **8**, 26 (1956)
54. Riehl, H. *Weather*, **9**, 335 (1954)
55. Riehl, H. *Tropical Meteorology.* 1954. New York: McGraw-Hill
56. Rossby, C. G. *J. Mar. Res.*, **2**, 38 (1939)
57. Rossby, C. G. *R. Met. Soc., Supplt. to the Quart. J.*, **66**, 68 (1940)
58. Rossby, C. G. 'The scientific basis of modern meteorology' in *U.S. Yearbook of Agriculture*, **1941**, 599 (1941)
59. Rossby, C. G. 'The scientific basis of modern meteorology' in *Handbook of Meteorology* (Berry, Bollay and Beers), Section VII, p. 502–529. 1945. New York: McGraw-Hill
60. Scherhag, R. *Met. Z.*, **51**, 129 (1934)
61. Scherhag, R. *Dtsch hydrogr. Z.*, **3**, 108 (1950)
62. Simpson, G. C. *Mem. R. Met. Soc.*, **3**, No. 23 (1928)
63. Simpson, G. C. *Quart. J. R. Met. Soc.*, **60**, 375 (1934)
64. Simpson, G. C. *Quart. J. R. Met. Soc.*, **83**, 459 (1957)
65. Starr, V. P. *J. Met.*, **5**, 39 (1948)
66. Sutcliffe, R. C. *Quart. J. R. Met. Soc.*, **65**, 519 (1939)
67. Sutcliffe, R. C. *Quart. J. R. Met. Soc.*, **82**, 385 (1956)
68. Sutcliffe, R. C. and Forsdyke, A. G. *Quart. J. R. Met. Soc.*, **76**, 189 (1950)
69. Sverdrup, H. U. *Oceanography for meteorologists.* 1942. New York: Prentice Hall
70. Sverdrup, H. U. *J. Mar. Res.*, **14**, 501 (1955)
71. Taulis, E. *Matér. Étude Calam.*, **33**, 3 (1934)
72. Wagner, A. *Klima-änderungen und Klimaschwankungen.* 1940. Braunschweig: Vieweg
73. Wexler, H. *Tellus*, **8**, 480 (1956)
74. Willet, H. C. *Mon. Weath. Rev.*, Supplt. No. 39, 126 (1940)
75. Willett, H. C. *Descriptive Meteorology.* 1944. New York: Academic Press
76. Willett, H. C. *J. Met.*, **6**, 34 (1949)
77. Lamb, H. H. and Johnson, A. I. *Geogr. Ann., Stockh.*, **41**, 94 (1959)

III

The Palaeoclimatological Significance of Desert Sandstone

N. D. Opdyke*

I. Introduction

Arid or semi-arid areas form an integral part of the climatic pattern of the continents, and deserts are present on every continent with the exception of Europe and Antarctica. High latitude deserts extend as far north as 45° (Gobi) and the most important of the earth's deserts exist along the Tropic of Cancer and the Tropic of Capricorn and in some instances extend almost to the equator, e.g. Atacama. These arid regions account for a considerable percentage of the total continental area; according to Shantz,[38] the semi-arid regions of the earth cover an area of 8 202 000 square miles, arid regions account for 8 418 000 square miles, and areas of extreme aridity cover 2 244 000 square miles or altogether 36 per cent of the total land area of 51 970 000 square miles. It may be expected, therefore, that sediments originating in an arid climate could form a significant portion of the sedimentary column.

II. Features of Arid Regions

II.1 *Arid Region Sediments*

Sediments formed in an arid climate are of several types. The most common of these are the result of sporadic aqueous action depositing thicknesses of conglomerates, sandstones and shales in alluvial fans, particularly in areas of interior drainage. Evaporites are the second major category of arid climate sediment. Chemically precipitated sediments containing such

* Department of Geology, The Rice Institute, Houston, Texas.

minerals as calcite, halite, sodium carbonate, sodium sulphate, potassium carbonate and borates are often precipitated in salt pans or salt lakes in areas of interior drainage. Of lesser importance are dark brown and black incrustations of secondary origin called 'desert varnish', which are seen on some outcrops in arid regions. These coatings consist of iron and manganese oxides deposited from evaporating moisture which has risen to the surface by capillary action. Another type of minor deposit caused by evaporation in arid and semi-arid regions is 'Caliche' which is a whitish limy deposit found where rising lime-bearing ground-water drawn up by capillary action has evaporated depositing its mineral content within the soil. Caliche deposits may range from mere films to layers several feet in thickness.[31]

Another kind of evaporite deposit which is very important in the geological column is one which is evaporated directly from sea water. Evaporite basins form in arms of the sea where circulation of sea water is impeded, which leads to the precipitation of gypsum, anhydrite, halite and potassium salts. Optimum conditions for the evaporation of sea water prevail in an arid climate where high temperature is combined with low precipitation so that evaporation will exceed inflow of water both from the ocean and the land. Modern evaporites are being deposited directly from sea water under natural conditions in only two areas of the world, one in the Bocana de Virrila near Bayovar, Peru,[27] which is bordered on the landward side by the Sechura desert and the other in the Gulf of Kara-Boghaz along the eastern side of the Caspian sea, Russia, which is backed on the landward side by the Kara-Kum desert.

The remaining major category of arid sediment is transported and deposited by aeolian action, the sand-size sediments being piled into sand dunes and the finer fraction deposited as loess, sometimes far from the confines of the desert. This type of sediment will be treated fully in Section III.

II.2 *Erosion Features of Arid Regions*

Erosion features produced under arid conditions are also sometimes preserved in the geological column. Aqueous erosion forms in arid areas differ considerably from erosion in more humid areas because the cover of vegetation is sparse and the rainfall sporadic and violent, which causes the desert landscape to be more intensely sculptured. Arroyes or Waddis with V-shaped profiles are incised in the landscape instead of valleys with gently sloping profiles which develop in the more humid climates. Desert erosion forms of this type have actually been preserved in the geological column. The most notable example is the exhumed Triassic desert landscape in Charnwood Forest, England.

Aeolian erosion is a common feature of some arid areas which are subjected to strong winds and have a supply of sand grains. Sand is transported by the wind principally by the process of saltation which moves the sand along in a low cloud usually only a few feet in height, and anything in the path of this cloud is subjected to abrasion which undercuts rock ledges, posts, etc.

Cobbles or pebbles which lie on desert surfaces are often faceted and polished by this sand blasting on the side of the pebble facing the prevailing wind; in some cases more than one side of the pebble is faceted due to the prevailing wind changing direction at different seasons of the year or to a change in position of the pebble. Shapes formed in this way are called ventifacts and are sometimes preserved in the geological column (e.g. Permo-Trias of Great Britain).

III. Aeolian Sands

One of the major sediments accumulated in desert areas and the one commonly associated with deserts is aeolian sand, and it is by the presence of such deposits that the ancient deserts of the world have been recognized. Wind artifacts, erosion features and evaporites are confirmatory evidence.

In desert areas the wind has ample opportunity to act upon and redistribute any sediment that is available on the desert surface. The sand fraction is piled into dunes and the finer fraction, except for small amounts trapped in salt pans, is transported and deposited as loess far beyond the desert confines. The dust-laden winds blowing from the Sahara, the Harmattan and Sirocco are acting this way at the present time.

The wind is a highly selective transporting agent, and consequently dune sandstones are usually very well sorted as can be seen from the size analysis (Fig. 1a) and from the sorting coefficient (Table I). For comparison, cumulative curves from the size analysis of several other sandstone types are shown in Fig. 1b, and their sorting coefficients in Table I. The measures of kurtosis and skewness, however, do not show marked differences from those of well sorted aqueous sandstones.

Table I. Sorting Coefficient (Trask)

	Number of analysis	Mean	Range	Locality	Reference
Beach sand	20	1·15	1·08–1·21	Texas Gulf coast	Strong, 1959
River sand	20	1·34	1·14–1·86	Texas Gulf coast	Strong, 1959
Dune sand	20	1·18	1·11–1·29	Texas Gulf coast	Opdyke, 1959

It can be seen from the figures given above that it is impossible to distinguish aeolian from beach sand on the basis of their sorting. However, the cross-stratifications in dunes dip very steeply (up to 33°) while those of a beach rarely exceed 12°, this permits differentiation of the two environments to be made on outcrop.

Grain shape and surface texture are characteristic. Millet seed sand grains are typical. They show very high sphericity and roundness values due to their mode of transport which tends to round off the individual grains while they are being saltated. Frosted surfaces are common in aeolian sands and sandstones due either to impact between the grains or to an unknown type of chemical action. Micaceous material is either present in very small amounts or absent because of its tendency to split along cleavage planes causing it to be readily carried away by the wind.

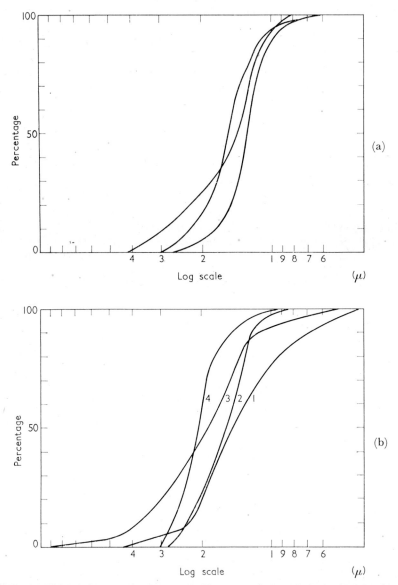

Fig. 1. (a) Cumulative curves of Texas Gulf coast aeolian sand. Logarithmic scale on the base from 60 to 900 microns, vertical scale in percentage. (b) Cumulative curves of Texas Gulf coast river and beach sand. 1. Guadalupe River; 2. Surfside Beach; 3. San Antonio River; 4. Sargent Beach. Logarithmic scale on base from 60 to 900 microns, vertical scale in percentage. Data from Cyrus Strong, unpublished M.A. thesis, The Rice Institute.

No significance, despite popular belief, can be attached to the colour of desert sands. Red sediments are accumulating today in the tropics and sub-tropics,[23] but they are not exclusively confined to these climatic belts. Red aeolian sand is accumulating in some modern deserts, sometimes apparently derived from underlying red beds. However, this is not true in all cases, for the sand dunes of the Australian desert are dominantly red in colour.[25] The causes of the formation of this red coating of haematite on desert sands is incompletely understood. Well known fossil dune sands occur as red (Lower Bunter, Wingate) or white (Coconino and Navaho) sandstones.

IV. The Importance of Wind Direction Studies

IV.1 *Aeolian Cross-Stratification*

The distinctive cross-stratification found in desert sand dunes is sufficiently characteristic to have been defined as aeolian or dune bedding. This cross-stratification is the remnant of the successive foreslopes of advancing sand dunes, which advance with the dominant wind. The foreslopes of sand dunes are inclined at an angle of approximately 33°, which is the angle of repose of dry sand. Laminations are sometimes present on the backslopes of sand dunes, but they have a characteristic low dip rarely exceeding 12° and are inclined upwind. As the dune advances, sand is moved up the backslope by a process of saltation[3] and dropped over the foreslope where it is trapped on the foreslope forming the laminations.

It is apparent that the direction of movement of the ancient dune field could be ascertained for one place if the direction of dip of a sufficiently large number of cross laminations were taken in order to average out anomalies caused by variations of dune form. Dips of less than 12° should be disregarded because of the possibility that they could be backslope deposits. In order to find the average direction of the wind through the period of time represented in any formation, readings should be distributed throughout the thickness of the formation. Different localities should be selected throughout the geographical extent of the formation under study so as to eliminate variation in wind direction due to local topography, and to arrive at an over-all picture of dune movement over as large an area as possible. The value of this type of study has been amply demonstrated by the work of Shotton[39, 40] and Rieche.[34] Consequently, it is apparent that measurement of the direction of cross-stratification will give a measure of the depositing wind, it being a particular form of current bedding.

Aeolian sandstones are, therefore, more useful to palaeoclimatic investigations than any of the other desert sediments because it is possible to derive more climatically significant information from them. These sandstones indicate not only an arid or semi-arid climate but give an indication of the direction from which the dominant wind blew during the time of deposition of the aeolian sandstones, an item of utmost importance in reconstructing the climates of the past. Brooks[7] recognized this fact and states, 'the weather at any place on any day is mainly governed by the winds which are blowing at the time; similarly, the climate is largely determined by the winds which blow most frequently. The winds in one place are closely related to the winds at other places, the whole forming a more or less orderly system which ultimately depends on the differences of temperature between different latitudes.'

IV.2 *Modern Dune Movement*

From a study of the direction of modern dune movement, it appears that there is a definite relationship between the direction of sand movement and the present air circulation of the earth. In Fig. 2 the pattern of dune movement is shown for areas from which information is available. Information is fairly complete on the low latitude deserts of the world, e.g. Sahara, Arabian, Indian, Kalahari, Namib, Australian and Atacama. Unfortunately, reliable information on the desert areas of central Asia is lacking; however, dune areas of the United States are much better known. The direction of movement of Pleistocene dunes are also given for the United States and Europe.

Sand is set in motion only when the wind rises above a certain force, usually about 4 on the Beaufort scale, so the resultant direction of dune movement is not the mean direction of all the winds throughout the year but is the resultant direction of the stronger winds.[3]

It can be seen from Fig. 2 that dune movement over the earth's surface corresponds in its over-all aspects to the general circulation of the earth. In latitudes below 22° dune movement conforms to the pattern of the prevailing easterlies or Trade Winds. This is true for the Sahara[4] and Arabian deserts in the northern hemisphere and the Australian[25] and Kalahari deserts[24] in the southern hemisphere. The Indian desert does not conform to this pattern because of the influence of the south-east Asian monsoon and the dunes move from the south-west to the north-east instead of from the north-east to the south-west, or east to west as in the remaining Trade Wind deserts. Above latitude 30° north or south of the equator, dune fields come under the influence of the prevailing westerlies and are moving from the south-west west and north-west, to the north-east east and south-east respectively. This applies to most of the dune fields of the middle latitudes, not only at the present day but also to the dunes of the late Pleistocene in the United States and Europe.[19, 42]

In some deserts of the world there are dune areas which lie, in part, in the zone of the prevailing westerlies and part in the prevailing easterlies; this leads to a regular alignment of the dunes, and a regular shift in direction of dune movement which results in an over-all pattern called the 'wheel-round'. The 'wheel-round' consists of a change in direction of dune movement through about ninety degrees of arc. The outstanding example of this effect is the eastern Sahara, where in the Libyan sand sea the dunes are aligned north-west to south-east; as latitude $23\frac{1}{3}$ (Tropic of Cancer) is approached, dune movement is from the north to the south, and south of the aforementioned latitude the dune movement is from the north-east to the south-west. This effect can also be seen in the Arabian, Kalahari and

Australian deserts, although in the Kalahari and Australian deserts this effect takes place at latitude 30° (Fig. 2). This phenomena is probably due to the fact that at these latitudes the prevailing easterlies give way to the prevailing westerlies.

A study of the dune pattern shown in Fig. 1 should be an aid in interpreting the direction of dune movement derived from cross-stratification studies of aeolian sandstones. The following generalizations from Fig. 2 should be applicable:

(*a*) Dune movement lower in latitude than 22° should be from the north, north-east, or east to the south, south-west or west, respectively, in the

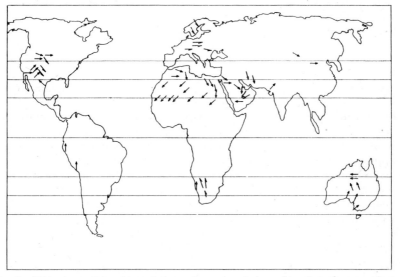

Fig. 2. Direction of modern dune movement (triangular tipped arrows) and Pleistocene dune movement (arrows with single barbs).

northern hemisphere and from the south, south-east or east to north, north-west, or west, respectively, in the southern hemisphere.

(*b*) Dune movement higher in latitude than 22° should be from the south-west, west or north-west to the north-east, east, or south-east, respectively, in both the northern and southern hemispheres.

(*c*) Major exceptions to this pattern are likely to be introduced by the monsoon systems which are sometimes dominant on the eastern side of large land masses.

(*d*) Minor exceptions could be introduced by the Trade Wind system becoming dominant in the region between 22° and 30° because of local geography or changed pattern of wind movement. It is unlikely that the influence of the Trade Wind would reach above 30° or the westerlies below 22°.

It is highly improbable that the general circulation of the earth has altered in any of its major components because the pattern of the earth's circulation is formed by the Coriolis forces (which is an effect of the conservation of angular momentum) operating because of the rotation of the earth. In a non-rotating earth, a single cell would be produced rising at the equator, flowing north and south to the poles, and returning to the equator along the earth's surface. This simple system does not exist because of the earth's rotation and the single cell is broken down into two or more components, the Tropical or Hadley cell causing the Trade Winds, the middle latitude or Ferrell cell causing the prevailing westerlies, and perhaps a polar cell.[8] It is difficult to see how this system could be altered or reversed while the earth is rotating in its present direction, and a reverse in the direction of rotation is extremely unlikely. Thus the wind direction derived from ancient sand dunes might be expected to represent the surface easterlies in the lower latitudes and the surface westerlies in the higher latitudes.

IV. 3 *Measurement and Statistical Treatment of Aeolian Cross-Stratification*

In measuring the direction of cross-stratification in aeolian sandstones with a Brunton compass, care must be taken to avoid false dips, and in general the magnitude of the angle of dip is a reasonable guide to nearness of approach to the true direction. Occasionally, two low dips in the same unit can be measured and the direction of maximum dip can be determined stereographically. Apart from the scale of the units involved, the techniques of measurement differ in no respect from cross-stratification measurements in aqueous sandstones.

Errors in measurement and variation of the shape of the slipface of the dunes will result in a scatter of the measured directions in any one site. Consequently, a sufficiently large number of readings must be made to average out these variations. As transverse dunes including barchans move in the direction of the dominant wind, the mean direction of any sufficiently large set of readings will represent the direction towards which the dominant wind blew, and by comparing results from different localities on as wide an areal extent as possible, the general pattern of the dominant wind will emerge on which may be superimposed irregularities due to local geography.

The readings taken at the different localities should then be subjected to suitable statistics. The type of statistics usually employed is vectorial statistics [12, 30, 34] which gives a suitable mean direction of transport and a measure of scatter. The vector mean is computed using the formula

$$\tan \bar{\theta} = \frac{\Sigma \sin \theta_n}{\Sigma \cos \theta_n}$$

where θ_n = azimuth from the nth observation or group of observations and $\bar{\theta}$ is the azimuth of the resultant vector. The value of vector addition is that it is partly a function of dispersion.

The second statistic used is derived from the magnitude of the resultant vector (r), which gives an adequate measure of the concentration or scatter of the individual vectors around the vector mean. It is obtained from the following formula:

$$r = [(\Sigma \sin \theta_n)^2 + (\Sigma \cos \theta_n)^2]^{\frac{1}{2}}$$

When the magnitude of the resultant vector (r) is divided by the number of readings (N) and multiplied by 100, using the formula

$$\bar{a} = \frac{r}{N} \cdot 100$$

where $\bar{a}$ = magnitude of the resultant vector in terms of per cent, a statistics is derived which is a percentage measure of the magnitude of the resultant vector. Therefore, it can be seen that the greater the concentration of the individual vectors about the vector mean $(\bar{\theta})$ the higher the magnitude of the resultant vector $(\bar{a})$ in per cent becomes. It is obvious that if the direction of dip of all the cross-laminae recorded at a locality lay along one azimuth, the vector magnitude would exactly equal the number of readings recorded, if each reading were given unit weight, and $\bar{a}$ would equal 100 per cent, which represents a perfect concentration.

V. Direction of Dune Movement through Geological Time

We have already seen (Fig. 2) that the dune movement of the late Pleistocene in North America and Europe conforms to the pattern which is expected from a study of modern dunes. In Europe, older dunes belonging to the Oligocene were present in the Paris basin[1] and were shaped by south-westerly winds. In North America, aeolian sandstones are present in the Miocene of Arizona and New Mexico in the Chuska Mountains. These sandstones (which are called the Chuska sandstone) have been thoroughly studied by Wright[43] who found that the dominant wind which transported these dunes blew from the south-west. As far as the writer is aware, no other Tertiary aeolian sands or sandstones have been studied. So we can see that in both North America and Europe the available evidence is in accord with the pattern of wind movement which can be observed today.

In Europe there appears to be no unequivocally aeolian sandstone known between the Tertiary and the Permo-Triassic; however, during the Permian, large dune fields came into existence over much of the British Isles[39, 40, 29] from Morayshire in Scotland to Devonshire in the south-west of England. It can be seen from Fig. 3 that the dominant wind which moulded and moved these dunes blew from the east north-east. This direction of transport is completely anomalous, differing from the direction which would be expected from the study of modern dune fields, and also from the present general atmospheric circulation of the earth. Aeolian sandstones older than the Permian are unknown or unreported from Europe.

In North America, conditions necessary for the accumulation and deposition of aeolian sandstones seem to be missing during the interval of time
between the Miocene and the Jurassic; however, during the Jurassic, large
accumulations of aeolian sandstone spread over the western part of the
United States during arid intervals. The youngest of these, the Cow Springs
sandstone of northern Arizona, was transported and deposited by dominant
north winds.[18] Unfortunately, there is little information available on the
next aeolian sandstone in terms of age: the Entrada sandstone. The next
formation to be considered is the Navajo sandstone of the Glen Canyon

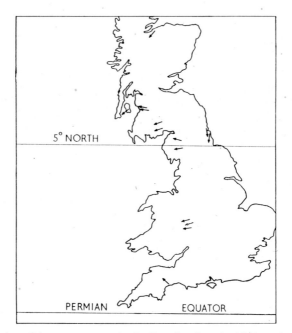

Fig. 3. Direction of dune movement in the Permian dune bedded sandstones of Great
Britain compared with the mean Permian palaeomagnetic equator.[39, 29]

Group. This widespread formation has been well studied by Kiersh,[22]
Poole and Williams,[33] and Opdyke,[29] and it was found that the dominant
wind throughout the time of the deposition of the Navajo blew from the
north or north-west, showing little deviation in direction throughout the
geographical extent of the formation which extends from Wyoming in the
north, to Arizona in the south and from Colorado to Nevada. In the lower
part of the Glen Canyon Group at the very end of the Triassic, the aeolian
Wingate formation was being deposited by the same dominant north to north-
west wind that was responsible for moulding the dunes of Navajo time.[33]
During the Lower Permian, arid conditions again became widespread in
the western United States and a dune field developed in Arizona which was

to become consolidated into the Coconino and DeChelly sandstones.[26, 34] The dominant wind during this time blew from the north or north-east.

The oldest aeolian sandstone that has been studied in North America is the Permo-Pennsylvanian Tensleep, Casper and Weber formations of Wyoming, Colorado and Utah.[30] The dominant wind during the period of deposition of these formations blew from the north-east.

The only aeolian sandstone that has been studied in order to determine its direction of transport outside of North America and Europe is the Botucatu

Fig. 4. Direction of dune movement in the Jurassic aeolian sandstones of the western United States (Navajo and Wingate [32] directions given by large solid arrow; Cow Springs direction [18] shown by the smaller arrow) compared with the Upper Triassic palaeomagnetic equator.

sandstone of late Triassic age of the Parana basin of Brazil and Uruguay. In the north of the Parana basin the Botucatu was transported toward the south by a dominant north wind,[2] but as the sampling was carried farther to the south in the Parana basin into Uruguay, it was found that the direction of the dominant wind changed to the west.[5]

If the direction of movement of the ancient dunes is compared with their expected direction of movement as indicated by modern dune movement, it is seen that there is little correlation; and in the cases of the English and American Permian and Permo-Pennsylvanian, respectively, the dominant wind came from a direction 180° away from the expected one. If the ice-caps were removed, it might be expected to alter the circulation somewhat over the continents. Brooks states that in this eventuality the dominant winds on the western sides of continents could be expected to blow from the south-west in the middle latitudes.[7] This hypothesis is valid for the Tertiary but for earlier periods it is not in agreement with the observed direction of dune movement except for the Botucatu desert of South America.

Recently, evidence derived from the study of palaeomagnetism has revived the controversy over the hypotheses of polar wandering and continental drift.[6, 14, 16, 20, 21, 36] If continental drift and polar wandering of the degree indicated by these palaeomagnetic measurements is a reality, then the wind system over any point on the continent's surface would be altered if there were a significant change of latitude of that point and the most significant of these changes would be a shift from the zone of the prevailing easterlies to that of the westerlies.

VI. Comparison of Palaeomagnetism and Palaeowind Directions

Irving[20] has shown that there are large discrepancies between palaeomagnetic results from the different continents which can only be explained on the basis of continental drift or a combination of continental drift and polar wandering. Therefore, he concluded that the proper way to compare palaeoclimatology and palaeomagnetism was within the continental block from which the palaeomagnetic measurements were obtained.

Unfortunately, at the present time the palaeomagnetic information is not as complete as one would wish. Some periods have remained unstudied in both Europe and North America and others have been inadequately studied. Fortunately, the Permian of Europe is among the periods that have been most intensely studied.[10, 14, 28, 35, 37] Ten localities have been investigated which give a mean pole positive of 166° east, 41° north, with the results spread over 15° of latitude and 20° of longitude. A Permian pole at this point on the earth's surface places the English Permian desert within 20° north of the equator, placing Great Britain in the zone of the prevailing easterlies, and in a position in perfect accord with the observed direction of transport of the Permian dune fields, Fig. 2. This position of Western Europe in relation to the prevailing wind system leads to a ready explanation of the aridity of western Europe during the Permian which is evident not only in the dune fields of the time but also in the development of great thicknesses of evaporites. These relationships would be impossible to explain if Western Europe were being swept by the moist prevailing westerlies during the Permian as they are today.

The palaeomagnetic results from the Tertiary of North America[9] indicate that the position of North America relative to the poles was much the same as it is today, which is in good agreement with the observed direction of transport in the Miocene Chuska sandstone, and not significantly different from the present direction of dune transport in the American south-west.[17]

Unfortunately, palaeomagnetic information from the Jurassic is very unsatisfactory for North America just when the development of dune deposited aeolian sandstone was at its peak in the western part of North America. The most reliable palaeomagnetic information which is closest in time to these sandstones is from the upper Triassic,[15] which places the pole at 56·7°N, 94·5°E. A pole position at this point would place western North America north of the equator but in the low latitudes and the observed north and north-west winds into north-east and north winds which would be expected

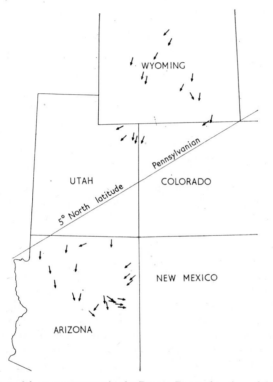

Fig. 5. Direction of dune movement in the Permo-Pennsylvanian of the United States compared with the palaeomagnetic equator for the Upper Pennsylvanian.[29–33]

at these latitudes. A more precise correlation must wait for the acquisition of more complete palaeomagnetic information from the Jurassic, but the true position of these sandstones would seem to lie between the Upper Triassic pole and the present pole. The directions of transport of these sandstones would seem to be in harmony with such a position, Fig. 4.

The palaeomagnetic information available from the Permian would place Western North America very close to the equator.[16, 36] Most of this information comes from one formation, the Supai of Arizona, but Graham gives information from other formations which were not submitted to statistics;

E

however, these stereograms from formations in New Mexico would place the state on the equator in some instances.

It has already been shown that the wind which deposited the Coconino and DeChelly sandstones blew from the north and north-east. These observed directions would be in accord with the palaeomagnetic information if they were north of the equator in the lower latitudes. It would be impossible to reconcile the observed direction of transport with a position south of the equator.

The palaeomagnetic information available from the Pennsylvanian is restricted to a pole position derived from the Naco formation of Arizona,[36] which places the equator diagonally across North America (Fig. 5). This pole position places the Upper Pennsylvanian aeolian sandstones of Wyoming, Colorado and Utah within 20° north of the equator. This position would change the observed dominant direction of transport in these sandstones from the north-east to a dominantly easterly wind. The observed direction of transport is, therefore, in accord with the position which is postulated by palaeomagnetism.

The remaining aeolian sandstone to be compared with palaeomagnetic results is the Botucatu of the Parana basin. Creer,[11] from palaeomagnetic results derived from the Botucatu sandstone and the overlying basalts, would place the Parana basin within approximately 5° of its present position at the time of the formation of these rocks. The palaeowind directions previously described from the Botucatu would compare favourably with this postulated position as well as its position today.

From the preceding discussion, it can be seen that the observed directions of transport in fossil dune sands is consonant with their position relative to the pole postulated from palaeomagnetic study (Figs. 3 and 5). It is also seen that the directions of the dominant wind at the time of formation of these sandstones is not consistent with their present geographical positions based on the available data of modern dune movement. It would seem, therefore, that the data from aeolian sandstones support the degree of continental drift which palaeomagnetism indicates based on the information which is available at the present time.

VII. Conclusions

Aeolian sandstones are of greater climatological importance than other types of arid sediments, for not only are they a clear indication of arid conditions, but they give an indication of the dominant wind at the time of formation. Meteorological considerations and present-day observations on dune movement indicate that the direction of dune movement can reasonably be expected to coincide in a general way with the pattern of the general circulation of the earth except under monsoonal conditions which develop on the eastern sides of major continents.

As the wind directions of all European and North American pre-Tertiary rocks conflict with the current wind patterns of those areas, it is logical to inquire whether a change of latitude is feasible, and it has been found that the latitudes and orientations suggested by palaeomagnetism permit a meteorologically feasible interpretation of the results so far obtained. Thus recognition of ancient deserts not only indicates predominantly arid climatic conditions but also gives meteorological information which must accord in a general way with the surface pattern of world air circulation.

References

1. Aliman, H. *Mém. Soc. géol. Fr.*, **14**, 1 (1936)
2. Almeida, F. M. de. *Int. Geol. Cong. Comtes rendus de la 19th sess.*, *Algiers* **1952**, **7**, 9 (1953)
3. Bagnold, R. A. *The Physics of Blown Sand and Desert Dunes.* 1941. London: Methuen and Co.
4. Bagnold, R. A. *Geogr. J.*, **117**, 78 (1951)
5. Bigarella, J. J. In Press
6. Bradley, J. *N.Z. J. Sci. Tech.*, **38**, 354 (1957)
7. Brooks, C. E. P. *Climate Through The Ages.* 1949. New York: McGraw-Hill
8. Byers, H. R., in *The Earth as a Planet.* 1955. Chicago University Press
9. Campbell, C. D. and Runcorn, S. K. *J. geophys. Res.*, **61**, 449 (1956)
10. Creer, K. M., Irving, E. and Runcorn, S. K. *J. Geomagr. Geoelect., Kyoto*, **6**, 163 (1954)
11. Creer, K. M. *Ann. Géophys.*, **14**, 373 (1958)
12. Curray, J. R. *J. Geol.*, **64**, 117 (1956)
13. Dubief, J. *Trav. Inst. Tech. Sahariennes*, **8**, 123 (1952)
14. DuBois, P. M. *Advances in Physics*, **6**, 177 (1957)
15. DuBois, P. M., Irving, E., Opdyke, N. D., Runcorn, S. K. and Banks, M. R. *Nature, Lond.*, **180**, 1186 (1957)
16. Graham, J. W. *J. geophys. Res.*, **60**, 329 (1955)
17. Hack, J. R. *Geogr. Rev.*, **31**, 240 (1941)
18. Harshbarger, J., University of Arizona. Unpublished Doctoral Thesis, 1949.
19. Hogbom, I. *Geogr. Ann., Stockh.*, **5**, 113 (1923)
20. Irving, E. *Advances in Physics*, **6**, 144 (1957)
21. Irving, E. and Green, R. *Geophys. J.*, **1**, 64 (1958)
22. Kiersch, G. A. *Bull. Amer. Ass. Petrol. Geol.*, **34**, 123 (1950)
23. Krynine, P. D. *Amer. J. Sci.*, **29**, 353 (1935)
24. Lewis, A. D. *S. Afr. geogr. J.*, **19**, 121 (1936)
25. Madigan, C. T. *Geogr. Rev.*, **26**, 205 (1938)
26. McKee, E. D. *Publ. Carneg. Instn*, **440**, 77 (1933)
27. Morris, R. C., Dickey, P. A. *Bull. Amer. Ass. Petrol. Geol.*, **41**, 2467 (1957)
28. Nairn, A. E. M. *Bull. Soc. géol. Fr.*, **7**, 721 (1957)
29. Opdyke, N. D., King's College, Durham University. Unpublished Doctoral Thesis, 1958
30. Opdyke, N. D. and Runcorn, S. K. *Bull. geol. Soc. Amer.*, **71**, 959 (1960)
31. Pettijohn, F. J. *Sedimentary Rocks*, 2nd edn. 1957. Harper & Bros.
32. Pincus, H. J. *J. Geol.*, **64**, 533 (1956)
33. Poole, E. G. and Williams, G. A. *Int. Conf. on the Peaceful Uses of Atomic Energy, U.N.*, 326 (1956)
34. Rieche, P. *J. Geol.*, **46**, 905 (1938)

35. Roche, A. *C.R. Acad. Sci., Paris,* **244**, 2952 (1957)
36. Runcorn, S. K. *Bull. geol. Soc. Amer.,* **67**, 301 (1956)
37. Rutten, M. G., Everdingen, R. O. van and Zijderveld, J. D. A. *Geol. en Mijnb.,* **19**, 192 (1957)
38. Shantz, H. L., in *The Future of Arid Lands,* Amer. Assoc. Adv. Sci. Publ. no. 43, 3 (1956)
39. Shotton, F. W. *Geol. Mag.,* **74**, 534 (1937)
40. Shotton, F. W. *Lpool. Manchr. Geol. J.,* **1** (1956)
41. Strong, C. Rice Institute, Houston, Texas. Unpublished M.A. Thesis, 1959
42. Thorp, J. and Smith, H. T. U. *Pleistocene Eolian Deposits of the United States, Alaska and Parts of Canada,* (Map) Geol. Soc. Amer. Publ., 1952
43. Wright, H. E. *Bull. geol. Soc. Amer.,* **67**, 413 (1956)

IV

Palaeoclimatic Significance of Evaporites

ROBERT GREEN

I. Introduction

The geology and chemistry of evaporites have been studied by many workers. Large amounts of data have been collected, data which are in some cases contradictory. In all aspects of interpretation of evaporite sequences differing opinions have been formulated. Interpretation of the palaeoclimatic significance of evaporites is based in many instances on theoretical data and on interpretations, made from evaporite sequences, of the conditions of evaporite deposition. Thus a number of assumptions and qualifications are made and these are set out in the following discussion; upon these depends much of the validity of the conclusions concerning the palaeoclimatic significance of evaporite deposits.

The importance of evaporites in palaeoclimatic interpretation is particularly significant where their associated non-evaporitic deposits are also taken into consideration. The following discussion is, however, concerned predominantly with evaporite deposits alone.

II. General Aspects of Evaporite Deposition

The presence of evaporite deposits at any point in space or time indicates the existence shortly prior to, and at, the time of deposition of a climate with a moisture deficit. Such a region, where total evaporation (E) is in excess of total precipitation (P) plus runoff, is said to have a positive E–P budget. If a body of water containing dissolved salts is present in a region of this type, and if the influx (I) of oceanic or other water is limited so that $E > P + I$, then that body of water will gradually evaporate, and salts will be deposited when their solubility coefficients are exceeded; an evaporite deposit will result. In the case of a similar body of water where $P < E < P + I$ no evaporite deposition will take place. Thus the presence of evaporites indicates semi-arid to arid climates, but evaporites may not be produced in all such climatic regions. Semi-arid and arid climates may be warm or cold. Warm arid climates predominate on the earth's surface, and few evaporite deposits are found in cold dry regions; hence this discussion is concerned mainly with the evaporite deposits of the warm arid regions.

Evaporites can be marine or non-marine in origin. Non-marine evaporites, deposited as the result of evaporation of lake waters, are highly variable in composition, and because of this great variability little detailed interpretation can be made of such evaporite sequences. Physical and chemical factors which vary with the composition of the brines exert strong influences upon the order and temperatures of deposition of salts. Thus in the absence of information concerning original contents of dissolved solids in former lake waters, no estimates can be made of water temperatures and temperature variations in such former lakes. Palaeoclimatic significance of non-marine evaporites is thus limited to qualitative interpretation only, and little further discussion will be made of such sequences.

Evaporites are deposited from marine waters if suitable physical as well as suitable climatic conditions exist. Physical conditions are a shallow sea, basin or inlet with access to the open ocean limited so that water evaporated is replaced, but so that most or all of the denser brines are trapped within the basin. Interpretation of the climatic significance of evaporites is dependent on other conditions. A basis for comparison is necessary, which can only be that of the present; this assumes relative uniformity of composition of oceanic waters throughout geological time, or at least as far back as the late Pre-Cambrian or early Cambrian period. To reject the principle of uniformitarianism places climatic interpretation based on marine evaporite sequences in the same vague state as that based on non-marine sequences. A second necessary assumption is that unless it can be shown otherwise the basic controls of present climate have remained the same throughout geological time. Also, until it can be shown otherwise, it is assumed that the climate of the earth's surface and the distribution of climatic belts was the same during the past as at present.

III. Extent of Present Warm Arid Climates

The distribution of warm arid homoclimates on land areas of the present day is between the latitudes of 50°N and 60°S:[25] extremely arid regions are distributed between the latitudes of 45°N and 35°S, with the largest areas lying between 15° to 35°N and 15° to 30°S. Arid climates are of several types: for example, some arid regions have summer rain, some winter rain, some limited all-year-round rain, and others are practically rainless. In many semi-arid regions the moisture deficit is small, such that if a large body of water were present there would be no moisture deficit, the region would no longer be semi-arid, and no evaporites could be deposited.

The E–P budget for a region is determined on the basis of the difference between total mean annual evaporation and rainfall. The standard methods of determining annual evaporation involve the use of shallow open pans, water-filled and exposed to the open air. Evaporation from a pan, which is a small body of water, causes no significant change in the humidity of the air of the surrounding region. Evaporation from the surface of a large body of water in the region, however, would materially increase the humidity of the air passing over much of that body of water, and hence would decrease the total amount of evaporation. Thus direct pan evaporation measurements over land areas cannot be used as a direct indication of the amount of evaporation that would take place from a shallow sea covering that same area. Thornthwaite[47] showed that pan evaporation measurements (275 to 490 cm annually) in the region of the Salton Sea, southern California, were from 80 to over 200 per cent in excess of actual evaporation from the Sea (152 cm, mean annual evaporation). The relative humidity of the air in arid regions may be as low as 5 per cent,[47] and the amount by which humidity would increase if a large body of water entered an arid region is not known, hence decrease in evaporation rate is not known. Thornthwaite's data for evaporation over the Salton Sea, a relatively small body of water with an area of approximately 1 500 square kilometres (in 1910) show a decrease from measured pan evaporation over land of approximately 66 per cent. As an estimate, then, evaporation from a hypothetical large body of water may be approximately one third of that measured from pans over land.

Detailed data for evaporation over land regions of the world are generally lacking. Thornthwaite[47] stated, however, that maps were in preparation which would show, on a world-wide basis, the distribution of evaporation over land surfaces.

It is probably more relevant for the purposes of this study to consider evaporation rates over the open oceans and seas, as evaporite deposits in many cases have been the products of evaporation of very large bodies of water. The best guides for evaporation rates over the oceans are the data of Wüst[57] and the maps of Meigs.[25] The regions with annual net evaporation of approximately 50 cm or greater lie between the latitudes of 15° to 30°N and 15° to 30°S. The highest net evaporation of approximately 125 cm takes place over the Atlantic Ocean at 10° to 15°S; the highest gross evaporation value is 154 cm, over the Atlantic Ocean at 20°N. Annual gross evaporation of approximately 150 cm takes place over the Atlantic Ocean between latitudes 15° and 25°N, 5° and 15°S, and over the Indian Ocean between latitudes 20° and 25°S.

The above figures are average annual values of evaporation for various latitudinal belts. Meigs' maps show the variation in evaporation rates within specific latitudinal belts.

Comparison of the above generalized net evaporation data with those data inferred from evaporite deposits may indicate whether major climatic changes have taken place in the past, or whether climates have been in general relatively uniform. In order to derive climatic data from evaporite deposits, the chemical and physical conditions of deposition must be examined. Less information is available in this field of study than might be expected.

IV. Mechanism of Marine Evaporite Deposition

No discussion will be made of the relative merits of various theories of evaporite deposition. In the light of present knowledge of seas and oceans, the mechanism of deposition outlined by Scruton[37] appears to be widely applicable to evaporite studies. The synopsis of Scruton's theory given below is necessarily brief.

From studies of circulation in restricted arms of the sea[11, 15, 58] it has been established that in those bodies of water where evaporation is greater than precipitation plus runoff, salinities increase away from the source of normal sea water, and that there is a movement of surface waters towards the head of the arm, this drift being caused by a surface slope produced by the evaporation. A bottom current flows seaward carrying water of increased density, the density increase being due to concentration of dissolved salts. Restriction to the basin of the major portion of this water of increased salinity is necessary to bring about sufficient concentration of salts so that evaporite deposition can commence. The primary restricting factor must be a sill, bar, reef or similar feature which limits influx of ocean water. Dynamic barriers are also established because of the layering in the basin of waters of varying densities. The inflow of sea water through the restricted connecting channel brings about a friction barrier, the importance of which increases as the channel becomes more restricted.[44] Outflowing waters of high salinity mix with inflowing ocean water in the channel, so that the water actually entering the basin from the seaward direction may be of considerably higher salinity than are normal ocean waters. Continual evaporation of the surface water as it flows headward increases salinities further, and eventually chemical deposition of dissolved salts begins in the portions of the basin farthest from the sea.

Data on the actual deposition of evaporites from sea water are mainly adapted from the work of Usiglio.[49] Deposition of individual salts takes place in succession as salinity and density increase, and each salt is deposited within particular density and salinity ranges. Thus, at any one point within a depositional basin a characteristic evaporite sequence will be developed. As salinity in the basin gradually increases the successive zones of deposition migrate towards the basin entrance. Thus, as detailed by Scruton,[37] there is both a horizontal and a vertical segregation of deposits within a basin. If quasi-equilibrium conditions are established at any period of time and at any concentration of salts, then the position of the horizontal salinity gradient is stabilized. In such a case Scruton points out that the thickness of each particular evaporite unit could be a measure of the length of time that the material in question was being deposited over each particular portion of the basin floor. A change in the character of a salt or change of type of salt at any one point may be due to seasonal or to long-term variations in rainfall, temperature, wind, sea level, the character of the basin or the character of the barrier cutting off the basin from the open sea.[23, 37]

As the deposition of several salts may take place at the same time within an evaporite basin, the presence of an early-depositing salt, such as gypsum, in one region and of a later-depositing salt, such as halite, in another does not necessarily imply a difference of climate, but more likely a difference in basin conditions or in salinities. The presence of evaporites in any part of the geological column does not necessarily imply the development of arid climatic conditions during that period of time, but perhaps only the development within an arid climate of a suitable basin with physical barriers in which evaporite deposition could take place. An evaporite succession such as the following, limestone–dolomite–anhydrite–halite–anhydrite–dolomite–limestone, may indicate a gradual climatic change from a negative E–P budget to a positive E–P budget and back to negative E–P. It may, however, indicate the gradual development of a restricted basin within a region with a positive E–P budget, followed by gradual disappearance of physical barriers separating that basin from the open sea.

Thompson and Nelson[46] have described a mechanism by which evaporites can be deposited as a result of freezing of the water containing the salts. Sodium sulphate deposits in lakes commonly originate by this mechanism, but as indicated by Bain[4] there is no evidence that important evaporite deposits have formed by freezing of sea water.

V. Theoretical and Experimental Conditions of Deposition

The main emphasis of this discussion is placed on the more common members of evaporite sequences, rather than upon the more complex end-members which may be produced by several different processes.

The sequence of deposition of salts from sea water was established by Usiglio,[49] and much of the more recent work is based on his data. Usiglio evaporated samples of water from the Mediterranean Sea at 40°C, and at various densities analysed brines and materials deposited. He found that deposition of calcium carbonate began at a density of approximately 1·0500 (salinity of 70·5‰) and ended at 1·1264 (195‰), calcium sulphate deposition began at 1·1264 (195‰) and ended at 1·2570 (427‰), sodium chloride deposition began at 1·2138 (352‰), with magnesium sulphate and magnesium chloride, and continued through into the last highly saline residues where potassium salts and double salts were deposited.

Although the general order of deposition of salts from sea water is widely accepted, the physical and chemical conditions under which deposition takes place have been a source of contention. The classic works on the subject are those of Van't Hoff and his associates who published extensively; the work is summarized by Van't Hoff.[50] Elaborate studies were carried out of conditions and results of deposition, using the Permian Stassfurt deposits of Germany as a source of materials. The temperature at which a particular salt will begin to separate is dependent upon the degree of saturation of the solution for various other salts, and also upon which particular salts are present in the solution. Sea water evaporated until it is saturated for sodium chloride is not saturated for other salts except for calcium sulphate. Thus the order of separation of salts at 25°C from water saturated for sodium chloride, potassium chloride, magnesium chloride and magnesium sulphate[50] is probably not applicable to studies of sea-water evaporation, unless concern is with the complex end-members of the sequence of deposition. As pointed out by Clark[10] a particular salt in the latter stages of deposition may be produced by several different reactions, thus it is difficult to determine the temperature or salinity at which it may have been deposited. The conclusions of Van't Hoff regarding the temperature conditions of deposition of the Stassfurt salts give the following minimum temperatures of deposition:

Glauberite ($CaSO_4 \cdot Na_2SO_4$): 10°C
Langbeinite ($2MgSO_4 \cdot K_2SO_4$): 37°C
Loeweite ($2MgSO_4 \cdot 2Na_2SO_4 \cdot 5H_2O$): 43°C
Vanthoffite ($MgSO_4 \cdot Na_2SO_4$): 46°C
Loeweite with glaserite ($3K_2SO_4 \cdot Na_2SO_4$): 57°C
Loeweite with vanthoffite: 60°C
Kieserite ($MgSO_4 \cdot H_2O$) with sylvine (KCl): 72°C

Such water or brine temperatures are not beyond present limits, as Kaleczinsky[20] recorded temperatures of over 70°C in natural saline lakes in Hungary, temperatures which he explained as being due to adsorption of the sun's heat by dense brines in the lower levels of the lakes.

As noted by Ochsenius,[28] a salt such as carnallite ($KCl \cdot MgCl_2 \cdot 6H_2O$), which requires a temperature of 120°C to crystallize out of a saturated solution, will crystallize out also as the mother liquor is cooled—such as during night time or during winter.

One of the most controversial problems in evaporite studies is that of gypsum–anhydrite relationships, and many palaeoclimatic interpretations are based on the temperatures of deposition of these two closely-related salts. Studies were carried out from an early date, and Vater[51] found that gypsum was deposited at normal temperatures from solutions saturated for sodium chloride or for magnesium chloride. Anhydrite was deposited only at temperatures above 30°C, and at such temperatures aragonite was deposited in place of calcite. The work of Posnjak[30] showed that in a solution saturated for calcium sulphate only, if the solution temperature exceeded 42°C all deposits were anhydrite. At 30°C the calcium sulphate was deposited as gypsum until the brine concentration reached 4·8 times that of normal sea water, after which point anhydrite was deposited. Sea water, however, is not saturated for calcium sulphate, but contains only 1·26 grams of calcium sulphate per litre of sea water. Posnjak[31] showed that total salinity of sea water must be increased by 3·35 times (from $35\%_0$ to $117\%_0$) to obtain saturation with respect to calcium sulphate. At this salinity the gypsum–anhydrite transition temperature was stated to be 34°C.

On the basis of thermodynamic calculations, MacDonald[26] detailed the history of crystallization of gypsum–anhydrite from sea water at a temperature of 25°C. At this temperature evaporation leads to a concentration of sea water until a salinity of $117\%_0$ is reached, then gypsum precipitates until the salinity reaches $215\%_0$, beyond which point anhydrite precipitates. When the salinity of the sea water becomes greater than $204\%_0$, all previously deposited gypsum is unstable and breaks down to anhydrite. For solutions saturated for sodium chloride, gypsum can precipitate only at temperatures below 14°C. In concentrated sea water, gypsum and halite can precipitate together at a salinity of $332\%_0$ and at temperatures below 7°C. The presence of other salts in concentrated sea water lowers the maximum temperature at which gypsum and halite can coexist from 14°C to 5°C.[26]

Posnjak and MacDonald both show that in solutions of sodium chloride and in concentrated sea water the gypsum–anhydrite transition temperature is lowered with increase in salinity. However, a number of workers, in particular Conley and Bundy,[12] have presented evidence showing that the presence of salts, such as those in sea water, activates the hydration of anhydrite to gypsum. Conley and Bundy's experimental data show that if anhydrite crystallites do form in sea water, then the activating constituents of the water would bring about a rapid conversion to gypsum or double salts, or both. For formation of primary gypsum, temperatures must not greatly exceed 42°C. The experimental evidence showed that at 25°C anhydrite is converted to gypsum at salinities well above $214\%_0$, whereas previous work based on theoretical vapour pressure calculations showed that above 25°C only anhydrite would be formed at such salinities. Conley and Bundy consider that such earlier thermodynamic work is incomplete, as lattice alterations and activator complexes which influence gypsum–anhydrite reactions were not taken into account. On the basis of their work these authors consider that it is highly unlikely that primary anhydrite forms in sea water.

VI. Present Evaporite Deposition

In one area of present evaporite deposition, there are sufficient observed data available to enable comparison with data derived from theoretical and experimental work. Gypsum and halite are being deposited in the Bocana de Virrila, a shallow marine inlet, 20 km long, in the Sechura Desert region of north-western Peru.[27] At the landward end of the estuary a saline environment, in the classification of Sloss,[38] exists, where gypsum and halite are being deposited in approximately 30 cm of water, at temperatures of 25° to 27°C. The salinities of the waters above the gypsum are between $191\%_0$ and $354\%_0$, and above the halite $355\%_0$. The salinity values for the lower limits of gypsum and halite deposition are in close agreement with those determined by Usiglio.[49] MacDonald's data,[26] however, indicate that gypsum deposition should commence at a salinity of $117\%_0$, and that where salinity rises above $204\%_0$ the gypsum is unstable and should break down to anhydrite. This is not in agreement with Morris and Dickey's observations. Conley and Bundy's results[12] are apparently more applicable to these observed data, for they showed that at $25°C$ gypsum can exist at salinities of $350\%_0$ or even greater, that gypsum is stable at temperatures up to $42°C$, and that this salt may exist indefinitely as a metastable phase at temperatures between $42°$ and $98°C$.

Unfortunately, few such detailed observed data as those of Morris and Dickey[27] are available for comparison with theoretical and experimental data. Partial data are available for the commonly cited classical example of present-day evaporite deposition: the Gulf of Karabugas, a barred basin less than 14 m deep on the east side of the Caspian Sea. Evaporation is high in the Gulf and a continual current flowing into the basin from the west carries in 355 000 metric tons of dissolved salts daily. The salinity of the Caspian Sea is only $12·9\%_0$,[5] one third that of the open ocean. Thus if the Gulf lay adjacent to the open ocean over one million metric tons of salts would be carried in daily, and deposition would be almost three times as great as at present. Present deposition is in the form of gypsum near the margins of the Gulf, particularly on the west side adjacent to the inlet, halite in the centre, and magnesium sulphate towards the centre during winter when the water temperature falls; the magnesium and sulphate contents of the Caspian Sea are higher than those of the open ocean. According to Andrussov[2] halite was not being deposited in the years 1896 and 1897 as the water was not saturated with respect to sodium chloride. He reported that salinities in the Gulf ranged up to $285\%_0$. Saturation with respect to sodium chloride was reached in 1942[7] and halite has been deposited since that time.

In shallow evaporating pans in the Nile River delta approximately 7 to 15 cm of salts are deposited annually,[54] and if this region were subsiding, considerable evaporite deposits might accumulate. To the south-east, natural salt pans exist adjacent to the Gulf of Akabar on the east side of the Sinai Peninsula; similar pans lie along the Red Sea coast of Eritrea, where periodic flooding by sea water permits deposition of alternating halite and gypsum.[53] When the Suez Canal was cut, the Great Bitter Lake was found to contain an evaporite deposit 13 km long by 6·4 km wide, with an average thickness of 8 m.[28] The evaporites consisted of gypsum and halite layers, averaging 5 cm thick, separated by thin beds of silt.

Evaporation from the Red Sea amounts to approximately 345 cm annually.[52] According to Sverdrup, Johnson and Fleming[45] evaporation is most intense during winter, when water temperatures in the northern end of the sea may drop as low as $18°C$, from the summer average of $30°C$. The excessive evaporation increases salinities which in the northern part of the Red Sea reach values of $40\%_0$ and $41\%_0$.[45] No rivers flow into the Red Sea, and as precipitation is extremely low, a significant shallowing of the sill separating the Gulf of Aden from the Red Sea would lead to the sea's becoming an evaporite basin.

The waters of the Gulf of Mexico during the summer reach temperatures of 29°C, and salinities are at least 36‰.[45] Numerous coastal lagoons border the north-west side of the Gulf, a region where annual rainfall ranges from 50 to 90 cm. Strong winds prevail, and with mean monthly temperatures ranging between 15° and 28°C, evaporation is high. At Amarillo, Texas, between 1907 and 1914, gross annual evaporation was 188 cm, and net evaporation 150 cm.[24] On the landward sides of many lagoons calcium carbonate, gypsum and halite are being deposited. In one lagoon near Tampico, Texas, salt has been deposited for over 500 years.[5]

In many other regions both natural and artificial small evaporite basins exist. Some are fed by marine waters, others derive their salts from re-solution of older deposits, from connate waters, and from magmatic and juvenile waters.[16]

VII. Paragenesis and Replacement of Evaporites

Before ancient evaporites are discussed mention should be made of paragenesis and of replacement of one salt in a deposit by another. These are of importance because palaeoclimatic interpretation must be made on the basis of the salts originally deposited, and not on those salts formed at a later date under different conditions of temperature and pressure.

Gypsum will dehydrate to anhydrite at varying depths of burial, depending upon the local temperature gradient, and upon the concentration of dissolved salts in interstitial liquids. MacDonald[26] considers that gypsum is not in equilibrium with buried halite except at temperatures below 14°C, as pore liquids are saturated for sodium chloride under such conditions. He stated that above the Sulphur salt dome, Louisiana, gypsum would not be in equilibrium with pore water at depths greater than 555 m. In the Miocene evaporite deposits of Sicily, gypsum was noted at depths up to 509 m.[29] The Permian evaporites of north-eastern Yorkshire contain no gypsum[43] as these strata now lie between depths of 1 000 and 1 500 m below the surface. Stewart reports temperatures of 34°C at 790 m, and 41°C at 1 280 m.

Carnallite in the Stassfurt deposits of Germany is considered to have formed from bischofite and sylvine;[50] Grabau,[16] however, points out this would involve a 4·95 per cent increase in volume, and considers it to be an unlikely process.

Replacement of one salt by another is apparently common, and in many cases nearly all traces of the original salt have been destroyed. Careful examination can reveal sufficient evidence of the original salts to permit reconstruction of the succession of changes. Armstrong and others,[3] and Stewart,[40-43] have shown the following series of replacements which have taken place in the Upper Permian deposits of north-eastern England:

(1) Gypsum replaced by anhydrite and halite, replaced by carnallite and rinneite, replaced by anhydrite, halite, sylvine and magnesite

(2) Gypsum replaced by halite, replaced by gypsum, replaced by anhydrite or halite, or both
(3) Anhydrite replaced by gypsum, replaced by halite
(4) Anhydrite replaced by halite
(5) Anhydrite and halite replaced by polyhalite, replaced by kieserite
(6) Dolomite replaced by anhydrite
(7) Dolomite replaced by halite

Thus detailed examination must be made of evaporite sequences for pseudomorphs of earlier minerals, particularly where the earlier minerals may have been deposited at lower temperatures than the replacing minerals. If such detail is not known, palaeoclimatic interpretations made may be subject to gross error.

VIII. Palaeoclimatic Interpretation of Evaporite Sequences

Palaeoclimatic reconstruction which has been carried out based on data derived from evaporites may be of uncertain validity. Many of the inferences drawn are based on the work of Posnjak [30, 31] and MacDonald. [26] The data of Conley and Bundy [12] were not then available, thus the value of interpretation based on gypsum–anhydrite transition temperatures is in doubt.

A limited number of evaporite deposits are known in detail sufficient to permit workers to reconstruct their past history. Four deposits have been selected for discussion.

VIII.1 *The Upper Permian Evaporites of Western Europe*

The most extensive and detailed studies of evaporite genesis and paragenesis have been carried out on the Permian evaporite deposits of Western Europe. The work of Van't Hoff and his associates constituted the earliest part of an intensive study carried out for almost 60 years, yet all problems of the conditions of deposition are not solved, and there exist diametrically opposed schools of thought on the subject.

Salt deposition in Germany began during Rotliegende (early Permian) time in the lower Elbe region; maximum extent of evaporite deposition was reached during Zechstein (late Permian) time when salts were deposited in a basin extending from west central Poland to north-eastern England, and from Denmark to southern Germany. Salts were deposited also during the Triassic period: both the upper Bunter and middle Muschelkalk contain extensive evaporite deposits in Germany, but during Keuper time evaporites were more restricted in extent, and halite deposition was confined to the lower Elbe region. [6] Salts of Malm age are present in the Hamburg–Bentheim region of Germany.

Many studies have been made of the Zechstein deposits. Lamination in the evaporites is found in many places, and on the basis of these annual laminae Richter-Bernburg [33] has estimated the duration of Zechstein sedimentation at 500 thousand to 1 million years. As this time interval represents only a small portion of Permian time, the breaks in sedimentation are probably more significant than the periods of deposition and thus the palaeo-climatic conclusions drawn possibly apply only to a small portion of Permian time. Richter-Bernburg considers that the cyclic sedimentation reflects annual climatic changes, and he attributes irregularities in the evaporite cyclic succession to sun-spot activity.

The average surface temperature of late Permian time has been estimated at 23·1°C by Quiring.[32] This estimate is based on calculations of water temperature and solar radiation constants necessary for the precipitation of potassium and magnesium salts. Quiring states that this figure is in agreement with that temperature calculated on the basis of geological criteria. At a water temperature of 23°C the first calcium sulphate deposits in a restricted basin would be gypsum. Stewart[43] and Borchert and Baier[8] consider that the present massive basal anhydrite beds of the upper Zechstein deposits were originally laid down as gypsum. Weber,[55] however, studying upper Zechstein gypsum beds along the south-east borders of the evaporite basin in Thuringia, believes that the strata were originally deposited as anhydrite. This opinion, on the basis of Posnjak's[31] data, infers a minimum water temperature of 34°C, and following the work of Conley and Bundy[12] infers a minimum water temperature of 42°C.

Stewart[40-43] has made detailed petrological studies of the Zechstein deposits of north-eastern England. Three evaporite sequences have been proved during drilling for potash, and the ideal succession in each sequence is as follows:

    (6) Carnallitic marls
    (5) Halite–sylvine zone
    (4) Halite zone: minor anhydrite
    (3) Halite–anhydrite zone: alternating beds of halite and anhydrite
    (2) Anhydrite zone: massive anhydrite with minor dolomite beds
    (1) Dolomite zone: dolomite and dolomitic marl

Evidence of the presence of early gypsum, probably primary, was found in the massive basal anhydrite zones,[43] and in the halite–anhydrite zones.[40-42] Stewart suggests that much of the massive basal anhydrite was deposited as gypsum, and that the original basal gypsum gave place upwards to primary anhydrite alternating with halite. The primary anhydrite is present in the main halite zones; during deposition of the beds of the anhydrite–halite and halite zones physical conditions were such that slight fluctuations of temperature, or salinity, or both, would cause differences in the nature of the primary calcium sulphate salt. Detailed examination of strata in the halite–anhydrite zone showed the following repeated succession:[43] anhydrite–gypsum–gypsum with halite–gypsum–anhydrite. The anhydrite typically contains some carbonate, and the gypsum is now represented by pseudomorphs of anhydrite and halite. This cyclic succession of units forms a series in which layers range in thickness from a few millimetres to fifteen centimetres. Stewart considers that the above sequence can be explained on the basis of seasonal temperature variations. Alternating gypsum and anhydrite layers may be annual, and are explained by a temperature fluctuation above and below the gypsum–

anhydrite transition point, gypsum being deposited in winter and anhydrite in summer; seasonal water temperature variations will be considerable in a shallow evaporating basin in a warm arid climatic region. As salinity increases, the gypsum–anhydrite succession gives place to anhydrite deposition during summer, gypsum during spring and autumn, and halite with varying amounts of gypsum during winter.[43] Further salinity increases inhibit deposition of gypsum and the annual succession becomes one of halite and anhydrite.

Definite evidence of seasonal changes of climate are thus presented by Stewart. The evidence is, however, only qualitative, and actual seasonal temperature variations are not known. In concentrated sea water, gypsum and halite will precipitate together at a salinity of 332‰ and at temperatures below 7°C,[26] or at slightly lower salinities only with lower temperatures. At a salinity of 332‰ and at approximately 7°C, anhydrite and halite are deposited, and anhydrite alone at higher temperatures.[26] With salinities slightly less than 332‰ halite and gypsum are deposited at temperatures several degrees below 7°C, gypsum alone at approximately 7°C, and anhydrite alone at temperatures several degrees above 7°C.[14]

The presence of gypsum and halite in close association indicates low water temperatures—according to MacDonald,[26] but not according to Conley and Bundy[12]—which can be explained climatically in several ways, as discussed by MacDonald:

(1) A cold dry climate, with water temperatures varying within a few degrees of 7°C.

(2) A cold winter and warm summer, thus with considerable annual temperature variations.

(3) If the gypsum and halite were not deposited at the same time, Stewart's observed sequence could be explained as follows:

(a) Gypsum deposition
(b) Anhydrite deposition, with gypsum converting to anhydrite
(c) Halite and anhydrite deposition
(d) Influx of fresh water, salinity is reduced, halite dissolves, anhydrite converts to gypsum
(e) Gypsum deposition

In the case of the third explanation the salinity increases steadily through stages (a) to (c); stage (d) is presumably the time of seasonal precipitation which brings about runoff into the basin. For this sequence of events to take place, the water temperature must remain below 34°C. In terms of an annual climatic cycle, the rainfall would probably be in late autumn or winter, and salinity would gradually increase during spring, and would reach a stage permitting halite–anhydrite deposition during summer. Briggs,[9] however, considers that precipitation and runoff into an evaporite basin will not mix significantly with the denser brines, but will form a thin layer on the surface; thus salinity would not be significantly reduced, and precipitation of salts would be inhibited until evaporation of the fresh water was complete. Over a long period of time, however, mixing of runoff waters with those in a basin would probably take place, as exemplified by the Black and Caspian Seas, the salinities of both of which are considerably below that of the open ocean.

As the Zechstein evaporite basin had a great extent, and as an enormous volume of water must have been evaporated annually, the aridity of the region probably approached a maximum. Grabau[16] indicated that maximum aridity is achieved in regions of constant planetary winds, and also where cold dry winds pass over warm waters. On this basis, the Zechstein climate in western Europe was probably one with strong planetary winds, a warm summer perhaps with water temperatures rising to well above the 23°C average temperature of Quiring,[32] and a cold winter with water temperatures falling below 7°C. The winter temperature value assumes uniformity of Permian seas with those of the present and MacDonald[26] notes that if the concentrations of salts, other than sodium chloride and calcium sulphate, were less in Permian seas then the maximum temperature at which gypsum and halite could deposit simultaneously would increase, but in no case could the temperature be above 14°C. The presence of abundant potassium and magnesium salts in the deposits suggests, however, that other salts were present in quantity in Permian seas, and so presumably winter surface temperatures close to 7°C were probable.

VIII.2 *The Permian Evaporites of the South-western United States*

The Permian rocks of the south-western United States are known in considerable detail as a result of extensive drilling for oil and for potash. The Delaware basin, in which the evaporites were laid down, was approximately 265 km long and 155 km wide[1] and connected with the open sea to the south-west.[21] Anhydrite, the Castile formation, is present in the basin in considerable quantity, and commonly shows lamination of anhydrite and bituminous calcite, which is probably annual. From study of these annual laminae Udden[48] calculated the average annual rate of anhydrite deposition to be 1·63 mm, and the duration of Castile time to be 306 000 years. By use of the data of Udden and of Adams, King[22] was able to arrive at a figure of 290 cm for the average net annual evaporation over the basin—an area of 26 000 square kilometres.

Scruton,[37] commenting on the fine lamination of the anhydrite, considers that the lamination was probably due to short-term annual fluctuations of salinity of the water. The salinity changes may have been caused by temperature variations, or by evaporation rate changes in as much as these will affect the position of the horizontal salinity gradient, or by sea-level changes perhaps caused by changes in wind strength.

The small amounts of clastic materials present in the evaporite sequence indicate that runoff from adjacent land areas was small, thus precipitation was probably low. Schaller and Henderson[36] found that the basal evaporite beds were massive anhydrite, and were overlain by anhydrite with halite pseudomorphs after gypsum, which in turn graded upward into halite. They

F

suggested that the original gypsum in the halite–anhydrite zone formed at an early stage in the unconsolidated primary anhydrite, and it was presumably replaced at a later stage by halite. If the basal anhydrite was primary, as was suggested, then the water at the time of deposition must have been at a minimum temperature of 34°C and have had a minimum salinity of 117‰.[31] The evidence of the presence of gypsum at a later stage in the depositional history indicates that the water temperatures must have dropped considerably below 34°C, to permit deposition of gypsum closely associated with halite. Stewart[43] has indicated how easily traces of primary gypsum can be destroyed when it breaks down into anhydrite and when a whole evaporite bed undergoes recrystallization. If Stewart's thesis that the massive basal anhydrite beds of evaporite sequences are deposited as gypsum is correct, and that conversion to anhydrite takes place as the salinities of the brines increase, then less drastic changes of water temperatures are necessitated to explain observed sequences of evaporite deposits. In particular, if the basal massive anhydrite bed of the Delaware basin evaporites was deposited as gypsum, then the original evaporite sequence closely resembles that of the Permian of western Europe, and thus the environments of deposition were probably similar. If this were the case then it can be postulated that climatic conditions may have included: (1) net mean annual evaporation: 290 cm; (2) mean annual rainfall: low; (3) mean annual temperature: 23°C; and (4) mean minimum surface water temperature: 7°C.

Comparison of the annual net evaporation value with those presented by Wüst[57] shows that no present-day net evaporation figures for open-sea regions approach 290 cm; only smaller lakes have data which are at all comparable. The studies of Harbeck and others[18] on Lake Mead, Colorado, perhaps form the best basis for comparison. The mean net annual evaporation from Lake Mead is 215 cm, annual precipitation is less than 13 cm, mean annual temperature is 19°C, and in winter the water surface temperature drops to 10° to 11°C; winds are light and average approximately 11 km per hour throughout the year.

According to most empirical formulae used for the calculation of evaporation rates, evaporation increases with increase in wind speed, with decrease in humidity of the air, and as water surface temperature approaches or becomes higher than air temperature. For a direct comparison of evaporation rates over Lake Mead and over the Castile Sea the effect of the salinity of the latter, 275‰ to 300‰,[22] must be taken into account. Harbeck's data[17] indicate that evaporation from such a brine would be at a rate 0·70 to 0·75 of that from fresh water, and also that the brine temperature would be from 2·5° to 3·0°C higher than that of fresh water under the same climatic conditions. Thus the rate of evaporation from a brine-filled Lake Mead would be slightly more than half that from the Permian Castile Sea. If winds in the Lake Mead region were strong instead of light, then, using Dalton's formula,[13] the evaporation rate from the brine could rise to over 230 cm annually. Strong winds from a landward direction—the north-east

—would certainly have been necessary in the region of the Castile Sea in order to remove the evaporated moisture and so keep the humidity over the Sea low. Strong wind alone may not have been sufficient to increase the evaporation rate to 290 cm annually, and thus the region may have been somewhat warmer than at present. Wind strength, however, was probably the major controlling factor in evaporation rate, more especially so because of the postulated low winter water temperatures.

VIII.3 *The Pennsylvanian Evaporites of the Paradox Basin, Western United States*

The Paradox basin is situated in the Four Corners region of the western United States, and lies mainly in south-eastern Utah and south-western Colorado. The deposits are in the Paradox formation and are somewhat unusual in that the evaporites are associated with black shales. The maximum depositional thickness was approximately 1 500 m.[56] The strata are of cyclothem type, the ideal cyclothem being as follows:[19]

> (11) Shale, black, fetid, calcareous, with local plant debris
> (10) Limestone
> (9) Dolomite, chalky to sucrosic
> (8) Dolomite, aphanitic
> (7) Anhydrite, laminated, massive
> (6) Halite, anhydrite inclusions at top and at base
> (5) Anhydrite, laminated, massive
> (4) Dolomite, aphanitic, commonly interlayered with anhydrite
> (3) Dolomite, sucrosic, with anhydrite inclusions
> (2) Limestone
> (1) Shale, black, fetid, calcareous

In the lower and upper parts of the Paradox formation the halite unit is absent, but this unit predominates in the middle member of the formation. The black shales, which are believed to be euxinic, grade north-eastward and south-eastward into calcareous siltstones and silty arkosic sandstones; this detrital material was derived from adjacent highlands.[56] The open sea lay to the north-west.

Wengerd and Strickland consider that the sequence of strata in the Paradox formation is the product of an interplay between fresh-water runoff from the land, normal sea water from the west, and an arid climate in the region of the basin. The basin of deposition was cut off periodically from the open sea by depositional barriers[56] or by dynamic barriers,[19] and the evaporites were the product of evaporation from the restricted basin. Gradual breakdown of the physical barrier would permit reversal of the typical evaporite sequence and a return to normal marine conditions, thus producing a cyclic succession of strata as outlined above.

The presence of black shales at practically any position in the succession is somewhat anomalous, particularly where they are present interbedded with halite or with anhydrite. Wengerd and Strickland consider that if the black shale represents suspended clays, the colloidal particles could not have travelled great distances across brines of high salinity and have remained unflocculated. Thus they postulate deposition of the black clays on broad mud flats after complete evaporation of the shallow brine, deposition being followed rapidly by subsidence and ingress of marine waters of the next evaporite cycle. These authors also consider the possibility of clay particles, protected by organic colloids, being swept out in fresh water over the denser brines, and that eventual mingling allowed flocculation and resulted in the association of black shales with halite and anhydrite. Whichever explanation is accepted, climatically the same conditions prevailed. Strong evaporation took place over the evaporite basin, induced by dry winds blowing from the land regions to the east and north-east. Periodic reversal of wind direction would lead to induction of orographic rains in the highlands flanking the basin to the east. Clastic material would be carried down slope by runoff, and be deposited interfingering with evaporites. The concept of a dominant easterly or north-easterly wind direction is in accordance with wind directions inferred from studies of aeolian sands of Pennsylvanian sandstones.[35]

Thus, in mid-Pennsylvanian times a warm arid climate prevailed in the western United States, probably with dominant north-easterly winds, and seasonal rainfall in upland regions bordering the seas.

VIII.4 *The Miocene Evaporites of Sicily*

The evaporites of the late Miocene Sulphur series of Sicily consist of gypsum and anhydrite, with local halite and potash salt beds up to 480 m thick.[29] The Gypsum formation contains most of the evaporites; typically these consist of alternating marl and gypsum layers with local salt beds. Ogniben[29] states that the strata show annual layering within a characteristic sequence, which is as follows:

> (3) Marl and shale
> (2) Thick zone of gypsum with swelling structures
> (1) Thin zone of microcrystalline gypsum

The lower zones average 1·6 m in thickness and contain laminae 2 to 3 mm thick. Ogniben considers that the lamination is caused by an inverse graded bedding. The gypsum deposited early in the season when salinity was low consists of fine-grained material; as salinity of the waters increased later in the season material of increased grain size was deposited.

The middle zones average 5·9 m in thickness and consist of secondary gypsum. These strata are considered to have been deposited as primary anhydrite, and to have hydrated to gypsum, producing the swelling structures described by Ogniben.[29] Occasionally, residual shreds of anhydrite may be found in these strata.

In areas where halite beds are developed, thin interbeds of primary anhydrite may be present which contain varves 2 to 2·5 mm thick separated by thin shaly layers. These varves also exhibit inverse graded bedding.

Several palaeoclimatic inferences may be made from these data. As primary gypsum was deposited the water temperature must have been below 34°C. Approximately 20 per cent of the total calcium sulphate was deposited as gypsum and 80 per cent as anhydrite; if other factors, such as evaporation rate and rate of inflow of sea water, be assumed relatively constant for the period of deposition of the calcium sulphate, then by extrapolation from D'Ans data,[14] minimum water temperature can be estimated at roughly 28°C. The presence of varves shows a seasonal climate, and the presence of terrigenous material in the interlayers indicates runoff from adjacent land areas at the end of the evaporation season, in late autumn or winter. In the anhydrite–halite sequence, anhydrite would be deposited during summer, and halite in winter, unless winter rainfall and runoff could mix with the brines sufficiently to bring about dilution and also inhibit evaporation.

The conclusions drawn are that water temperatures probably lay between 28 and 34°C and that the region had rainfall in late autumn or winter. At present the Mediterranean region has a mean surface water temperature of approximately 20°C, with an annual water temperature variation of approximately 10°.[45] Rain falls mainly during autumn and winter, and approaches 50 cm annually. Probably the Miocene climate of the Mediterranean region was not drastically different from that of the present, and the Sicilian region lay in the lower latitude portion of a present Mediterranean-type climatic belt rather than in the centre.

IX. Gross Distribution of Evaporites in Space and Time

Detailed analysis of specific evaporite deposits, if those deposits are known in sufficient detail, can give information concerning the climate at the time of deposition. Such information, however, covers only fragments of geological time—several thousands of years or several tens of thousands of years.

Evidence from recent times and from Cenozoic strata where more precise climatic measurements can be made show that cyclic variation in climate is probable, and that climatic changes can take place quite rapidly. There are moderate limits, however, to this cyclic variation within any one period of time. Thus examination of the gross distribution of evaporites in time can perhaps indicate whether major arid climatic belts had a significantly different distribution in the past from that of the present: whether climatic belts have always lain parallel to the present equator, and whether they have been wider or narrower in their latitudinal extents.

The latitudinal distribution of evaporites in the various geological systems, based on data collected from numerous sources, and illustrated in Figs. 1 to 9, is as follows:

Tertiary: 10°–50°N
Cretaceous: 5°–40°N; 0°–20°S
Jurassic: 25°–50°N; 0°–35°S
Triassic: 25°–55°N; 3°–5°S
Permian: 25°–55°N; ? 25°S
Carboniferous: 35°–55°N; 0°–15°S
Devonian: 45°–65°N (?75°)
Silurian: 35°–75°N
Ordovician: 35°–83°N
Cambrian: 25°–75°N

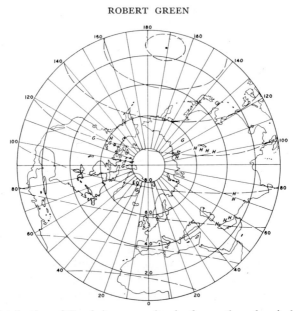

Fig. 1. Distribution of Cambrian evaporites in the northern hemisphere. Dashed lines represent lines of latitude relative to the palaeomagnetic pole, and are at 20 degree intervals starting at the equator: after Runcorn.[34] *Abbreviations: G*, gypsum, *H*, halite, EQ., palaeomagnetic equator.

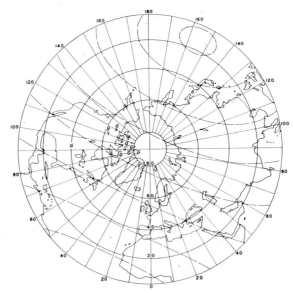

Fig. 2. Distribution of Ordovician evaporites in the northern hemisphere. Dashed lines represent lines of latitude relative to the palaeomagnetic pole, and are at 20 degree intervals starting at the equator: after Runcorn.[34] *Abbreviations: G*, gypsum, EQ., palaeomagnetic equator.

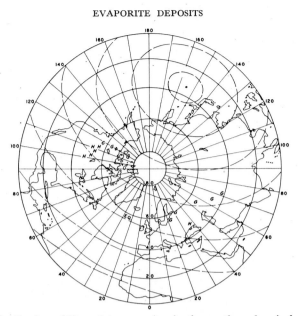

Fig. 3. Distribution of Devonian evaporites in the northern hemisphere. Dashed lines represent lines of latitude relative to the palaeomagnetic pole, and are at 20 degree intervals starting at the equator: after Runcorn.[34] *Abbreviations: G,* gypsum, *H,* halite, EQ., palaeomagnetic equator.

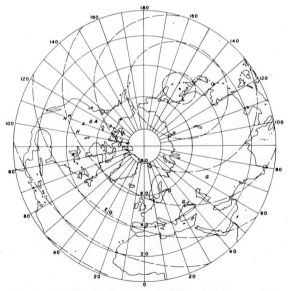

Fig. 4. Distribution of Carboniferous evaporites in the northern hemisphere. Dashed lines represent lines of latitude relative to the palaeomagnetic pole, and are at 20 degree intervals starting at the equator: after Runcorn.[34] *Abbreviations: A,* anhydrite, *G,* gypsum, *H,* halite, EQ., palaeomagnetic equator.

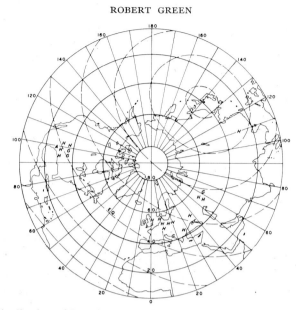

Fig. 5. Distribution of Permian evaporites in the northern hemisphere. Dashed lines represent lines of latitude relative to the palaeomagnetic pole, and are at 20 degree intervals starting at the equator: after Runcorn.[34] *Abbreviations: A*, anhydrite, *G*, gypsum, *H*, halite, EQ., palaeomagnetic equator.

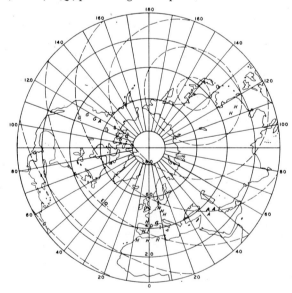

Fig. 6. Distribution of Triassic evaporites in the northern hemisphere. Dashed lines represent lines of latitude relative to the palaeomagnetic pole, and are at 20 degree intervals, starting at the equator: after Runcorn.[34] *Abbreviations: A*, anhydrite, *G*, gypsum, *H*, halite, EQ., palaeomagnetic equator.

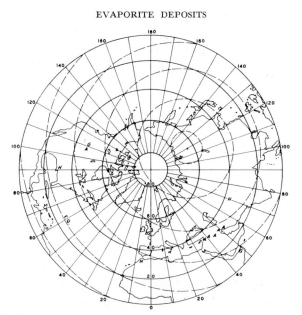

Fig. 7. Distribution of Jurassic evaporites in the northern hemisphere. Dashed lines represent lines of latitude relative to the palaeomagnetic pole, and are at 20 degree intervals starting at the equator: after Runcorn.[34] *Abbreviations: A*, anhydrite, *G*, gypsum, *H*, halite, EQ., palaeomagnetic equator.

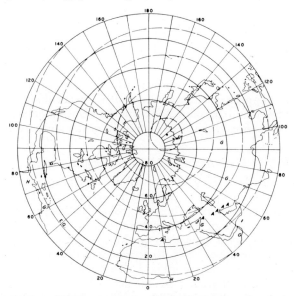

Fig. 8. Distribution of Cretaceous evaporites in the northern hemisphere. Dashed lines represent lines of latitude relative to the palaeomagnetic pole, and are at 20 degree intervals starting at the equator: after Runcorn.[34] *Abbreviations: A*, anhydrite, *G*, gypsum, *H*, halite, EQ., palaeomagnetic equator.

Extremely arid warm regions at present lie between 45°N and 35°S, and have their greatest extent between 15° and 35°N, and 15° and 30°S.[25] Arid homoclimates extend as far north as 50°, but as the moisture deficit in most of these regions is small they are not significant from the point of view of evaporite deposition.

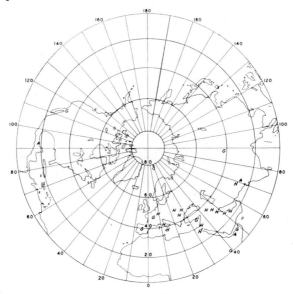

Fig. 9. Distribution of Tertiary evaporites in the northern hemisphere. Palaeo-magnetic pole almost coincident with present pole.[34] *Abbreviations: A*, anhydrite, *G*, gypsum, *H*, halite.

In the southern hemisphere, continental land masses are of relatively small extent, hence the geological record is limited, particularly for Palaeozoic strata. Thus the picture obtained of evaporite distribution is poor, and dis-cussion will be confined mainly to the record of the northern hemisphere.

IX.1 *Analysis of Evaporite Distribution*

In the northern hemisphere the distribution of evaporites indicates that salt deposition has taken place in the past far to the north of its present limits. The distribution of evaporites through geological time, relative to present latitudes, is shown in Fig. 10. The presence of evaporites at a particular point in time and space is dependent on two variables—suitable climate and suitable physical conditions. Fig. 10 represents an attempt to eliminate the variable of suitable physical conditions. Through geological time numbers of shallow basins with restricted oceanic access have probably been formed; a certain number of such basins will have lain within arid climatic belts, and in these evaporites will have been deposited. If the distribution of such basins through time has in general been random, then the distribution of evaporite deposits should permit general determination of the extent of warm arid climatic belts through geological time.

The significance of the relationship between geological time and the distribution of evaporites in terms of latitude may be evaluated by means of linear regression analysis. Assuming time to be the independent variable (x) and latitude the dependent variable (y), it is possible to set up an equation of the form $y = a + bx$ that will give the line of best fit for the scatter

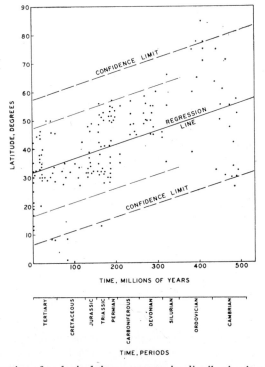

Fig. 10. Regression of geological time on evaporite distribution in terms of latitude. The outer dashed lines delimit the 95 per cent confidence belt for the regression line, based on all data. The inner dashed lines delimit the 95 per cent confidence belt, based on Silurian and later evaporite deposits.

diagram (Fig. 10). By following the procedure outlined by Snedecor[39] the regression coefficient (b) was obtained, and the contribution of time (x) to the regression on latitude (y) evaluated by means of an analysis of variance table (Table I).

The regression equation is:

$$y = 31 \cdot 55 + 0 \cdot 4929x$$

The significance of the regression of time is given by the ratio of the regression mean square over the residual mean square (Table I), which is significant at the 0·1 per cent level. This means that the probability that the relationship between time and distribution of evaporites shown in Fig. 10 could have arisen due to chance is less than 1 in 1000. The regression line itself is the line of best fit for the data used, and it indicates the mean position

Table I. Linear Regression Analysis of Variance of Geological Time (x) on Evaporite Distribution in Terms of Latitude (y)

Source of variation	Degrees of freedom	Sums of squares	Mean square	F-Ratio
Regression	1	8374·82	8374·82	51·79[a]
Deviations from regression	160	25874	161·71	
Total	161			

[a] Significant at the 0·1 per cent level.

of the belt of evaporite distribution through geological time. The confidence limits have been calculated and lie 25·4° to 25·7° either side of the regression line; 95 per cent of the points indicating evaporite deposits fall within these limits.

IX.2 *Interpretation of Analysis*

The regression line intersects latitudes of the present at 31·5°N, and so lies within a hot arid climatic belt. The warm desert and semi-desert regions of the northern hemisphere lie within the latitudes of the confidence limits. Water surface temperatures at the latitude of the southern confidence limit are close to 27°C, at the latitude of the regression line range from 20° to 25°C, and at the latitude of the northern confidence limit range from 7° to 14°C.[45] The present belt of north-east Trade Winds lies between the regression line and the southern confidence limit, and the present dominant westerly winds develop between the regression line and the northern confidence limit.

The climatic data for the present portion of the northern hemisphere lying within the confidence limits constitute a general basis on which to base interpretation of past deposits. As noted previously, however, cyclic changes of climate within the confidence limits are probable, and the relative positions of continents and oceans during geological time will have induced regional modifications of the major climatic belts. It is considered that these data can be applied to palaeoclimatic studies with a reasonable degree of confidence as far back as Silurian time. No significant changes in the mean width of arid climatic belts for the past 350 million years are apparent from the data presented. During Cambro-Ordovician time, however, the belt of potential evaporite deposition may have been 10° to 20° of latitude wider than the confidence limits indicate. This distribution suggests that relatively uniform warm dry conditions prevailed over most of the northern hemisphere. If the data for Cambrian and Ordovician evaporite deposits are eliminated from the linear regression analysis, the confidence limits then lie approximately 18° of latitude north and south of the regression line (Fig. 10) and delimit very closely the present warm desert and semi-desert belts of the northern hemisphere.

If the distribution of evaporites is considered in relation to lines of latitude constructed using palaeomagnetic data,[34] a general northward movement through geological time is indicated for the mean position of the arid climatic belt in the northern hemisphere. This infers an over-all warming trend in the earth's climate through time, an interpretation which is not in agreement with interpretations based on specific evaporite deposits (Section VIII). Certain deposits, such as the Carboniferous evaporites of Brazil, the Permian and Triassic evaporites of south-east Asia, the Cretaceous evaporites of Bolivia and the Jurassic and Cretaceous evaporites of Argentina occupy anomalous positions relative to the palaeomagnetic poles of their particular periods, anomalies which are explicable only by means of continental drift.

The palaeoclimatic interpretations made on the basis of the four evaporite deposits discussed in Section VIII are in agreement with the gross climatic interpretation based on the general pattern of evaporite distribution (Fig. 10). These conclusions regarding past climates do not eliminate the possibility of continental drift having taken place in the northern hemisphere. A relative east to west drift of continental masses would cause no changes in the latitudinal distribution of evaporite deposits, but any postulated relative northward movement of continents must be evaluated in terms of the effect on the distribution of evaporites relative to latitude. It is significant, however, that the distribution of evaporites through geological time can be explained on the basis of climatic change alone, without necessitating any changes in relative positions of continental masses, or in positions of the rotational poles of the earth, assuming that these poles are closely associated with palaeomagnetic poles.

X. Conclusions

The presence of evaporites indicates the existence at the time of evaporite deposition of a climate in which evaporation was greater than precipitation. The majority of present areas of evaporite deposition are located in warm arid regions—between the latitudes of 45°N and 40°S. Non-marine evaporite deposits are of qualitative value only in palaeoclimatic interpretation. Quantitative palaeoclimatic data must be inferred from marine evaporite deposits.

Theoretical and experimental work, supplemented by field observations, indicates that individual salts are deposited from marine waters within particular salinity and temperature ranges, and in general in a particular order. In the later stages of evaporite deposition the magnesium- and potassium-rich salts may be produced in a varying order by different reactions; the difficulty of determining which reactions took place in a particular deposit detracts from the usefulness of the complex end-members of evaporite deposition in palaeoclimatic interpretation. The relationship of gypsum and anhydrite is problematical. If the gypsum–anhydrite transition temperatures indicated by theoretical vapour pressure calculations are correct, then the presence of primary gypsum or anhydrite in evaporite deposits is of great significance in quantitative palaeoclimatic interpretation. Practically all such published palaeoclimatic data are based on this premise. Experimental work, apparently supported by field observations, indicates that primary anhydrite is never deposited from sea water, and thus that calcium sulphate salts are not of any great significance in quantitative palaeoclimatic interpretation.

There is abundant evidence which indicates that, following initial evaporite deposition, interaction takes place between salts, and that one salt may be replaced by another, the replacement in many cases obliterating practically all traces of the originally deposited salt. Thus great care must be taken to determine the succession of primary salts before any palaeoclimatic interpretation can be made.

The four specific evaporite deposits discussed indicate that during Pennsylvanian time in the western United States, during Permian time in the south-western United States and Western Europe, and during Miocene time in southern Italy and Sicily warmer and drier climatic conditions than those of the present existed. The quantitative climatic data concerning these specific deposits are based mainly on the theoretical thermodynamic data relative to gypsum–anhydrite transition temperatures, and thus may not be valid. Seasonal variation in climate is indicated by lamination of beds in all four evaporite deposits.

The gross distribution of evaporite deposits in space and time in the northern hemisphere, explained in direct terms, indicates an equatorward restriction of the northern limit of evaporite deposition from Cambrian to recent times. Linear regression analysis of the data indicates that this equatorward restriction is significant. The regression line constructed indicates the mean position of the warm arid climatic belt, and the confidence limits the probable extent of warm arid climates through geological time. The data for Cambrian and Ordovician evaporites are more scattered than those for later periods, possibly indicating more over-all uniform climatic conditions during early Palaeozoic time. If these data are eliminated from the analysis the closer confidence limits drawn delimit the present warm desert and semi-desert belts of the northern hemisphere.

It appears that the mean position of the warm arid climatic belt has moved equatorwards through geological time at a mean rate of 5° of latitude each 100 million years, and that the warm arid climatic belt has always lain grossly parallel to the earth's present equator.

Analysis of the gross distribution of evaporites considered relative to lines of latitude constructed using palaeomagnetic data indicates an over-all warming of the earth's climate through time, and that the mean position of the warm arid climatic belt has moved away from the equator through time. This analysis necessitates use of continental drift to explain various anomalies in evaporite distribution.

It is considered significant that the distribution of evaporites through geological time is explicable on the basis of a gross trend in climatic change, an explanation which necessitates large-scale change neither in the relative positions of continental masses nor in positions of the rotational poles of the earth.

References

1. Adams, J. E. *Bull. Amer. Ass. Petrol. Geol.*, **28**, 1596 (1944)
2. Andrussov, N. *Petermanns Mitt.*, **43**, 25 (1897)
3. Armstrong, G., Dunham, K. C., Harvey, C. O., Sabine, P. A. and Waters, W. F. *Miner. Mag.*, **29**, 667 (1951)
4. Bain, G. W. *Amer. J. Sci.*, **254**, 758 (1956)
5. Baker, C. L. *Univ. Tex. Bull.*, **2901**, 27 (1929)
6. Bentz, A. 'Germany', in *The Science of Petroleum*, Vol. VI, Pt. 1, pp. 24–33. 1953. Oxford University Press
7. Blumberg, J. B. *C.R. Acad. Sci. U.R.S.S.*, **114**, 1012 (1957)
8. Borchert, H. and Baier, E. *Neues Jb. Min. Geol. Paläont.*, **86**, 103 (1953)
9. Briggs, L. I. J. *J. sediment. Petrol.*, **28**, 46 (1958)
10. Clarke, F. W. *Bull. U.S. geol. Surv.*, **770** (1924)
11. Collier, A. and Hedgpeth, J. W. *Publ. Inst. Mar. Sci. Univ. Tex.*, **1**, 121 (1950)
12. Conley, R. F. and Bundy, W. M. *Geochim. et cosmoch. Acta*, **15**, 57 (1958)
13. Dalton, J. *Mem. Manchr lit. phil. Soc.*, **5**, 535 (1802)
14. D'Ans, J. *Naturwissenschaften*, **34**, 295 (1949)
15. Ewing, G. C. *U.S.N.R. Research Unit* 11-5, *Mimeographed Rept.* (1950)
16. Grabau, A. W. *Geology of the non-metallic Mineral Deposits other than Silicates. Vol. I. Principles of Salt Deposition.* 1920. New York: McGraw-Hill
17. Harbeck, G. E. *Prof. Pap. U.S. geol. Surv.*, **272**A (1955)
18. Harbeck, G. E., Kohler, M. A., Koberg, G. E. *et al. Prof. Paper U.S. geol. Surv.*, **298** (1958)
19. Herman, G. and Barkell, C. A. *Bull. Amer. Ass. Petrol. Geol.*, **41**, 861 (1957)
20. Kaleczinsky, A. *Uber die Hungarischen warmen und heiszen Kochsalzseen.* 1902. Budapest
21. King, P. B. *Bull. Amer. Ass. Petrol. Geol.*, **26**, 533 (1942)
22. King, R. H. *Bull. Amer. Ass. Petrol. Geol.*, **31**, 470 (1947)
23. Kuhn, R. *Fortschr. Min.*, **32**, 90 (1954)
24. Meigs, C. C., Bassett, H. P. and Slaughter, G. B. *Univ. Tex. Bull.*, **2234** (1922)
25. Meigs, P. 'World Distribution of Arid and Semi-arid Homoclimates', in *Reviews of Research on Arid Zone Hydrology*, U.N.E.S.C.O., 1952
26. MacDonald, G. J. F. *Amer. J. Sci.*, **251**, 884 (1953)
27. Morris, R. C. and Dickey, P. A. *Bull. Amer. Ass. Petrol. Geol.*, **41**, 2467 (1957)
28. Ochsenius, C. *Nova Acta Leop. Carol.*, **40**, 121 (1878)
29. Ogniben, L. *J. sediment. Petrol.*, **27**, 64 (1957)
30. Posnjak, E. *Amer. J. Sci.*, **35**A, 247 (1938)
31. Posnjak, E. *Amer. J. Sci.*, **238**, 559 (1940)
32. Quiring, H. *Neues Jb. Geol.*, **7**, 322 (1954)
33. Richter-Bernburg, G. *Naturwissenschaften*, **37**, 1 (1950)
34. Runcorn, S. K. *Bull. geol. Soc. Amer.*, **67**, 301 (1956)
35. Runcorn, S. K. *Science*, **129**, 1002 (1959)
36. Schaller, W. T. and Henderson, E. P. *Bull. U.S. geol. Surv.*, **833** (1932)
37. Scruton, P. C. *Bull. Amer. Ass. Petrol. Geol.*, **37**, 2498 (1953)
38. Sloss, L. L. *J. Sediment. Petrol.*, **23**, 143 (1953)

39. Snedecor, G. W. *Statistical Methods*, p. 122. 1937. Ames, Iowa: Iowa State College Press
40. Stewart, F. H. *Miner. Mag.*, **28**, 621 (1949)
41. Stewart, F. H. *Miner. Mag.*, **29**, 445 (1951)
42. Stewart, F. H. *Miner. Mag.*, **29**, 557 (1951)
43. Stewart, F. H. *Proc. Geol. Ass., Lond.*, **64**, 33 (1953)
44. Stommel, H. and Farmer, H. G. *Woods Hole Oceanographic Inst., Tech. Rept*, **52–63** (1952)
45. Sverdrup, H. U., Johnson, M. W. and Fleming, R. H. *The Oceans.* 1942. New York: Prentice-Hall
46. Thompson, T. G. and Nelson, K. H. *Amer. J. Sci.*, **254**, 227 (1956)
47. Thornthwaite, C. W. 'Climatology in Arid Zone Research', in *The Future of Arid Lands*, Publ. 43, American Association for the Advancement of Science, New York, 1956
48. Udden, J. A. *Bull. geol. Soc. Amer.*, **35**, 347 (1924)
49. Usiglio, J. *Ann. Chim. (Phys.)*, **27**, 92, 172 (1849)
50. Van't Hoff, J. H. *Zur Bildung der ozeanischen Salzablagerungen*, **1**. 1905. Braunschweig
51. Vater, H. *S.B. preuss. Akad. Wiss.*, **269**, 270 (1900)
52. Vercelli, F. 'Bilancio dello scambio di aqua fra Mar Rosso e Oceano Indiano', in *Campagna idrografico-scientifica nel Mar Rosso R. N.* Ammiraglio Magnaghi, 1923–24, Ricerche di oceanografia fisica, Parte 1, Correnti e Mareo, 1925, pp. 178–183
53. Von Buschman, J. O. *Das Salz*, Vol. II, p. 201. 1909. Leipzig
54. Walther, J. *Das Gesetz der Wustenbildung in Gegenwart und Vorzeit*, p. 241. 1900. Berlin: Reimer
55. Weber, H. *Hallesches Jb. Mitteldeut. Erdgeschichte*, **2**, 32 (1953)
56. Wengerd, S. A. and Strickland, J. W. *Bull. Amer. Ass. Petrol. Geol.*, **38**, 2157 (1954)
57. Wüst, G. *Festschr. Norbert Krebs (Landerkundliche Forschung)*, pp. 347–359. 1936. Stuttgart
58. Zenkevich, L. A. *Soviet Science*, **2**, 393 (1947)

V

Climatic Significance of Red Beds

F. B. Van Houten

'Geology is a particularly alluring field for premature attempts at the explanation of imperfectly understood data.' *Dana*
'Geology has to choose between the rashness of using imperfect evidence or the sterility of uncorrelated, unexplained facts.' *Gregory*

I. Introduction

Red beds were among the first sedimentary sequences to be considered climatic indicators. During more than 125 years of continuing interest in the origin of these rocks their common colour has been assumed to be their most significant feature, resulting from rather unique conditions of deposition. Indeed, most discussions have focused directly on climate as the principal cause of the colour, and interpretation of their origin has generally been assumed to be a simple matter.

Through the long course of speculation about red beds, which is summarized in Tables I and II, not only have countless geologists ventured unfounded opinions, but the conclusions of competent students have differed immensely as well. Most European geologists, impressed by the Permo-

G

Triassic red bed–evaporite sequences, have emphasized aridity and deserts, and they have supported their views with numerous references to many observations of modern deserts. American geologists, on the other hand, more commonly emphasized the rôle of red soils from warm, humid uplands, and fluviatile and deltaic deposition in savanna environments. But until recently there has been no adequate literature on modern tropics and subtropics to cite in support of this interpretation because so few explorers had described these realms.

Interpretations of red bed sequences have developed against a changing background of ruling hypotheses—first marine deposition, then lacustrine, then desert, red-soil origin, arid climates, deltaic, fluviatile, savannas and seasonally humid climate, and tectonic framework. Commonly the background has been accepted uncritically and employed with indefinite connotations. It is now realized that a significant characteristic of the subject is its complexity and the difficulty of simplifying it for analysis. The problems of the origin of red beds involve at least the material, climate, relief, and tectonic setting of the source area, and the climate, geography and tectonic setting of the basin of deposition. In addition, the investigation is made more difficult by the fact that no direct analogues of red bed sedimentation are widespread today, and those situations that may be analogous, such as the upper Amazon drainage system and the Gran Chaco of South America and the Rajputana Desert of India, have not been studied in detail.

Hypotheses that have been proposed to explain the origin of red beds can be arranged in the following categories:

Derivation of pigment	Condition at place of deposition
A. From Source Area	
1. Erosion of red soil containing anhydrous ferric oxide pigment *Primary detrital red beds*	Oxidizing; favoured by warm, dry climate; well-drained area
2. Erosion of red bedrock containing anhydrous ferric oxide pigment *Second cycle (secondary) red beds*	Oxidizing; favoured by warm, dry climate; well-drained area
B. Developed at Place of Deposition	
3. Dehydration of goethite, aging of hydrohaematite; alteration of ilmenite-magnetite or biotite *Post-depositional red beds*	a. Oxidizing; hot, dry climate produces anhydrous ferric oxide before burial b. After burial; produces anhydrous ferric oxide
4. Precipitation of anhydrous ferric oxide or of hydrated ferric oxide later dehydrated *Chemical red beds*	Oxidizing; favoured by warm, dry climate, and by saline water

Detailed analyses of many formations contribute basic information and ideas about red beds and variegated sequences. Amongst them are the Devonian Catskill facies of New York;[202] the Mississippian Bedford shale of Ohio;[229] the Permian Kaibab and Toroweap formations of Arizona and

Utah;[199] the upper Permian deposits of Kansas;[285] and the Rotliegende and Wadener beds of Germany;[96, 245] the Permo-Triassic Kagerödsformation of Sweden;[166, 293] numerous Triassic formations including Karroo red beds of S. Africa;[87] Buntsandstein of Germany;[297] Newark group of Connecticut and N. Carolina;[173, 246] Moenkopi formation of Arizona;[200] and the late Jurassic Morrison formation of the Colorado Plateau[54] and central Wyoming.[211] Early Cenozoic variegated deposits of the Rocky Mountain region[304] and the late Cenzoic Siwalik series of India[171] may also be cited.

The more general problems of red bed origin have been discussed by Russell,[257] Barrell,[19] Tomlinson,[291] Van Houten,[304] Krynine[172] and others[83, 231, 270]

The currently prevailing view holds that haematitic red pigment developed in upland soils in warm moist climates with seasonally distributed rainfall was deposited as a detrital sediment in an oxidizing environment. The favourable conditions for supply and burial of the pigment were controlled partly by the tectonic framework of the region.

This general explanation of red bed origin is corroborated by the occurrence of reddened rocks and palaeosols immediately below some red bed sequences whose pigment reasonably was derived from these red profiles of weathering. Throughout the Rocky Mountain region, for example, there are reddened strata, red residual soils and breccias, and intensely weathered crystalline rock beneath widespread Pennsylvanian red beds eroded from this regolith.[203, 204, 287, 313] Similarly, red Permian deposits in Great Britain locally overlie reddened upper Coal Measures[7, 10, 65, 294] that are presumably remnants of red soil profiles.[84] Moreover, these red soils developed during the time that the Keele and Etruria red beds accumulated along with the uppermost Coal Measures of England. A reddened zone below the Permian Rotliegende in central Germany affords further evidence of a primary detrital origin of the late Palaeozoic red beds.[24] In Oregon, red soil that developed on the Eocene Clarno formation was incorporated into the lower red part of the overlying Oligocene John Day formation.[316] The genetic relationship between red beds and red upland soils is also suggested by the fact that red sediments accumulated in the Ebro Basin[247] and on many of the pediments[174] in Spain, in the Auvergne District of France, and in the Molasse of Switzerland during a middle Cenozoic episode of very warm, humid climate with a prolonged dry season that produced red upland soil in Spain and laterite as far north as Ireland.[95]

In the following discussion analytical data and processes affecting the materials are emphasized. Interpretation of the climatic significance of red beds is reviewed briefly in the conclusions.

During the preparation of this paper I have enjoyed many profitable discussions with A. F. Buddington and A. G. Fischer. It is a pleasure to acknowledge their enthusiastic interest and help.

II. Facies of Red Beds

A thorough review of the rôle of ferric oxide as a pigment in sedimentary rocks should consider all red-coloured rocks, including red chert, red lime-stone and sedimentary iron formations. But the present concern with the climatic significance of red beds deals with those believed to be of primary detrital origin. Although this is the only adequate general explanation available, some of the formations included here, especially the variegated ones, may be second cycle (secondary) red beds which have inherited their pigment from older red beds eroded in the source area.

In addition to their colour, detrital red beds generally share several other characteristics. They are composed principally of rather poorly-sorted sand-stone and mudstone rich in feldspar or in rock fragments. Many of them contain layers of carbonaceous shale or lignite, or follow coal measure sequences without interruption. Mudcracks, ripplemarks and intraforma-tional (clay-pellet) conglomerates are common. Footprints occur widely but other fossils are rare, with the significant exception of Triassic red beds

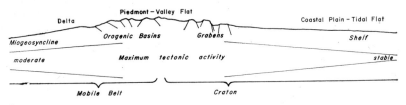

Fig. 1. Diagrammatic distribution of major facies of primary detrital red beds.

In Mobile Belts
1. Delta
2a. Piedmont-Valley Flat

On Craton
2b. Piedmont-Valley Flat
3. Coastal Plain–Tidal Flat

of 'Gondwanaland' which have yielded a magnificent tetrapod fauna. More-over, all of them required predominantly oxidizing conditions of deposition and most of the sequences were formed during episodes of tectonic activity, a relationship reflected in associated conglomeratic facies and volcanic rocks.

Although red beds possess these several common features they do not constitute a single lithofacies. Instead, they differ in important details, lithologic associations and tectonic background. And such features other than colour commonly provide the best evidence of origin. Yet these differ-ences have been obscured in the past by focus on redness alone.

The more distinctive facies described here briefly are essentially the ones first pointed out by Krynine[172] and then elaborated by Dunbar and Rodgers.[83] Such a classification, expressed very diagrammatically in Fig. 1, helps to emphasize similarities and differences among red bed sequences. Nevertheless, it can become arbitrary when applied specifically because major deposits of detrital red beds have accumulated in almost every geographical environment of predominantly non-marine deposition and in every tectonic framework except the eugeosyncline.

Many of the assignments suggested here are tentative at best, but they have been proposed with the conviction that rearrangement of the items will not weaken the usefulness of the general classification.

II.1 *Deltaic Red Beds in Mobile Belts*

Deltaic red beds are extensive, thick sequences of silty shale and sandstone rich in rock fragments (lithic arenite or subgraywacke). The beds are generally rather persistent, and cross-bedding is common. In this facies the red pigment is generally concentrated in dark red to reddish brown shale; most of the sandstone layers and lenses are drab.

Red detritus from upland soils was spread across broad expanses of prograding deltas. The red pigment prevailed in extensive oxidizing environments on flood plains, but was reduced in channels, in lakes and lagoons, and in most of the sediments carried to the sea.

Deltaic red beds commonly accumulated during the development of geosynclines, at times of orogenic activity when paralic or non-marine conditions encroached on the sea. They belong to the molasse facies of Van der Gracht,[299] Krynine[172] and Pettijohn.[231]

Typical examples of deltaic red beds:

Bays formation, middle Ordovician; Tennessee
Juniata and Queenston formations, late Ordovician; New York to Tennessee
Medina formation, early Silurian; New York
Bloomsburg and High Falls formations, late Silurian; New York to Virginia
Catskill facies, middle and late Devonian; New York to Virginia
Bedford shale, early Mississippian; Ohio
Upper part of Shikhotse series, Permian; north China
Late Jurassic and early Cretaceous deposits; eastern Gulf Coast
Ephraim formation, early Cretaceous; south-western Wyoming and adjacent Idaho
Variegated parts of Wayan formation, Cretaceous; south-western Wyoming and adjacent Idaho
Variegated Cenozoic deposits of Burma

Some mobile belt deltaic red beds, like the Bloomsburg and the Ephraim formations, grade laterally into cratonic red or variegated sequences.

Beds of red shale interfingering with, or laterally equivalent to drab deposit and coal beds are essentially a deltaic facies that accumulated in an environment dominated by swamps, lakes and lagoons. Throughout the region, in source area and depositional site as well, a warm, moist climate prevailed which supported extensive coal swamp vegetation. Accordingly, preservation of red sediments depended principally on local oxidizing conditions, and the sequences are commonly variegated.

Typical examples of deltaic red beds with coal measures:

Mauch Chunk and Hinton formations, late Mississippian; Pennsylvania to Virginia
Parts of Monongahela and Conemaugh series, Pennsylvanian; Pennsylvania
Barren Red Coal Measures, Pennsylvanian; Scotland
Keele series and Etruria marl, Pennsylvanian; England
Ottweiler beds, Pennsylvanian; Saar Basin

Shansi series, Pennsylvanian or Permian; north China
Lower Rotliegende, Permian; Hercynian basins, Germany
Dunkard series, Permian; south-western Pennsylvania and West Virginia
Upper part of Damuda series, Permian; India
Estancia series and Aquidauana facies, Permian; central Brazil
Upper part of Ecca series, late Permian; south-west Africa
Molteno beds, late Triassic; South Africa

Lower Carboniferous (Mississippian) Cementstone and Calciferous sand-stone series in northern England and Scotland are related to variegated Coal Measures sequences but also contain minor amounts of gypsum.

II.2 *Piedmont-Valley Flat Red Beds*

The Piedmont-valley flat facies consists of thick wedges of lenticular, poorly-sorted, dark red, maroon and reddish-brown sandstone and mudstone, and marginal conglomerates and breccias that accumulated in orogenic basins and in grabens. The coarse piedmont border facies grades laterally into stream-channel and flood-plain alluvium, with minor non-red lacustrine and swamp deposits.

(*a*) Those sequences that accumulated in *orogenic basins* are a molasse facies, but they differ from deltaic red beds in having been deposited in actively deformed basins at the time of final deformation of a geosyncline. Some of these molasse sequences were deposited in elongated foredeeps in front of rising mountain chains and are characterized by sandstone rich in rock fragments (lithic arenite or subgraywacke), as for example:

Andean red beds, Cretaceous and Cenozoic; Bolivia to Colombia
Red Molasse, middle Cenozoic; Switzerland
Siwalik series, late Cenozoic; India

Other Piedmont-valley flat sequences commonly classified as molasse are thick arkosic red and variegated deposits with associated acidic and inter-mediate volcanic rocks, that accumulated in smaller basins within mountain systems after the principal orogenic activity. Typical examples are:

Hazel formation, late Pre-Cambrian; Texas
Rotliegende and equivalent formations, Permian; Hercynian Basins, Germany, France, Great Britain
Permo-Pennsylvanian arkosic deposits; Ancestral Rockies basins, Oklahoma to Colorado
Andean red beds, Permian; Peru
Verrucano facies, Permo-Triassic; southern border of Hercynian chain, southern Europe
Early Cenozoic deposits; Rocky Mountain basins, Wyoming to New Mexico; central Mexico
Middle Cenozoic deposits; Ebro Basin, Spain

These arkosic sequences are listed here because they occur in mountain belts, but for the purposes of the present discussion there is little that distinguishes them from arkosic red beds that accumulated in grabens.[6] Furthermore, some of them are closely associated with other red bed facies. The poorly-sorted red beds of the Ancestral Rockies basins (Fountain, Maroon, Rico, Cutler, Abo, etc.) grade laterally into extensive finer-grained red deposits and marine limestone sequences. Similarly, the widespread Bunter and Keuper (Triassic) red beds of northern Europe have arkosic basin-border facies that overlie the poorly sorted Rotliegende red beds in Hercynian basins.

Feldspar-rich variegated beds of the Beaufort series and the Stormberg red beds of the Karroo system of South Africa, equivalent red beds in northern Argentina, and the Narrobeen formation in New South Wales are thick Triassic alluvial deposits suggestive of a molasse facies associated with final Gondwanide deformation of the Cape (Samfrau) geosyncline.[87,309] King reference 162, p. 48) has recognized, however, that these 'Gondwanaland' sediments could not have been derived from a high narrow folded mountain system, for the arkosic sandstone and shale 'proclaim their derivation from a terrace of typically Archean rocks'. King then gives little impor-tance to the orogenic setting of the thick alluvial sequences, citing, instead, derivation from normal continental masses with an Archean basement like Africa itself, and (p. 61) broad epeirogenic movement creating axial upwarps that supplied the detritus.

North of the Gondwanide foredeep the Triassic Karroo red beds in central Africa, the Estrado Nova, Rio Do Rasto, Santa Maria, Piramboia, and related red beds of Brazil and Uruguay, and the feldspar-rich Roraima red beds (Triassic?) in south-eastern Venezuela and adjacent British Guiana and Surinam, are thinner, more extensive deposits of vast alluvial plains. Here the sites of deposition were broad cratons, rather than the margin of a deformed geosyncline. On the other hand, in Northern Rhodesia and Madagascar the Karroo system accumulated in grabens, as did equivalent deposits of the Gondwana system in India. This tectonic setting, together with the basaltic lavas associated with Triassic deposits of 'Gondwanaland', links them with sequences of the arkosic red bed–graben suite. More than any other deposits considered in this discussion, 'Gondwanaland' red beds reveal the fallacy of attempting too rigorous a classification of sedimentary sequences.

(b) Piedmont-valley flat red beds in *grabens* are arkosic deposits that accumulated in actively sinking fault basins, and they are commonly associated with basic volcanic rocks. Many of the basins lie along trends of old mobile belts but were faulted after the main deformation of the geo-synclinal mountain system. Red bed sequences in these basins are essentially the same as molasse deposits of intermontane basins. Some of the graben-basins, however, are apparently unrelated to the development of a folded mountain system.

Typical examples of the arkosic red beds in grabens:

Keweenawan series, late Pre-Cambrian; Great Lakes region
Van Horn formation, late Pre-Cambrian?; Texas
Upper Copper Mine River series, late Pre-Cambrian; North-west Territories
Signal Hill formation, late Pre-Cambrian; eastern Newfoundland
Torridon sandstone, late Pre-Cambrian; Scotland
Sparagmite, late Pre-Cambrian; Norway
Jotnian and Dala sandstone, late Pre-Cambrian; Sweden
Waterberg system, late Pre-Cambrian or early Palaeozoic; South Africa
Hankao system, late Pre-Cambrian; China

Old Red Sandstone, Devonian; Great Britain, Norway, Greenland, Spitzbergen
Kagerödsformation, Permo-Triassic; southern Sweden
Newark group, Triassic; eastern North America
Middle Gondwana system, Triassic; India
Upper Karroo system, Triassic; Northern Rhodesia and Madagascar
Cretaceous and early Cenozoic red beds; Gobi Desert to south-eastern China
Sespe formation, Oligocene; southern California
Middle Cenozoic deposits; Auvergne district, France

Many graben red bed sequences grade rapidly into other facies. The Old Red Sandstone, for example, interfingers with marine deposits in south-western England and into an evaporitic facies in the Baltic countries. Late Devonian and Mississippian red beds of Nova Scotia and Quebec are poorly-sorted arkosic basin deposits that interfinger with marine strata and are succeeded by coal-bearing beds. The thick, extensive upper Vindhyan series (late Pre-Cambrian or Cambrian, India) comprises arkosic red beds of a transitional type, for they include deposits of periodic marine invasions, and the Permo-Triassic 'red beds in the (United) States afford, indeed, an almost exact analogy with the Vindhyan-Cambrian beds in the gradation from fluviatile to marine gypsiferous and dolomitic deposits' (reference 9, p. 152).

II.3 *Coastal Plain—Tidal Flat Red Beds on Cratons*

This most familiar and distinctive type of red bed generally consists of extensive, rather well-bedded and well-sorted quartzose to feldspathic, red to orange-red sandstone, siltstone and shale with layers and lenses of evaporites and aeolian sandstone.

Red detritus of these sequences accumulated in a warm to hot, semi-arid to arid climate with a long dry period, on broad featureless flood plains and coastal plains with local dunes and lakes, on wide tidal flats and in shallow restricted seas. Because of the very low gradient, minor changes in topography effected extensive advances and retreats of the sea. Moreover, maximum deposition of gypsum in many of the sequences accompanied the marine incursions, whereas aeolian sand accumulated at times of major regressions.

Typical examples of evaporite-bearing red beds on cratons:

Vernon shale, late Silurian; New York
Permian red beds; Kansas and adjacent Oklahoma
Wichita, Clear Fork, Whitehorse and related groups, Permian; north and central Texas and Oklahoma
Dewey Lake red beds, Permian; west Texas
Yeso and Chalk Bluff formations, Permian; New Mexico
Supai and Hermit formations, Permian; Arizona
Kaibab and Toroweap red beds, Permian; Arizona
Opeche red beds, Permian; South Dakota
Goose Egg formation, Permian; eastern Wyoming
Satanka shale, Permian; Southern Wyoming
Red beds associated with Magnesian limestone, late Permian; England
Ufimian red beds, Permian; Russia
Lykins formation, Permo-Triassic; central Colorado
Shihchienfeng series, Permo-Triassic; north China
Pierce Cányon and Dockum red beds, Triassic; Texas and adjacent New Mexico
Moenkopi and Chinle formations, Triassic; Colorado Plateau
Dolores formation, Triassic; south-west Colorado

Spearfish, Chugwater, and Jelm formations, Triassic; South Dakota, Wyoming and
   adjacent Montana
Bunter and Keuper red beds, Triassic; northern Europe
Tartarian series, Triassic; Russia
Kayenta formation, Juro-Triassic; Colorado Plateau
Gypsum Spring formation and equivalent red bed sequences, middle Jurassic; Wyoming,
   Montana, North Dakota and adjacent Canada
Carmel formation, middle Jurassic; Colorado Plateau
Summerville formation, late Jurassic; Colorado Plateau
Sundance red beds, late Jurassic; Wyoming and South Dakota, North Dakota and
   adjacent Canada
Late Jurassic and early Cretaceous red beds in eastern Mexico

In their setting on cratons, members of this facies are tectonically related
to the graben red-bed suite, but they accumulated farther from their source
and on more stable parts of the cratons. Accordingly, these evaporite-bearing
sequences commonly grade into coarser arkosic basin-border deposits in one
direction. Some cratonic red beds, such as the Moenkopi, Chinle and
Chugwater (Triassic) formations that extend westwards to the Rocky Mountain geosyncline, form red-bed tongues without evaporites (Woodside,
Ankareh, Wood shale and equivalent red beds in south-western Wyoming
and adjacent Utah and Idaho) that interfinger with thick marine sequences.[176]
The Sundance red beds (late Jurassic) also extend westwards to the Rocky
Mountain geosyncline, but here they grade into the thick evaporite-bearing
Preuss red beds with a marine limestone tongue.[148]

   The widespread variegated Morrison (late Jurassic) and Cloverly (early
Cretaceous) and equivalent formations of the Rocky Mountain region
resemble red bed–evaporite sequences in their extensive distribution and their
cratonic setting, but differ in being deposits of broad alluvial plains without
marine incursions and accordingly contain insignificant amounts of evaporite.
To the west these thin alluvial sheets grade into variegated deltaic deposits
(Ephraim and Wayan formations) of the Rocky Mountain geosyncline.
Similarly, the thin sequences of Triassic red beds of eastern South America,
and south and central Africa are extensive cratonic deposits of alluvial plains
that contain no evaporite.

II.4 *Distribution of Red Beds*

   Confirmation of the importance of tectonic control of primary detrital red
beds and variegated sequences comes from the observation that the sequences
are not scattered randomly through space and time. Instead, certain general
areas were sites of red bed accumulation during several geological periods:

Great Britain and Norway: late Pre-Cambrian, Devonian, Pennsylvanian, Permian,
   Triassic
Eastern North America: Ordovician, Silurian, Devonian, Mississippian, Pennsylvanian,
   Permian, Triassic
Southern and Central Rocky Mountain region: Pennsylvanian, Permian, Triassic,
   Jurassic, early Cretaceous, early Cenozoic
East flank of central Andes: Permian, Triassic, Jurassic, Cretaceous, early Cenozoic
China: late Pre-Cambrian, Permo-Triassic, late Jurassic, late Cretaceous, early Cenozoic,
   late Cenozoic

Table III. Distribution of Red Beds in Time and Space

	China	Europe	North America	Western South America	Eastern South America	Africa	India	Australia
Jurassic	Aeolian sands	Marine	Marine / Aeolian sands	Aeolian sands	Aeolian sands		Aeolian sands	
Triassic	RED BEDS	RED BEDS	RED BEDS	?	RED BEDS	RED BEDS		RED BEDS
Permian	Evaporites / Coal measures	Evaporites / Aeolian sands / Marine tongues	Evaporites / Aeolian sands / Marine tongues	RED BEDS	Coal measures	Coal measures		Coal measures / Glacial / Coal measures
Pennsylvanian		Coal measures	Coal measures	Marine	Glacial	Glacial		Glacial
Mississippian				Coal measures	Glacial			

Each area had its own distinctive tectonic development and consequent succession of red bed facies, however. In the southern and central Rocky Mountain region late Palaeozoic block faulting and early Mesozoic cratonic conditions were followed by a late Mesozoic geosynclinal setting and early Cenozoic intermontane basins. In China, on the other hand, repeated block faulting following intense orogeny in late Palaeozoic time produced a succession of fault basins filled with non-marine red beds locally associated with lignite and gypsum.[323]

Late Palaeozoic and early Mesozoic events occurred in a rather similar sequence in the northern and southern hemispheres. In each continent, except in western South America, extensive deposits of red beds followed accumulation of coal measures. This succession, and the common association of variegated deposits with coal measures in both hemispheres, points to a close relationship between the geographic–tectonic setting of red beds and coal measures.

The fact that the succession started about a period later throughout much of 'Gondwanaland' implies that the development of widespread Permo-Triassic red beds was not dependent on some global control alone. Other factors, perhaps partly tectonic, must have affected first Europe, North America, and western South America, and then the other continents. Red beds in 'Gondwanaland' never reached the stage of extensive evaporite deposition, but the episode ended with widespread aeolian sands, as it did in North America and China.

III. Analytical Data

III.1 *Detrital Grains*

Most red beds contain considerable feldspar or rock fragments and magnetite, ilmenite and specularite among the sand and silt grains. Those deposits containing abundant feldspar accumulated in tectonically active basins as a result of deep erosion of crystalline rocks of crustal blocks, whereas most of the red beds containing abundant fragments of sedimentary and low-grade metamorphic rocks accumulated in mobile belts during or at the end of a geosynclinal cycle (reference 172, pp. 64–65; reference 229, pp. 628–630).

The presence of abundant feldspar in many red sequences has often been taken as evidence of restricted chemical weathering in cold or arid climates. But weathering of feldspar in the source area depends not only on a suitable climate but also on sufficient time. In regions of high relief and rapid dissection feldspar may be eroded before it is decomposed, even though the climate favours alteration. Krynine[169] has described the accumulation of arkose in tropical climates with heavy rainfall in Tabasco, southern Mexico; his review (references 170, 173, pp. 132–143) of processes in humid tropical uplands emphasizes this as a normal situation. In spite of the fact that the mountain slopes are blanketed with red soil, it is protected from rapid erosion by dense vegetation. But the slightly weathered bedrock, such as described by Harrison (reference 130, pp. 60–77) as lying below lateritic profiles in

Table IV. Chemical Analyses of Red and Drab Sedimentary Rocks. With numbered references to bibliography.

	Pre-Cambrian Signal Hill	Silurian Vernon shale				Devonian Old Red Sandstone					Mississippian Bedford shale		Penn. Coal Measures	Upper Permian of Kansas			
	red-brown arkose						Lower		Upper				shale	shale		Taloga shale	
	red	red	red	drab	drab	red	red	red	red	drab	red	drab	red	red	red	red	drab
SiO₂	71·38	52·30	56·90	57·79	33·14	70·87	73·32	59·24	85·68	92·13	57·20	61·70	64·06	50·66	47·49	60·86	50·50
Al₂O₃	14·25	18·85	24·14	16·15	11·26	11·66	11·31	6·65	11·76	4·42	13·06	18·68	20·6	16·29	18·17	10·42	12·74
Fe₂O₃	4·75 }6·55	6·26	— }5·20	2·31	2·31	2·38	3·54	2·02	0·52	0·37	14·08	3·36	6·84	6·30	8·82	— }3·35	3·84 }9·28?
FeO	0·46	1·26	5·20	1·06		1·81	0·72	0·31	0·23	0·33	1·36	1·68	0·32	0·89	0·84	3·35	2·13
TiO₂						0·54					1·20	1·12	0·62	0·74	0·80	0·96	0·94
P₂O₅						0·11					0·15	0·08		0·04	0·08	0·12	0·06
CaO	3·01	3·36	0·94		16·50	1·79	1·35	16·04	1·0	1·27	0·65	0·48	0·12	1·36	1·26	0·81	12·88
MgO	0·46	4·49	1·37		8·77	3·03	0·24	0·12	Tr	0·14	1·62	1·38	0·04	7·47	6·92	12·88	19·54
MnO				0·21		Tr	Tr	0·50	Tr	0·24	0·04	0·02	0·09	0·05	0·05		
Na₂O	2·28	1·35	1·0	1·22	1·21	1·77	2·34	0·19	0·12	0·11	0·35	0·2	0·44	0·52	0·60	0·24	0·20
K₂O	1·99	4·65	3·69	4·11	2·56	2·29	6·16	2·30	1·57	0·72	2·60	2·9	0·91	3·17	4·37	3·57	2·13
SO₃												0·22					
CO₂	3·04		1·08	3·42	20·48	1·09	0·92	12·16	0·07		0·25	0·12			0·41	0·04	
Cl																	
H₂O⁻	0·21	5·30 }	4·36 }	4·50 }	2·88	0·26 }	0·30 }	1·0		0·43 }	1·96	1·17		5·94	4·21 }	6·52 }	9·28
H₂O⁺	1·20					2·50 }	1·29 }	Tr	1·57	0·42	5·45	4·50	5·85	6·37	6·23 }		
organic matter											0·18	0·68					
Fe‴ : Fe″	10·3	4·97		2·19		1·31	4·9	6·5	2·26	1·12	10·4	2·0	21·6	7·1	10·5		
Ref.	42			3		250		6·5		192	177		197	305			285

igneous loss

Table IV—*continued.*

	Permian — Lower Rotliegende mudstone		Lower Triassic — Bunter sandstone					Upper Triassic — Keuper marl											
	red	drab	red	drab	red	red	red	red	drab	red	drab	red	drab	red	drab	red	drab	red	drab
SiO_2	62·86	64·04	93·4	94·0	87·1	55·58	60·58	49·67	50·37	50·91	50·84	48·22	48·91	52·11	45·46	55·08	56·46	53·62	53·40
Al_2O_3	17·63	17·10	1·77	2·35	3·9	10·26	22·3	14·16	14·78	12·98	13·12	16·40	15·15	18·06	14·40	14·16	13·52	20·53	24·49
Fe_2O_3	7·53	2·79	1·33	0·53	1·3 }	3·83	8·25	3·12	1·12	3·8	0·87	3·94	0·92	3·66	0·05	3·20	0·87	3·19	1·79
FeO	0·14	0·83	0·15	0·07		3·01		1·65	1·73	0·91	0·96	1·03	1·62	1·16	1·14	1·12	1·43	1·60	1·77
TiO_2	2·35	1·26	0·12	0·16		0·54	0·69	0·62	0·57	0·33	0·42	Tr	Tr						
P_2O_5	0·14	0·12					0·37	Tr	Tr	Tr	Tr	Tr	Tr						
CaO	0·56	2·42	Tr	Tr	2·7	5·66		4·73	5·31	5·18	7·37	4·21	6·10	5·74	13·31	6·13	7·44	5·49	4·32
MgO	0·64	1·18	0·33	0·25	1·1	11·30	0·68	3·81	4·90	5·42	6·10	3·44	4·3	0·73	2·10	0·90	1·26	4·75	3·28
MnO	0·05	0·06				0·05	Tr												
Na_2O	0·18	0·19	0·25	0·3	0·8	0·19	0·4	9·79 }	7·08	6·43 }	4·20 }	9·81 }	8·05					2·91 }	2·37
K_2O	2·90	2·93	1·66	1·7	1·3	3·01	3·4												
SO_3								Tr	Tr	Tr	Tr	Tr	Tr					0·09	0·08
CO_2		2·55		1·4				8·10	10·16	10·21	13·01	8·79	11·60	5·31	12·12	6·23	7·46	3·31	4·74
Cl							Tr	Tr	Tr	Tr	Tr	Tr	Tr						
H_2O^-	0·30	0·30																	
H_2O^+	4·96	4·32	0·83 }	0·56 }	0·5 }	3·45 }	9·62 }	4·22 }	3·8 }	3·72 }	3·01 }	4·16 }	3·35 }	4·04	2·71	4·97	4·31	4·45 }	3·71 }
organic matter								0·12	0·17	0·10	0·09								
$Fe'''; Fe''$	50·2	3·35	8·87	7·58		155	inf.	1·89	1·69	4·17	0·91	3·83	0·56	3·16	0·04	2·85	0·60	1·99	1·01
Ref.	96	96	233	215	215	155	215	213	213	213	213	213	213	213	213	213	213	197	197

Table IV—continued.

	Triassic					Upper Triassic — Newark group										Eocene	
	Spearfish shale		Chugwater			red-brown sandstone					red shale					Wasatch mudstone	
	red	red	siltstone red	siltstone drab	clay drab											red	drab
SiO₂	56·20	58·32	69·77	72·21	47·35	88·13	80·53	77·70	69·94	76·43	73·0	51·02	51·2	58·6	44·88	59·83	60·16
Al₂O₃	11·50	8·59	9·35	9·21	20·05	5·81	9·92	11·81	13·55	10·65	3·20	22·45	20·2	20·66	20·29	16·26	15·53
Fe₂O₃	3·64	2·04	2·84	0·64	2·78	1·77 }	1·99 }	1·89 }	2·48 }	7·13 }	10·0 }	9·42 }	8·1 }	5·86 }	16·46 }	4·31	2·67
FeO	0·65	0·18	0·35	0·28	0·29	0·31										1·40	0·70
TiO₂	0·77	0·48	0·55	0·57	0·43											0·58	0·74
P₂O₅					0·08												
CaO	5·83	8·45	4·11	4·94	3·78	0·20	0·63	0·55	3·09	0·84	4·93	2·63	3·8	4·76	5·10	1·56	0·37
MgO	4·23	3·65	3·02	2·95	2·40	0·53	0·63	0·43	Tr	0·92	0·90	3·37	5·4	0·65	5·20	1·96	3·57
MnO	0·10	0·07					Tr	Tr	0·70	Tr		0·93	0·10		Tr	0·03	0·02
Na₂O	0·98	0·72	1·75	1·52	0·17	2·63	5·67	6·89	5·43	0·97		2·18		6·48	2·42	0·82	1·44
K₂O	3·74	2·71	3·03	2·06	4·31	0·06			3·30	0·73		1·38		1·44		3·87	2·96
SO₃	2·26	0·43	0·43	0·08												0·91	0·62
CO₂	5·72	12·08	3·80	4·32						Tr	Tr	2·81	5·6	0·80		0·10	0·08
Cl	Tr	Tr										1·30				0·02	0·02
H₂O⁻	1·60	0·52			5·36	0·26 }	1·14 }	0·82 }	1·01 }	2·20 }	1·0 }	2·54 }	1·7 }	0·65 }	5·55 }	3·28	5·52
H₂O⁺	2·84	1·40	1·69	1·43	12·98	0·23										4·71	5·79
organic																0·17	0·04
Fe''':Fe''	5·6	11·3	8·1	2·28	9·6	5·7										3·08	3·83
Ref.	248	248	156	156	157	80	71	268	268	50	52	52	52	52	52	265	ᵃ

ᵃ W. H. Bradley personal communication.

British Guiana and by Brückner (reference 41, p. 308) as rotten country rock at the base of lateritic profiles in central Africa, can readily be eroded in steep canyons during periodic downpours. Floras associated with several arkosic red bed sequences[173, 242, 304] point to their origin in warm, humid climates, thus implying that erosion must have outstripped decomposition. The mixture of fresh and decomposed feldspar in these deposits is additional evidence of just such a process.

Magnetite and ilmenite have been reported as the most abundant accessory minerals in many red beds, and commonly, but not invariably, they are rare in associated drab beds. These detrital minerals, and feldspar, point to igneous and metamorphic source rocks for many red beds. But the data do not mean that 'the prime requisite for red bed formation is an igneous or metamorphic source rich in these minerals' as claimed by Miller and Folk.[205] On the contrary, some red beds undoubtedly have been derived from weathered sedimentary rocks. The New Red Sandstone of England, for example, was derived at least in part from red soils developed on the upper Coal Measures.[84] The *sine qua non* for accumulation of red beds, rather than being ilmenite–magnetite-bearing source rocks, is an actively eroded upland weathering in a warm moist climate, as pointed out long ago by Raymond (reference 239, p. 241). Although this requisite is essentially independent of the mineral composition of the source rock, detrital magnetite–ilmenite grains do provide an important clue to conditions of accumulation. Their presence emphasizes the rôle of oxidizing environments in preserving red pigment as well as magnetite and ilmenite at the place of deposition, and the importance of local reducing environments in eliminating both pigment and the 'iron ores', regardless of the climate at the depositional site.

In recent palaeomagnetic investigations of red beds by Creer, Irving, and Runcorn,[59] Blackett,[27] Irving,[149] and Creer,[57] X-ray analyses of the black ferromagnetic grains in the Torridon and Old Red sandstones reveal that the mineral is principally specularite (haematite) with intergrowths of ilmenite or leucoxene, a triangular texture indicating a cubic host and small remnants of magnetite. In fact, no magnetite grains have been found in any normal red sandstone analysed so far. Creer (reference 57, p. 127) has shown that iron oxide grains in a black Pre-Cambrian sandstone consist of titaniferous magnetite with a triangular texture, and that some grains are altered to haematite in varying degrees. This observation, together with the fact that specularite is not widely known in source rocks, suggests that the haematite grains in red beds may have been derived from titaniferous magnetite in the source rock. Irving (reference 149, p. 101) on the other hand, implies without adequate evidence that source rocks containing magnetic specularite are common in many parts of the world. The absence of magnetite and ilmenite in the Torridon and Old Red Sandstones is inconsistent with most reports on the mineral content of red bed sequences. Proper understanding of the situation requires many more detailed data regarding the distribution of iron and iron–titanium oxide minerals in sedimentary rocks and red soils. Furthermore, it is not known whether the magnetic intensity of the grains is due to the specularite or to the small quantities of magnetite which they appear to contain (reference 149, p. 103).

Table V. Iron Oxide Content of Red and Drab Sedimentary Rocks

	Reference		Fe_2O_3	FeO	Fe''' : Fe''
Pre-Cambrian Signal Hill arkose	42	red	4·75	0·46	10·3
		drab	2·54	2·82	0·9
Silurian Vernon shale	207	red	2·25	0·75	3·0
		drab	0·0	1·19	0·0
Permo-Pennsylvanian Maroon mudstone	352	red	2·79	0·6	4·64
		red	7·0	1·0	7·0
		drab	3·63	1·0	3·63
Permian of Texas	123	red	5·15	*1·28	4·02
		drab	1·71	1·28	1·34
		red	6·0	0·29	20·7
		drab	1·28	1·02	1·78
Lower Triassic Bunter sandstone	215	red	1·20	0·38	3·15
		drab	0·15	0·07	2·14
Upper Triassic Keuper marl	213	red	3·39	0·97	3·5
		drab	0·87	1·12	0·78
		red	3·12	0·87	3·6
		drab	0·66	0·92	0·71
		red	3·14	1·45	2·16
		drab	1·04	1·64	0·63
Triassic Spearfish shale	248	red	4·61	1·24	3·72
		drab	1·85	1·04	1·78
Triassic Chugwater siltstone	291	red	3·50	1·04	3·02
		drab	1·03	1·04	0·99
	304	red	3·28	0·28	11·7
		drab	2·34	0·63	3·7
		red	1·75	0·49	3·5
		drab	0·86	0·31	2·66
Lower Eocene Wind River mudstone	304	red	7·91	0·19	41·6
		drab	6·24	0·38	16·5
Willwood mudstone	304	red	4·18	0·58	7·2
		drab	2·77	0·52	5·32

III.2 Chemical Composition

Chemical analyses of red beds and associated non-red beds are presented in Tables IV and V, and their iron oxide contents summarized in Figs. 2 and 3. Similar, but less inclusive, data have been assembled several times in earlier studies of red beds (Table II). It must be emphasized that direct comparison of these analyses will be misleading because the samples differ in grain size and their chemical composition is closely related to their texture. Furthermore the state of hydration of the ferric oxide, which is a basic control of the colour of the rocks, can not be determined by chemical analysis.

The data reveal the following relationships:

(1) Although red rocks do not owe their colour simply to a greater total iron content or to a greater ferric iron content than non-red rocks, there is more of both in most red specimens.

(2) In any pair of samples from the same formation the red one, with rare exceptions, contains more Fe_2O_3 than the drab one.

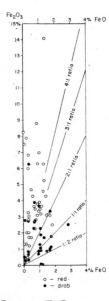

Fig. 2.
FeO and Fe_2O_3 content of red and drab sedimentary rocks.

Data from Tables IV and V.

(3) Almost all red rocks contain an excess of Fe_2O_3 over FeO greater than about 2:1. Some drab rocks also have ratios exceeding 2:1, but most of them are less than 2:1.

(4) The general difference between the iron content of red and non-red rocks suggests that drab beds have been derived from red ones not just by

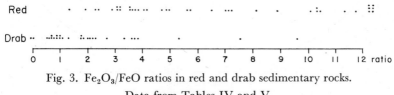

Fig. 3. Fe_2O_3/FeO ratios in red and drab sedimentary rocks.
Data from Tables IV and V.

reduction of ferric oxide, which would result in a corresponding increase in the amount of FeO in drab beds, but also by the removal of iron oxide, as proposed by Keller[156] and Eichhoff and Reineck.[92]

(5) Those drab beds that have a high ferric oxide content probably contain it in a silicate,[156] presumably a clay mineral, rather than in a yellow, brown, or red ferric oxide mineral. Recently, Keller[160] has identified

H

glauconitic mica in a drab bed containing 13·11 per cent of Fe_2O_3 and 1·31 per cent of FeO. On the basis of this evidence all drab beds are not the result of simple reduction and solution. Some apparently form under conditions with an oxidation potential high enough to maintain the iron in the ferric state, but combined with a silicate rather than with oxygen as a free ferric oxide.

III.3 *Clay Fraction*

A. *Red Upland Soils*

The presumption that the clay fraction of most detrital red beds was derived from red upland soils makes information about the clay minerals and iron oxides in this source material especially significant in the present inquiry.

The abundant literature on laterites and lateritic soils published during the last twenty years[212] reveals that they occur extensively throughout tropical and subtropical regions (Fig. 4) with seasonal rainfall, having

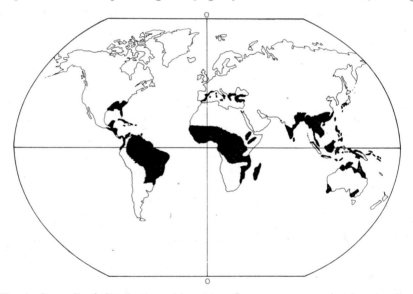

Fig. 4. Generalized distribution of lateritic soils, terra rossa, and red and yellow podsolic soils.

developed on a variety of bedrock in well-drained uplands with a fluctuating water table. With few exceptions these soils form in acidic, oxidizing environments where rainfall exceeds 40 in. (102 cm) a year and the mean annual temperature is above 60°F (16°C). Terranes of more easily weathered limestone and basic igneous rocks produce red soil in a mean annual temperature of 55 to 60°F and with annual rainfall of 20 to 40 in. In fact, the general climatic requirement for the development of red soil is so fundamental that many writers[46,53,89,115,172,212] have postulated earlier, warm, moist episodes to explain red soils now found in arid regions.

Detailed analyses of the clay fraction of laterites and lateritic soils[2,46,89,95,129,174,298,301,306] show that they are characterized by hydrated aluminium oxides, kaolinite minerals of the 1 : 1 or 2-layer clay mineral group, and haematite (anhydrous ferric oxide), especially in the upper part of the profile. Under certain conditions the aluminum hydrates (bauxite) are produced directly from the parent material, but commonly the minerals of a lateritic soil result from successive stages of desilication and dehydration accompanied by the removal of alkalis and alkaline earths.[121,128,160] Earlier stages still in effect in the lower part of the profile, are characterized by goethite (hydrated ferric oxide), probably by hydrohaematite, and by 2 : 1 and 2 : 2 clay minerals, and these products may dominate the entire profile under conditions of less intense weathering. In terra rossa of the drier Mediterranean belt, for example, illite is commonly the most abundant clay mineral,[180,216] perhaps derived in part at least from parent material.

B. *Ferric Oxide Minerals in Soils*

Basic information about the ferric oxide minerals and relationships among them (Fig. 5 and 6) have been discussed by Posnjak and Merwin,[235] Palache, Berman and Frondel,[226] Van Houten[304] and others.[30,105,106,107,175,190,260,295]

Lepidocrocite (γ-$Fe_2O_3 \cdot H_2O$ or γ-$FeO \cdot OH$), a hydrated ferric oxide dimorphous with goethite which is generally ruby-red to reddish brown and orange, is prepared as a yellow colloidal precipitate which will form along with goethite from the same chalybeate solution. Lepidocrocite is not as stable as goethite, for it dehydrates to haematite (α-Fe_2O_3) on grinding, and slowly at temperatures as low as 95°C,[107] and to maghemite (γ-Fe_2O_3) on heating to high temperatures (170° to 400°C).

The natural occurrence of lepidocrocite is similar to that of goethite but apparently it is rarer. It forms some iron rust and concretions in hardpans, and has been found in some British soils,[40] as well as in a relict lateritic soil in the east-central part of the Sahara Desert (reference 174, p. 130).

Maghemite (γ-Fe_2O_3), an anhydrous ferromagnetic oxide with crystal structure and magnetic properties like those of magnetite, is typically brown, but the colour varies from yellow to dark red according to particle size. It can be prepared by dehydrating lepidocrocite at high temperatures and by oxidizing magnetite. Maghemite is metastable with respect to haematite, altering to it extremely slowly at ordinary temperatures, and at an increasing rate with rising temperature.

Maghemite is formed in nature by supergene processes, especially by weathering of magnetite and rusting of iron and steel. Although commonly said to be rare, maghemite has been recorded in most of the detailed analyses of lateritic soils, such as those by Allen,[2] Carroll and Woof,[46] Eyles,[95] Henin and Le Borgne,[137] Edwards,[89] Kubiena,[174] and Stavrou,[278] in Dutch soils by Van der Marel[300] and in early Cretaceous bauxite by Gladpovsky and Sharovo.[109] Van Kersen (reference 306, p. 363) has reported a magnetic

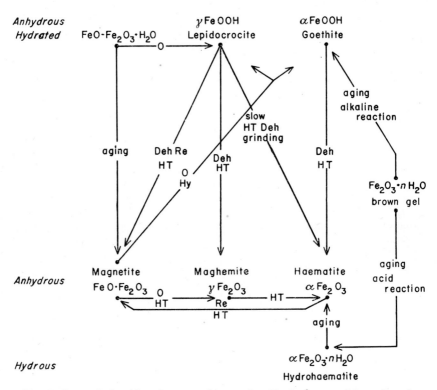

Fig. 5. Interrelationship of some oxides and oxide hydrates of iron, based on laboratory studies. Deh—dehydration; HT—high temperature; Hy—hydration; O—oxidation; Re—reduction

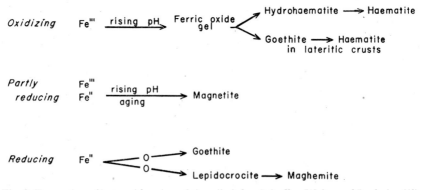

Fig. 6. Formation of iron oxide minerals in soils (after Scheffer, Welte and Ludwieg [260])

haematite in British Guiana laterites, which may be maghemite, and Bock (reference 30, p. 155) states that maghemite is found in many soils and rock formations, but he cites few examples.

Goethite (α-$Fe_2O_3 \cdot H_2O$ or α-$FeO \cdot OH$) is a hydrated ferric oxide which is yellow to brown. It forms from a common colloidal precipitate in laboratory preparations at normal temperatures and pressures, and in nature it is the ubiquitous brown alteration product of iron-bearing minerals weathered in an oxidizing environment, even in arid climates. Goethite is stable under normal conditions, dehydrating to haematite at about 130°C. It has been assumed to be the pigment of most yellow and brown soils, but some of this may be hydrohaematite.

Haematite (α-Fe_2O_3), is an anhydrous ferric oxide which is dull to bright red in ochrous varieties. The degree of agglomeration or particle size affects the colour: minute particles produce a brown colour, larger particles redder colours. Haematite is the most stable form of Fe_2O_3 and the only one stable at all temperatures. In laboratory preparations a brown colloidal ferric oxide in a neutral to acidic reaction ages to amorphous brown hydrohaematite and finally to crystalline anhydrous red haematite.

Haematite is the principal pigment in red soils, presumably formed by the aging of brown colloidal ferric oxide (see reference 190, pp. 307–308; 260, p. 55) under conditions of intense weathering accompanied by bacterial action.[127, 240] Gheith,[107] however, thinks that the notion that there is a yellow colloid which yields goethite and a brown one which yields haematite is erroneous, because both yellow and brown varieties occur side by side in nature and both age to goethite. Red haematite is also formed by weathering under the dehydrating influence of saline solutions,[125, 277]

Available information about the iron oxide minerals of particular interest in a study of red beds shows that under laboratory conditions the hydrated oxides, lepidocrocite and goethite, can be produced from colloidal gels by chemical reactions different from those producing hydrohaematite and haematite. Excess water can be removed from all of these forms at surface temperature. Only at high temperature, however, can the hydrates be altered to anhydrous oxides. Accordingly, the two common ferric oxide minerals, goethite and haematite, are stable at normal temperatures and pressures.

Theoretically brown goethite in soil cannot produce red haematite by spontaneous dehydration or aging. Yet the presence of goethite in the lower part of lateritic profiles and of haematite in the upper part points to the conclusion that the haematite was derived from goethite by aging of the hydrate (reference 95, p. 41; reference 272, p. 157; reference 212, pp. 301–302; reference 306, pp. 320, 326, 363; and reference 260, pp. 57–60). This interpretation is not necessarily a direct contradiction of the laboratory data, however, for dehydration and aging in soils are processes far more complex than the dehydration of laboratory experiments. Moreover, Scheffer, Welte and Ludwieg[260] believe that the reaction occurs only in lateritic crusts (Fig. 6). Evidence that the process in nature is not simple dehydration with heating is afforded by the persistence of both lepidocrocite and goethite in an ancient laterite exposed in the central part of the Sahara Desert for many thousands of years.[174]

Mackenzie (reference 190, pp. 307–310) and Scheffer, Welte and Ludwieg (reference 260, pp. 57–60) have recently emphasized the importance of brown ferric oxide gel or amorphous hydrohaematite as a pigment in brown soils and the precursor of haematite in red soils (Fig. 6), and Hamdi and Iberg[126] found that an amorphous brown ferric oxide gel is the main iron oxide in the clay fraction of alluvium of the lower Nile. The fact that the amorphous ferric oxide cannot be identified by X-ray methods may explain why it has not been reported more widely. Furthermore, Scheffer, Welte and Ludwieg (reference 260, p. 60) have suggested that hydrohaematite may be the principal ferric oxide in brown soils of cooler climates where aging to haematite has been retarded. In warmer climates, on the other hand, the process of laterization not only concentrates ferric oxide in the profile but it also favours complete aging of hydrohaematite, thus producing the abundant red haematite pigment.

C. *Transportation and Deposition of Clay Fraction*

(1) *Ferric Oxide Pigment.* X-ray analyses show that haematite is the predominant ferric oxide present in almost all of the red beds tested,[280] and it may confidently be assumed to be the principal pigment in most red beds. But just as detailed analyses of soils continue to expand the known occurrences of ferric oxides other than the common ones, so many more detailed analyses of red beds are needed before we know much about their iron oxide mineral content. The fact that some red upland soils contain lepidocrocite and maghemite in addition to haematite and goethite, suggests that these minerals may also have been inherited in some red beds. Moreover, Hofer and Weller[141] and Bock (reference 30, p. 155) cite evidence that maghemite is the principal iron oxide in some red sandstones.

In most red beds the pigment is very finely diffused, permeating the entire rock mass. It occurs in mudstone layers, in the matrix of poorly-sorted sandstone, and as coating on sand grains. Commonly, shale and mudstone are redder than associated sandstone because the pigment is concentrated in the clay fraction. On the other hand, the finer-grained rocks, because of the greater total surface area presented by the many small grains, require more haematite to produce a colour comparable to that of a coarser-grained red rock. Particle size and degree of agglomeration of the ferric oxide crystals are also important factors controlling its colouring effect. The fact that agglomeration of haematite in soil is retarded by the presence of calcium[234] may account for non-red beds commonly having a higher calcium content than associated red beds.

The way the ferric oxide in red beds was probably transported from the source areas has been elucidated by detailed investigations of the rôle of clay minerals in the transportation of iron oxides.[45,103] Iron oxide is held as coatings on the surface of clay mineral platelets and on mineral grains of silt and sand size as one of the effects of weathering and soil-forming processes. The kaolinite clays of the tropics with their bright red colouration due to haematite and other ferric oxides is a conspicuous example of this process, but iron oxide probably occurs as a coating on other clay minerals as well. Carroll (reference 45, p. 25) found that ferric oxides remain attached to clay particles deposited in oxidizing environments, but are changed to the ferrous state and taken into solution under reducing conditions, as through metabolic processes of bacteria.

Preliminary calculations of the thermodynamic properties of goethite and haematite by Schmalz [261] also corroborate a primary detrital origin of the red pigment. These data suggest that, except where present in the late members of an evaporite sequence or where precipitated by organic agencies, haematite in sediments is the product of subaerial weathering in the source area.

The pigment in most red beds presumably originated in soils developed on the more common types of igneous, sedimentary and metamorphic rocks. Locally, however, some of it was eroded from volcanic terranes. Red mudstone in the Calciferous sandstone series (Carboniferous) of Scotland (reference 250, p. 132) and in the Etruria marl of England [253] was apparently derived in part from weathering of contemporaneous basalts. Similarly, Pocock (in reference 253, p. 26) has suggested that the variegated early Eocene Reading beds of the London Basin may have been derived from decomposition of early Cenozoic volcanic rocks of Great Britain. These examples call to mind the rather common association of red beds and volcanic rocks, implying that weathering of relatively easily decomposed volcanic rocks in the source area may have produced some of the red pigment in other red sequences.

Although many lines of evidence suggest a detrital origin of the pigment in red beds, the proposition is not supported by our meagre information about recent alluvium of tropical rivers. Contrary to the implications of the hypothesis, apparently there is no widespread accumulation of red sediment in the tropics today. Some rivers draining lateritic uplands have deposited red to reddish-brown alluvium, as in Surinam (reference 147, p. 62) and in the Gran Chaco (reference 124, pp. 159–160); but many tropical rivers do not carry red detritus. For example, the lower Amazon River, though commonly said to transport red mud, actually has dirty yellowish-red water and light gray to gray-brown alluvium (reference 154, pp. 45, 57; reference 275, p. 609), and the Senegal River in west Africa deposits yellow-brown detritus. [292] It should be noted, however, that these are large through-flowing rivers contaminated by numerous tributaries and incessantly moving their sediments toward the sea. By this continual reworking considerable organic matter is incorporated in the alluvium. Rivers that deposited many of the red bed sequences in the past, on the other hand, were probably shorter streams flowing directly from upland areas to continually aggrading lowlands. In addition to this source of uncertainty about the effectiveness of a direct derivation of red pigment from lateritic soils, the hypothesis does not adequately account for the familiar observation of a predominance of red and reddish-brown colours and a paucity of yellowish-brown colours in ancient mudstones compared with modern alluvium.

In order to account for these observations a supplementary process of aging of hydrohaematite is apparently required. According to the supplemented proposition ferric oxides concentrated in red upland soils provide an adequate supply of potential pigment. Rapid deposition in an oxidizing environment preserves the inherited oxides, and with burial and aging brown hydrohaematite is converted to additional haematite. In contrast, mud that receives little free oxide from the source area or is deposited in reducing environments, produces drab sedimentary rock. As a result of this process most yellow-brown sediments are converted either to drab or to red rocks. But the conversion is not universal or complete, especially in porous sandstone. The possible rôle of hydrohaematite in the formation of red beds, as outlined here, cannot be evaluated until the distribution and behaviour of the mineral has been investigated in detail.

The essence of this supplementary process was put forward by Crosby [62, 63] and accepted by Barrell (reference 19, pp. 287–293) and Krynine.[173] Krynine believes that 'dehydration of yellow iron oxide into red anhydrous oxide takes place at surface temperatures in many warm regions, but it can not be duplicated in the laboratory unless much higher temperatures are used' (p. 144). 'It seems that some of the red color of the Triassic is due to early post-depositional subaerial weathering of the deposited sediments' (p. 159), 'and is nothing but the formation of a red soil on alluvium' (p. 145). Considered in detail, however, leaching and other soil-forming processes of upland areas where haematite is readily produced, are less effective in lowland areas of aggradation. Here continual accumulation hinders the development of soil profiles, thus retarding the aging and dehydration of ferric oxides. It is possible, of course, that very slow aggradation in warm, humid climates may enable inherited hydrohaematite to age more rapidly to haematite, or alluvium containing easily-altered volcanic debris may produce haematite directly. Distinctive dark red to lavender mudstone in the Chinle (late Triassic) red beds of the Colorado Plateau, and the variegated Morrison (late Jurassic), Cloverly (early Cretaceous) and early Cenozoic deposits in the Rocky Mountain region probably resulted in part from weathering of volcanic debris as it accumulated slowly on broad flood plains. Nevertheless, flood-plain weathering probably did not operate as a general process in the origin of red bed pigment.

Much of the past prejudice favouring deserts as the environment of red bed deposition has stemmed from the assumption that aridity was required to produce haematite-rich deposits, even though Russell [257] and Blanckenhorn [28] pointed out long ago that deserts are not characterized by red soil. The minor amount found there has inherited its pigment from older red sediments or was formed during earlier, more humid times. Admittedly, many of the common features of red bed sequences, such as mud-cracks, salt casts, mud-pellet conglomerate and interbedded evaporite do form in deserts, but the most important characteristic, sediment rich in free ferric oxide, is not produced there.

Deep burial and high temperature have also been cited as producing red beds through the dehydration of goethite. The fact that there is no consistent relationship between depth of burial and redness of formations shows that this process alone does not explain the origin of red beds.

Robb[252] and Valeton[297] maintain that haematitic pigment of some red beds was derived from alteration of biotite during and after sedimentation. Miller and Folk[205] also believe that 'most of the red color develops at the site of deposition' (p. 344), principally by destruction of magnetite, ilmenite and other iron-bearing minerals in reducing environments and precipitation of the released iron as haematite coatings on sand grains and in the clay minerals in oxidizing areas.

A post-depositional precipitation of haematite is not an adequate general explanation of the origin of red bed pigment. Nevertheless, some modification of the inherited pigmenting material may have taken place, especially in extensive red beds associated with evaporites. Swineford[285] believes that the upper Permian red beds of Kansas are primary detrital deposits but that the uniform orange-red colour may be attributed to thorough redistribution of ferric oxide from complex colloids in contact with highly alkaline Permian sea water. Moreover, redistribution of haematite probably produced the red coating on sand grains in porous aeolian sandstone in some red bed sequences. The actual process by which the red carapace was deposited after rounding of the grains at the place of deposition is difficult to decipher, however. Dunham[84] has suggested 'that finely-divided iron oxide was in suspension in the lagoon waters in which these sandstones accumulated, and that each grain became coated during sedimentation. The alternative possibilities that the ferric oxide was in solution or in colloidal dispersion in the waters, seem less likely.' Shotton[273] has pointed out, on the contrary, that muddy lagoons are not common features in vast areas of dune sand, yet great thicknesses of aeolian sand do have haematite-coated grains.

The nature and origin of the pigment in red beds has recently become a subject of speculation in palaeomagnetic investigations. But there is no consistency of interpretation and no evidence adduced to support one or another assumption, even though the situation bears directly on a proper understanding of the magnetic characteristics of red beds.

Blackett[27] followed Jones[152] in stating that some part of the red haematite in the Old Red Sandstone may be detrital. Yet he claimed (p. 12) without supporting evidence, that the magnetization of many red beds was acquired during chemical changes after deposition 'for petrologists affirm that without doubt much of the haematite (α-Fe$_2$O$_3$), which is responsible both for their red colour and for their natural magnetism, is not an original constituent of the rock at all but has been produced *in situ* by subsequent chemical changes'. In addition, Blackett quoted with approval the notion that haematite-bearing red beds are the result of deep burial of goethite-bearing deposits. Creer, Irving and Runcorn[59] and Blackett[27] have also suggested that the red

Table VI. Clay Mineral Groups in Red Bed Sequences

B—Biotite   Ch—Chlorite   I—Illite   M—Montmorillonite   S—Sepiolite
C—Corrensite   G—Glauconitic mica   K—Kaolinite   M-l.—Mixed layer   V—Vermiculite

Formation	Predominant	Subordinate	Reference
Miocene			
Ebro Basin; Spain	I	M-l. M-I	Riba, 1955, p. 368
Oligocene			
Eocene			
Sespe; southern California	I, M		
Willwood (red and drab); Wyoming	I	M, K	Van Houten, 1948, p. 2100
Wind River (red and drab); Wyoming	I, K	M	,, ,,
Wasatch (red and drab); Wyoming	I	M, K	,, ,,
DeBegue (red and drab); Colorado	I, K	M	,, ,,
Galisteo (red and drab); New Mexico	I	M	,, ,,
San José (red and drab); New Mexico	M-l. M, I, Ch		Droste, 1955, p. 126
Lower Cretaceous			
Cloverly; north-central Wyoming			
Upper claystone	K	M, I	Moberly, 1960, p. 1163
Lower mudstone	M	I	
Upper Jurassic			
Brushy Canyon (Morrison); Utah	M		Weeks, 1953, p. 10
Brushy Canyon (Morrison); Colorado	I, K		,, ,,
Brushy Canyon (red; Morrison); Colorado	M		Keller, 1958a, p. 124
Brushy Canyon (drab; Morrison); Colorado	G		Keller, 1958a, p. 124
Brushy Canyon (drab; Morrison); Colorado	I	Ch	Keller, 1958a, p. 124
Morrison red unit; Colorado	I	K	Keller, 1953b, p. 98
Morrison; eastern Wyoming—South Dakota	I	K, M	Tank, 1956, p. 875
Morrison; north-central Wyoming	I	M	Moberly, 1960, p. 1163
Triassic			
Beaufort; South Africa	K, M, M-l. M-I		Van der Merwe and Heystek, 1955, p. 487
Newark red beds; North Carolina	I, M	K, V	Hooks and Ingram, 1955, p. 21
Brunswick shale (Newark); New Jersey	I	Ch	Van Houten, 1948, p. 2100
Newark red shale; Connecticut	I	Ch	
Chicopee shale (Newark); Massachusetts	I		Van Houten, 1948, p. 2100
Spearfish red siltstone; South Dakota	I		Van Houten, 1948, p. 2100
Chugwater (red and drab); Wyoming	I		Keller, 1953a, p. 5
Chinle (red and drab); Colorado Plateau	I		Schultz, 1955, p. 124–125
Uppermost	M-l. M-I	V, Ch or K	
Upper	I		
Middle	M-l. M-I		
Lower	K		

Moenkopi; Colorado Plateau	I	M-l. M-I, K	Schultz, 1955, p. 125
Keuper marl; England	S	K	Keeling, 1956
Keuper marl; England	C	I	Stephen and MacEwan, 1950
Keuper marl; England	C	I	Honeyborne, 1951, p. 154
Keuper marl; Germany	C	I, Ch	Lippmann, 1954
Keuper marl; Jura, France	C, I		Vivaldi and MacEwan, 1957
Keuper marl; Spain			,,
Bunter sandstone; Germany			
Upper	C		,,
Middle	I		Lippmann, 1956
Hauptbuntsandstein; Germany			
red	I, B	I	Huffman, 1954
drab	I, Ch, K	Ch	Valeton, 1953, p. 349–350
Bunter; Spain	I, K		Vivaldi and MacEwan, 1957
Kagerödsformation; Sweden	M		Troedsson, 1942, p. 326
Permian			
Unterrotliegende; Germany	I	Ch or K	Falke, 1954, p. 334–335
Derived till; Scotland	I	M	Mitchell and Mitchell, 1956, p. 96
Upper Permian; Kansas	I	Ch, K, M	Swineford, 1954, p. 97, 108
Hermit mudstone; Arizona	M-l. M-Ch	K	
Yates (drab); Texas			Earley, *et al.*, 1956
Permo-Pennsylvanian			
Maroon; Colorado			
red	I, B		Robb, 1949, p. 101
drab	I		
Pennsylvanian			
Fountain; Colorado	M		Weaver, 1958a, p. 162
Mississippian-Pennsylvanian			
Molas (lower and middle); Colorado	K	I	Merrill and Winar, 1958, p. 2115
Mississippian			
Mauch Chunk; Pennsylvania	Ch		
Devonian			
Old Red Sandstone; Scotland	I	Ch	Mackenzie, 1957b
Catskill mudstone; New York	I	Ch	Weaver, 1958a, p. 162
Catskill; Pennsylvania	I		
Silurian			
Bloomsburg shale; Pennsylvania	I		
Salina red shale; New York	I		
Ordovician			
Juniata; Pennsylvania	I		Weaver, 1953, p. 283
Pre-Cambrian			
Torridon arkose; Scotland	I		
Keweenawan arkose; Michigan	I		

pigment is a chemical cement derived from the alteration of magnetite during transportation and deposition. Moreover, Irving[149] has stated that the cementing haematite may have been derived from redistribution of specularite or by direct chemical deposition from interstitial water, and Creer[58] has claimed that most geologists believe that the pigment in red beds is postdepositional.

The problems of the red bed pigment are so manifold that current information and opinions cannot be summarized simply. While haematite undoubtedly is the most common oxide, others are probably also present. Most of the haematite pigment is apparently of detrital origin. Yet, some of the iron oxide may have been redistributed in colloidal form after deposition, and some of it altered diagenetically. Furthermore, the stable natural remanent magnetization in some rocks is due to black detrital grains and in others to haematite pigment.

(2) *Clay Minerals*. Illite commonly accompanied by a subordinate amount of chlorite is the characteristic clay mineral assemblage in most red beds (Table VI), as it is in many sedimentary rocks, generally predominating in both red and associated drab beds. Montmorillonite present in many of the analysed red beds, was derived at least in part from volcanic debris produced by volcanic activity attending deposition of many sequences.

Corrensite (interlayered chlorite–vermiculite) and mixed-layer montmorillonite–chlorite have been reported from Permian and Triassic evaporite-bearing red beds. This implied environmental distribution may be due to incomplete information about clay minerals in other sedimentary rocks, however, because corrensite has also been found in a non-red limestone and shale. Some of the corrensite in red beds apparently resulted from degradation of detrital chlorite by post-depositional leaching.[182]

Most of the kaolinite in red beds is probably of detrital origin. The abundant kaolinite in the upper Cloverly claystone, on the contrary, was apparently produced at the place of deposition by prolonged weathering of very slowly accumulating tuffaceous sediments (reference 211, p. 96).

Sepiolite in the Keuper marl resulted from deposition in highly basic, saline lakes with abundant SiO_2 derived from a lateritic source area.[155] This association accords with Millot's[208] suggestion that a supersaline continental facies favours the development of sepiolite, palygorskite and attapulgite (see also reference 121, p. 250), and with Grim's (reference 120, p. 341) conclusion that sepiolite is likely to be a significant component of desert soils.

The principal clay mineral assemblage in red beds presents a perplexing contradiction which emphasizes the incompleteness of both our data and the leading explanations of clay mineral genesis. Many of these illite–chlorite-bearing red bed sequences are non-marine to tidal flat deposits that accumulated in a very warm climate. But most of the recent sediments that have been analysed for clay mineral content are marine and deltaic deposits of temperate regions. We know very little about the clay mineral composition of alluvium in tropical and subtropical regions.

A common concept of clay mineral origin holds that the assemblage in sedimentary rocks is largely the product of adjustment to conditions of deposition.[119, 208] According to this view kaolinite is likely to be the prominent constituent of non-marine deposits whereas illite and chlorite are likely to predominate in marine deposits.

An alternative interpretation of inheritance from the source area has been proposed by Riviere,[251] Weaver,[320, 321] and Milne and Earley.[209] The latter investigators have shown, for example, that clay minerals in recent sediments in south-eastern United States strongly reflect the character of their source material and are only slightly modified by depositional environments. Especially at sites of rapid deposition the clay minerals are dependent largely on products from the source area, whereas in environments of slow accumulation they may be altered to illite to some extent. Milne and Earley did find some variation with depth of burial, however, showing (pp. 332–333, 335) that there is a gradual decrease in the amount of kaolinite and a slight increase in the amount of illite. But the observation was interpreted to mean that no significant changes in the mineralogy had occurred during the time of burial (p. 336) and that compaction and burial of mud apparently produce very little alteration of the clay minerals except possibly in the exchange ions (p. 338). Similarly, Weaver has concluded that it is difficult to explain the known distribution of clay minerals in sedimentary rocks as a modification by environments of deposition, and that the clay minerals are therefore largely detrital materials inherited from the source area.

In addition to a general disagreement about clay mineral origin, there is specific contradiction about the origin of the clay minerals in normal non-marine sediments. Grim (reference 121, p. 250) believes that 'there seems to be no indication of change in clay mineral composition on passing from the weathering to the fluviatile environment', whereas Weaver concludes that (reference 321, p. 258) 'there is strong evidence that clays are altered (usually degraded) to some extent in fluviatile and subaerial continental environments', and that 'there is little question that clay minerals form by authigenesis and diagenesis under continental conditions' (reference 320, p. 169).

Abundant data (reference 321, p. 258) suggest that kaolinite is dominant in fluviatile deposits. Direct evidence for this conclusion is afforded by analysis of the alluvium of the Neuces River of North Carolina [39] which drains an upland of kaolinite-rich red and yellow podsolic soils.[223] Kaolinite inherited from the soil predominates in the alluvium, but it does decrease in abundance downstream whereas illite, chlorite and mixed-layer illite and chlorite increase downstream, possibly the result of diagenetic trends principally in an estuarine environment.[118] On the other hand, illite predominates in the alluvium of the lower Nile,[126] even though its headwaters drain extensive lateritic uplands.

According to current notions about the origin of red beds and of clay minerals, kaolinite and aluminium hydroxides derived from lateritic soils should predominate in non-marine red beds (see reference 96, pp. 335–337). But instead, most of them contain abundant illite and chlorite. Before attempting to evaluate the situation it is well to recall that illite is the abundant clay mineral in most fine-grained sedimentary rocks and chlorite is present in many of them. In this connection Weaver (reference 321, p. 260) has remarked that 'on an over-all basis illite is probably as abundant in clay-size material as quartz is in sand- and silt-size material. The fact that illite is so frequently a dominant mineral would make it appear doubtful if in itself it has any more environmental connotation than does quartz.' The present concern, therefore, is not just the prevalence of illite and chlorite, but more specifically the widespread absence or paucity of kaolinite in red beds.

In order to explain this anomaly Hooks and Ingram[143] and Droste[82] have postulated that the abundant illite, chlorite and other 2 : 1 clay minerals in some non-marine red bed sequences are detrital fractions of red upland soils eroded before deep weathering had produced kaolinite throughout the profile, either because of continued rapid erosion or of moderate weathering conditions. Similarly, Lippmann (reference 182, p. 137) has suggested that the chlorite which altered diagenetically to corrensite was inherited from the source area, and he interpreted this to mean that the source area weathering had not been intense, even though red pigment was produced. Admittedly, illite and chlorite in some sequences were derived from red upland soil where they persisted under moderate weathering conditions, particularly in those soils developed on sedimentary and metamorphic rocks which could supply these clay minerals abundantly. But as a general explanation to account for the rarity of kaolinite, this proposal ignores the fact that kaolinite predominates throughout the profile of most red upland soils, including only moderately lateritized ones in south-eastern United States. [223]

The widespread occurrence of illite and chlorite and the insignificant amount of kaolinite in the many facies of red beds vitiate any claim that these minerals are simply detrital, and at the same time suggest the operation of a process more universal than local environmental modification. Consequently it appears that the paucity of kaolinite in most analysed red beds may be partly the result of diagenetic alteration of the mineral. Swineford (reference 285, p. 161) has postulated that the illite and chlorite in the upper Permian marine red beds of Kansas were diagenetically developed within the sediments, and that 'they were probably produced at the expense of kaolinite and gibbsite'. Capewell (reference 44, p. 160) also suggested a diagenetic origin for the chlorite in the Old Red Sandstone in Ireland.

Most discussions of diagenesis of clay minerals in sedimentary rocks have emphasized environmental modification at the place of deposition. Apparently very early diagenesis is not as effective as its most ardent advocates have claimed. But it may be that a prolonged diagenesis can alter the original clay minerals appreciably. Grim (reference 120, p. 357) has pointed out that 'since montmorillonite and kaolinite tend to disappear in sediments of increasing age, it follows that very ancient sediments must be composed largely of the illite and chlorite types of clay minerals'. Because little change in composition of recent sediments seems to result from burial Grim (reference 121, p. 251) has added that 'any substantial change in clay mineral composition after deposition is likely to be slow'. Nevertheless, if diagenesis is a major factor producing illite- and chlorite-rich rocks, it can apparently alter inherited kaolinite within a few tens of millions of years, for the illite-rich Miocene deposits of the Ebro Basin, Spain, presumably accumulated as kaolinitic alluvium derived from upland laterites.

Although a diagenetic alteration of kaolinite seems to be required by the relationships of clay minerals in most red bed sequences, the persistence of abundant kaolinite in a few reveals that there have been situations in which the process did not operate. As an example, residual red soil forming the lower member of the Molas formation (Mississippian–Pennsylvanian) in south-western Colorado and the red alluvial deposits of its middle member both contain abundant kaolinite unaltered by diagenesis.

Clearly, present information about the origin and fate of transported clay minerals is too meagre to permit formulating a satisfactory general theory. As now understood, no one process accounts for all of the facts; more reasonably several processes must have operated to produce the final clay mineral assemblage in red beds.

III.4 *Summary*

The three lines of inquiry expressed in the analytical data not only reveal what is known about the constitution of red beds, but they also indicate the scope of our ignorance and help to formulate meaningful questions for future investigation. Some suggested by the present discussion are:

1. Are the black detrital grains magnetite, ilmenite or specular haematite?

2. Were the black haematite grains derived from source rocks, or were they produced by weathering of magnetite grains in the source area? Or produced by weathering at the place of deposition?

3. Is all of the red pigment finely disseminated haematite? Is it all detrital? Was some of it produced by aging of detrital hydrohaematite?

4. Is there any geothite, lepidocrocite or maghemite in the rock?

5. Is any of the pigment chemically precipitated haematite cement? If so, what was the source of this material?

6. In connection with these questions, it should be emphasized that the problem of the nature of the iron oxide minerals in red beds is twofold. In the coarser fractions in siltstones and sandstones the iron oxides are essentially detrital, relic minerals (magnetite, ilmenite, etc.), inherited from the source rocks, whereas the pigment minerals in the mudstones and shales are new products of weathering in the source area and of possible additional alteration at the place of deposition.

7. If kaolinite is the characteristic clay mineral of lateritic soils today why isn't it common in red beds presumably derived from red soils?

8. If inherited kaolinite has been altered diagenetically in most red beds to an illite–chlorite assemblage, how is kaolinite preserved in some red beds as well as in non-red Cretaceous deposits associated with widespread intervals of bauxitization?

9. Why are there so few ancient yellow-brown mudstones when yellow-brown alluvium is so prevalent today?

10. Is there any substantial accumulation of recent bright red alluvium?

11. What is the iron oxide and clay mineral content of the more common dull reddish-brown to yellow-brown alluvium that characterizes much of the deposits derived from lateritic terranes today?

IV. Conclusions

Investigation of the origin of red beds does not lead to simple or final statements. Nevertheless, reasonable conclusions based on available data may be summarized.

IV.1 *Source of Ferric Oxide*

The ferric oxide in most red beds probably originated in red upland soils developed in a tropical or subtropical climate. Most of the oxide accumulated as detrital haematite; some of it may have been inherited hydro-haematite that aged to haematite after deposition.

Presumably the need for a red soil source and its associated warm, humid climate as an explanation of red bed origin may diminish to the extent that future investigation shows that hydrohaematite is abundant in non-red soils and consistently converts to haematite.

IV.2 *Possible Unique Ancient Environments*

Absence of well-developed land floras before Devonian time may have imposed somewhat different conditions on source area weathering and erosion, as well as on organic accumulation at the place of deposition. During the interval of extensive red bed development from Devonian to Jurassic time essentially the same general type of vegetation prevailed. Later, the evolution of grasses in the Cenozoic era probably affected soil-formation and erosion, especially in savannas, so that some of the processes in savannas today may differ at least in intensity from those of late Palaeozoic and Mesozoic time.

Although the late Palaeozoic and Mesozoic floras provide considerable information about environments of red bed deposition, there are no really reliable criteria for estimating the temperature in which they grew. Accordingly, estimates of the climate of Pennsylvanian coal measures in the northern hemisphere range from temperate to tropical, with the consensus favouring a rather warm climate. In contrast, the consensus prefers a cool climate for Permian coal measures in 'Gondwanaland'.

IV.3 *Basic Rôle of Oxidizing Conditions*

The essential condition for preservation of transported ferric oxide pigment is an oxidizing environment at the place of deposition. The importance of reducing conditions in eliminating inherited pigment is demonstrated both by the development of local non-red lenses and layers and by lateral gradation of red deltaic facies, such as the alluvial Catskill and Bedford deposits, into non-red sediments of swampy coastal lowlands and shallow seas. Similarly, the red arkosic alluvial deposits of the Sespe formation grade outward from their source into a non-red marine facies.

The common conditions of restricted oxidation that produce non-red sediments are poor drainage, as with deposition below the water table, and abundant organic matter that escaped complete decay. In addition to the alteration of ferric oxide under these reducing conditions, partially decayed organic matter is transformed into dark colloidal humus which easily imparts drab colours to the sediments by its adsorption on clay mineral platelets. By this process dark gray sediments may have a low organic content, just as only a small amount of haematite dispersed as coatings on clay minerals can produce red pigment.

Oxidizing conditions are largely related to local geographical factors, rather than to climatic ones. But they may be controlled partly by climate. The warm, moist environment that produces red upland soils also encourages rapid bacterial decay of organic matter at the place of deposition; and a climate somewhat drier than that of the source area will support less abundant vegetation and a lower water table, thus favouring preservation of red pigment. Mudcracks, footprints, salt casts and evaporites in many red bed sequences point to just such a drier climate at the place of deposition.

IV.4 *Rôle of Tectonic Setting*

The tectonic behaviour of the source area and the site of deposition is a basic factor controlling the origin of red beds, not only in simply being responsible for rapid burial, but also in determining the framework of the different facies of red beds outlined in Section II. Its importance is emphasized by the association of widespread tectonic activity and attendant non-marine environments with the Permo-Triassic climax of red bed deposition, most of which occurred on cratons.

The tectonic framework may participate in determining whether or not red soil develops in the source area, even in a favourable climate. The Cretaceous period, for example, was characterized by a warm, moist climate, but this was also a time of stability in much of Europe, north Africa, and North America, with planation of the continents and the spread of epicontinental seas. As a consequence, bauxite developed extensively on broad lowland source areas and was preserved as residual deposits[285, 298] and in kaolinite- and gibbsite-rich detrital formations. During the same period red beds accumulated in tectonically active fault basins in China and in the Andean mobile belt in western South America.

IV.5 *Climate at the Place of Deposition*

The climate at the place of deposition is one of the basic factors involved in preservation of red pigment. Inasmuch as all of the red bed floras are

I

warm-temperate to subtropical or warmer assemblages, red detritus apparently was not carried far from the climate realm in which it originated.

The depositional climate also shares in controlling the nature of associated features and sediments. Aeolian deposits, desiccation marks and evaporites, for example, indicate at least temporary dry conditions during deposition, and in some cases local desert environments. But they do not imply accumulation in vast deserts like the great high pressure or trade wind deserts today.

IV.6 *Climatic Significance of Red Bed Facies*

Many of the red bed sequences yield inadequate information about the depositional climate when they are considered individually. Significant data become available when the red beds are assembled in several geographic-tectonic facies (Fig. 1).

(a) Red beds and red lenses associated with coal measures probably accumulated in a warm, humid climate with insignificant seasonal dryness, like that of their source area. Preservation of red detritus results from local oxidizing conditions.

The climate of many deltaic red beds without coal measures cannot be interpreted directly. Some that are closely related to sequences with coal measures presumably also accumulated in a warm, humid environment on oxidizing sub-aerial alluvial plains. Those red deltaic deposits that grade into evaporitic facies, like the Silurian red beds of the Appalachian geosyncline and the late Jurassic and early Cretaceous red beds of the Gulf Coast geosyncline, undoubtedly accumulated under drier conditions than prevailed in the source areas.

(b) Piedmont-valley flat red beds and variegated sequences in grabens and in molasse basins accumulated in tropical to subtropical savanna climates well-documented by associated floras. The fact that these deposits accumulated relatively near their source areas implies a rather similar climate in the uplands. Basin deposits with lenses and layers of gypsum, such as the Miocene red beds of the Ebro Basin, Spain, and the Cretaceous and Cenozoic red beds of China, and those associated with evaporite-bearing formations, such as the Rotliegende and Verrucano red beds of Europe, probably accumulated in a warm, humid climate with a marked dry season.

(c) Most of the extensive 'blanket' red beds of the coastal plain–tidal flat facies accumulated some distance from their source in a climate which was much drier than that in the uplands, as suggested by the widespread evaporites and local aeolian deposits and by associated floras. For example, the flora of the Permian red beds with evaporites in western United States indicates a drier climate (subtropical to tropical with a long dry season) than that of the Permian Dunkard coal measures red beds in eastern United States[327] or that of the late Triassic Chinle red beds with only a minor amount of associated evaporite and a more humid subtropical to tropical climate, with ample rainfall but a distinct dry season.[74]

Cratonic red beds that accumulated on broad alluvial plains, like those of the Karroo system and the Morrison formation, are rather similar to some deltaic red beds. They were deposited far from their source, they are non-marine and contain little or no evaporite, and yield no clearly diagnostic evidence of the depositional climate. Some geologists argue that the abundant herbivorous dinosaurs in the Morrison formation imply a lush vegetation and much moisture, whereas others point to the associated aeolian deposits and minor amount of gypsum and postulate a very dry climate.

IV.7 Red Bed–Evaporite Facies and Marine Environments

Some red beds with evaporites, such as the Cretaceous and Cenozoic sequences in China, the middle Cenozoic deposits of the Ebro Basin, Spain, and the Permian red beds of England [84] may have accumulated in large lakes in dry non-marine basins. Most red beds with extensive evaporite deposits, on the other hand, reflect the influence of marine environments. Indeed, many of them contain tongues of marine limestone and dolomite, as illustrated by the red beds associated with the Permian Magnesian limestone of England, the Permian red beds of north Texas and the Buntsandstein, Keuper, Supai, Hermit, Kaibab, Toroweap, Moenkopi, Spearfish, Chugwater, Carmel and Preuss red beds. Furthermore, the evaporite content commonly decreases in the manifestly non-marine facies of these deposits.

The accumulation of cratonic red bed–evaporite sequences on broad featureless coastal plains and tidal flats over which seas made repeated extensive shallow incursions and retreats has been nicely pictured by Wilfarth,[328] Burk,[43] Imlay[148] and Harshbarger et al.[131]

IV.8 Red Bed–Evaporite Facies and Deserts

Lateral gradation of red bed–evaporite sequences and aeolian deposits and the repeated replacement of red bed environments by wind-swept deserts, as depicted during late Triassic and Jurassic time in western United States by Imlay[148] and Harshbarger et al.,[131] resulted from successive shifting of geographic environments rather than from alternating climates.

Examples of red beds with interfingering aeolian sandstone:

Late Permian red beds associated with the Magnesian limestone in England
Late Permian Toroweap red beds on the Colorado Plateau
Early Triassic Buntsandstein in northern Europe
Late Triassic Keuper red beds of northern Europe
Late Triassic Chugwater red beds in Wyoming
Late Triassic Moenave formation on the Colorado Plateau
Late Triassic Piramboia red beds of Brazil
Middle Jurassic Carmel formation on the Colorado Plateau
Late Jurassic Sundance red beds in southern Wyoming
Late Jurassic Preuss red beds of south-eastern Idaho and adjacent Wyoming and Utah
Late Jurassic Summerville and Morrison formations on the Colorado Plateau

Examples of red beds succeeded by extensive aeolian formations:

Permian Chapiza red beds of Ecuador and Peru below the Saraiquillo formation
Permian Supai and Hermit red beds below the Coconino sandstone on the Colorado Plateau

Permo-Triassic lower Shihchienfeng red beds below the upper Shihchienfeng aeolian sandstone in north China

Early Triassic Chugwater red beds below the Jelm formation in Wyoming

Late Triassic Chugwater and Ankareh red beds below the Nugget sandstone in western Wyoming

Late Triassic Chinle red beds below the Wingate sandstone on the Colorado Plateau

Late Triassic Karroo red beds below the Cave and equivalent sandstone in central and southern Africa

Late Triassic Piramboia red beds below the Botucatu sandstone in eastern South America

Early Jurassic (?) Kayenta red beds below the Navajo sandstone on the Colorado Plateau

Middle Jurassic Carmel red beds below the Entrada sandstone on the Colorado Plateau

Late Jurassic Summerville red beds below the Cow Springs sandstone on the Colorado Plateau

Deposits of red mud and interbedded evaporites accumulating in a hot, dry climate graded laterally into marine sediments in one direction and in the other into alluvial deposits with little or no evaporite and into aeolian sands of deserts. With retreat of the sea and migration of these lateral facies, sheets of wind-blown sand succeeded red bed–evaporite sequences. The rapidity with which a desert environment can over-run a vast alluvial plain is illustrated by the transformation of the western part of the well-watered and wooded Indo-Gangetic plain into the Rajputana (Great Indian) Desert within the past several thousand years.[168]

IV.9 *Permo-Triassic Red Beds, Palaeomagnetism and Continental Drift*

If ancient red beds were derived from lateritic soils their sources and places of accumulation presumably lay in tropical and subtropical global girdles which were broader during much of the geological past when the earth's climate was warmer. Analysis of Permian invertebrate faunas of the northern hemisphere suggests a marked northward shift of the subtropical marine temperature belt (Fig. 7) approximately parallel to the present equator.[279] Such a poleward shift of warm-climate belts accompanied by a prolonged episode of tectonic activity may have led to the widespread red bed development in Permo-Triassic time. There is no evidence, however, that subtropical climates shifted far enough north to account for the very high latitude Permo-Triassic red beds.

With few exceptions the magnetic inclination of ancient red beds that have been analysed is small and indicates that they lay within 25° of their equator when they were magnetized. The few non-red high latitude deposits analysed (varved shale associated with the Dwyka tillite and late Cenozoic basalt in Iceland and north-western United States) have large inclinations. Although these are very limited data they do agree with the lateritic origin of detrital red beds, and thus appear to support the idea of polar wandering in the past. Nevertheless, so many poorly understood factors are involved in producing the inclination that this observation is no more than suggestive at the present time.

Permo-Triassic palaeomagnetic pole positions (Fig. 7) fit many of the red bed sequences as well as late Palaeozoic glaciation in the southern hemisphere and the early Permian tillite recently reported in Gondwana-like deposits in central Asia.[91] Significant contradictions are introduced, however (reference 150, p. 210). For example, red beds in China are almost on the location of the Permian pole based on American red beds and within 20° longitude of the Triassic pole. In addition, the Permian palaeomagnetic equators (Fig. 7) fall very near the boundary between Permian subtropical and temperate belts calculated by Stehli.[279]

Reconstruction of 'Gondwanaland' in an Antarctic region in order to account for late Palaeozoic glaciation denies the possibility of part of the

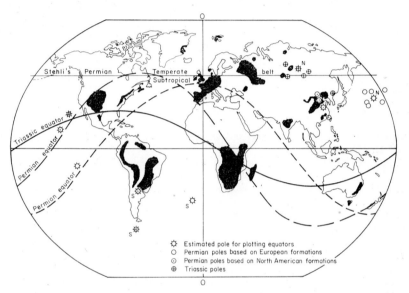

Fig. 7. Distribution of Permo-Triassic red beds, and estimated positions of Permian and Triassic palaeomagnetic poles, and of Permian marine subtropical-temperature belt.

'Gondwana' province in central Asia, and imposes the necessity of very rapid drift to get these southern continents into tropical or subtropical belts (reference 101, pp. 201, 203; reference 87) by Triassic time.

However the poles are shifted or the continents drifted, the rearrangements must provide a distribution of ancient red beds consistent with their derivation from lateritic soils or a more satisfactory general theory of red bed origin will have to be proposed.

References

1. Albareda, J. M., 'Spanish investigations on clay minerals and related minerals', in *Clays and Clay Minerals*, Nat. Acad. Sci., Nat. Res. Council, **456**, pp. 147–157 (1956)
2. Allen, V. T., 'Formation of bauxite from basaltic rocks of Oregon'. *Econ. Geol.*, **43**, 619–626 (1948)

3. Alling, H. L., 'The geology and origin of the Silurian salt of New York State'. *Bull. N.Y. St. Mus.*, **275**, 5–139 (1928)

4. Almeida, F. F. M., 'Botucatú, a Triassic desert of South America'. *Int. Geol. Cong.*, *19th, Algeria*, sect. 7, **f. 7**, 9–24 (1953)

5. Almeida, F. F., and Barbosa, O., 'Geologia das quadriculas de Piracicaba e Rio Claro, Estado de São Paulo'. *Div. Geol. Min. Brasil*, **143**, 96 p. (1953)

6. Amstutz, G. C., 'Kleintektonische und stratigraphische Beobachtungen im Verrucano des Glarner Freiberges'. *Ecl. geol. Helv.*, **50**, 141–159 (1957)

7. Anderson, W. and Dunham, K. C., 'Reddened beds in the Coal Measures beneath the Permian of Durham and South Northumberland'. *Proc. York. geol. (polyt.) Soc.*, **29**, 21–32 (1953)

8. Auden, J. B., 'Vindhyan sedimentation in the Son Valley, Mirzapur District'. *Mem. geol. Survey India*, **62**, 141–250 (1933)

9. Auden, J. B., 'Paleoclimates during the deposition of the Vindhyan and related systems'. *Int. Geol. Cong.*, *17th, U.S.S.R.*, 1937, *Rpt. 17th sess.*, **6**, 137–152 (1940)

10. Bailey, E. B., 'Subterranean penetration by a desert climate'. *Geol. Mag.*, **63**, 276–280 (1926)

11. Bailey, E. B., 'Climate in Torridonian and Dalradian time'. *Int. Geol. Cong.*, *17th, U.S.S.R.*, 1937, *Rpt. 17th sess.*, **6**, 255 (1940)

12. Bain, A. G., 'On the geology of southern Africa'. *Trans. geol. Soc. Lond.*, ser. II, **VII**, 175–192 (1856)

13. Bain, G. W., 'Northern area of Connecticut Valley Triassic'. *Amer. J. Sci.*, **23**, 57–77 (1932)

14. Baker, A. A., Dane, C. H. and Reeside, J. B., 'Correlation of the Jurassic formations . . .'. *Prof. Pap. U.S. geol. Surv.*, **183**, (1936)

15. Baker, C. L., 'Origin of Texas red beds'. *Univ. Tex. Bull.*, **29**, 3–8 (1916)

16. Baker, C. L., 'Depositional history of the red beds and saline residues of the Texas Permian'. *Univ. Tex. Bull.*, **2901**, 9–72 (1929)

17. Barrell, Joseph, 'Relative geological importance of continental, littoral, and marine sedimentation'. *J. Geol.*, **14**, 316–356, 430–457, 524–564 (1906)

18. Barrell, Joseph, 'Origin and significance of the Mauch Chunk shale'. *Bull. geol. Soc. Amer.*, **18**, 449–476 (1907)

19. Barrell, Joseph, 'Relations between climate and terrestrial deposits'. *J. Geol.*, **16**, 159–190, 255–295, 363–384 (1908)

20. Barrell, Joseph, 'Central Connecticut in the geologic past'. *Proc. Wyo. hist. geol. Soc.*, **12**, 25–54 (1912)

21. Barrell, Joseph, 'The upper Devonian delta of the Applachian geosyncline, pt. I'. *Amer. J. Sci.*, **36**, 429–472 (1913)

22. Barrell, Joseph, 'Dominantly fluviatile origin under seasonal rainfall of the Old Red Sandstone'. *Bull. geol. Soc. Amer.*, **27**, 345–386 (1916)

23. Barton, D. C., 'The geological significance and genetic classification of arkose deposits'. *J. Geol.*, **24**, 417–449 (1916)

24. Becksmann, Ernst, 'Geologische Untersuchungen an jungpaläozoischen und tertiären Landoberflächen im Unterharzgebiet'. *Neues Jb. Min. Geol. Paläont.* **64**, 79–146 (1930)

25. Beede, J. W., 'Origin of the sediments and coloring matter of the eastern Oklahoma red beds'. *Science*, **35**, 348–350 (1912)

26. Bell, W. A., 'Joggins Carboniferous section of Nova Scotia'. *Sum. Rpt. Geol. Survey Br. Dept. Mines Canada* (1911), 328–333 (1912)

27. Blackett, P. M. S. *Lectures on Rock Magnetism*. 1956. Jerusalem: Weizmann Science Press.

28. Blanckenhorn, M., 'Der Haupt-buntsandstein ist keine echte Wüsten Bildung'. *Z. Ges. Erdk. Berl.*, **59**, 297–311 (1907)

29. Blanford, W. T., 'On the manner of occurrence of the reptilean remains found in the Panchet beds. . . .', p. i–iii, appendix to Huxley, T. S., 'On a collection of vertebrate fossils . . .'. *Palaeont. indica, ser. IV*, **1** (1865)

30. Bock, Wilhelm, 'The oxides of iron and their thermo-magnetic properties'. *Proc. Pa. Acad. Sci.*, **28**, 143–172 (1954)

31. Bonney, T. G., Presidential address; *Geol. Sect., Rpt 56th meet.*, Brit. Assoc. Adv. Sci. (1886), 601–621 (1887)

32. Bonte, A. and Celet, P., 'Sur la significance des sédiments rouges et verts du Trias du Jura Français'. *Geol. Rdsch.*, **43**, 342–348 (1955)

33. Bornemann, J. G. *Über den Buntsandstein in Deutschland.* 1889. Jena: Gustav Fisher

34. Bosworth, T. O., 'The origin of the upper Keuper of Leicestershire'. *Geol. Mag.*, **44**, 460–461 (1907)

35. Bosworth, T. O. *The Keuper Marl around Charnwood.* 1912. Leicester: W. Thornby and Son

36. Bradley, W. F. and Weaver, C. E., 'A regularly interstratified chlorite-vermiculite clay mineral'. *Amer. Min.*, **41**, 497–504 (1956)

37. Branson, E. B., 'Origin of the red beds of western Wyoming'. *Bull. geol. Soc. Amer.*, **26**, 217–230 (1915)

38. Branson, E. B., 'Triassic-Jurassic "red beds" of the Rocky Mountain region'. *J. Geol.*, **35**, 607–630 (1927)

39. Brown, C. Q. and Ingram, R. L., 'The clay minerals of the Neuse River sediments'. *J. sediment. Petrol.*, **24**, 196–199 (1954)

40. Brown, G., 'The occurrence of lepidocrocite in some British soils'. *J. Soil Sci.*, **4**, 220–228 (1953)

41. Brückner, Werner, 'The mantle rock ("laterite") of the Gold Coast and its origin'. *Geol. Rdsch.*, **43**, 307–327 (1955)

42. Buddington, A. F., 'Pre-Cambrian rocks of southeast Newfoundland'. *J. Geol.*, **27**, 449–479 (1919)

43. Burk, C. A., 'Electric log correlation of the Triassic rocks of southeastern Wyoming'. *Wyo. geol. Assoc., Guide-book, 8th ann. field conf.*, 29–33 (1953)

44. Capewell, J. G., 'The Old Red Sandstone of the Inch and Annascaul district, Co. Kerry'. *Proc. R. Irish Acad.*, **54**, 141–167 (1951)

45. Carroll, Dorothy, 'Role of clay minerals in the transportation of iron'. *Geochim. et cosmochim. Acta*, **14**, 1–27 (1958)

46. Carroll, Dorothy and Woof, Marion, 'Laterite developed on basalt at Inverell, New South Wales'. *Soil Sci.*, **72**, 87–99 (1951)

47. Case, E. C., 'A great Permian delta and its vertebrate life'. *Pop. Sci. Mon.*, **73**, 557–568 (1908)

48. Case, E. C., 'The Permo-Carboniferous red beds of North America and their vertebrate fauna'. *Publ. Carneg. Instn*, **207**, 176 p. (1915)

49. Chamberlin, T. C., 'On the habitat of the early vertebrates'. *J. Geol.*, **8**, 400–412 (1900)

50. Clark, F. W., 'Report of division of chemistry and physics (1886–1887)'. *Bull. U.S. geol. Surv.*, **55**, (1889)

51. Coleman, A. P. *Ice ages, recent and ancient.* 1926. New York: Macmillan and Co.

52. Cook, G. H. *Geology of New Jersey.* 1868. Newark, N.J.

53. Cooke, H. B. S., 'Observations relating to Quaternary environments in east and southern Africa'. *Geol. Soc. S. Afr.*, annex **60**, 1–73 (1958)

54. Craig, L. C. *et al.*, 'Stratigraphy of the Morrison and related formations, Colorado Plateau region'. *Bull. U.S. geol. Surv.*, **1009**E, 125–168 (1955)
55. Crampton, C. B. and Carruthers, R. G., 'The geology of Caithness'. *Mem. geol. Surv. Scot.*, 194 p. (1914)
56. Credner, H. *Versuch einer Bildungsgeschichte . . . Thüringer Waldes.* Erfurt, Denk-schriften, 1854
57. Creer, K. M., 'The nature of remanent magnetism of certain stable rocks from Great Britain'. *Phil. Trans.*, **250**A, 111–129 (1957)
58. Creer, K. M., 'The remanent magnetization of unstable Keuper marls' (V). *Phil. Trans.*, **250**A, 130–143 (1957)
59. Creer, K. M., Irving, E. and Runcorn, S. K., 'The direction of the geomagnetic field in remote epochs in Great Britain'. *J. Geomagn. Geoelect., Kyoto*, **6**, 163–168 (1954)
60. Cresswell, Frank, 'The conditions under which the Triassic deposits of England were formed, with special reference to the Keuper marls'. *Trans. Leicester lit. phil. Soc.*, **14**, 21–27 (1910)
61. Crosby, W. O., 'Color of soils'. *Proc. Boston Soc. nat. Hist.*, **23**, 219–222 (1888)
62. Crosby, W. O., 'Geology of the Black Hills of Dakota'. *Proc. Boston Soc. nat. Hist.*, **23**, 488–517 (1888)
63. Crosby, W. O., 'On the contrast in color of the soils of high and low latitudes'. *Amer. Geol.*, **7**, 72–82 (1891)
64. Cumming, J. G. *The Isle of Man, its history, etc.*, 376 p. 1848. London
65. Daglish, John and Forster, G. B., 'On the magnesian limestone of Durham'. *Trans. N. Engl. Inst. Min. mech. Engrs.*, **13**, 205–213 (1864)
66. Dana, J. D. *Manual of Geology.* 1863. Philadelphia: Theo. Bliss and Co.
67. Dana, J. D., 'On some results of the Earth's contraction from cooling . . .'. *Amer. J. Sci.*, **5**, 423–443 (1873)
68. Dana, J. D. *Manual of Geology*, 2nd edn. 1875. New York: Ivison, Blakeman, Taylor, and Co.
69. Dana, J. D., 'The physical history of the Triassic formation of New Jersey and the Connecticut Valley'. *Amer. J. Sci.*, **17**, 328–330 (1879)
70. Dana, J. D., 'Subaerial decay of rocks and origin of the red color of certain formations'. *Amer. J. Sci.*, **39**, 317–319 (1890)
71. Darton, N. H., 'On the disintegrated sandstone at New Durham, New Jersey'. *Trans. N.Y. Acad. Sci.*, **2**, 117–119 (1883)
72. Darton, N. H., 'Geology of the Bighorn Mountains'. *Prof. Pap. U.S. geol. Surv.*, **51**, 129 p. (1906)
73. Darton, N. H., 'Geology and underground water of the Arkansas valley in eastern Colorado'. *Prof. Pap. U.S. geol. Surv.*, **52**, 90 p. (1906)
74. Daugherty, L. H., 'The upper Triassic flora of Arizona'. *Publ. Carneg. Instn.*, **526**, 108 p. (1941)
75. Davies, Edward, 'Action of heat on ferric hydrate in presence of water'. *J. chem. Soc.*, **19**, 69–72 (1866)
76. Davies, W. M., 'The Triassic formation of Connecticut'. *Rep. U.S. geol. Surv.*, pt. 2, 1–192 (1898)
77. Dawson, J. W., 'On the colouring matter of red sandstone and of greyish and white beds associated with them'. *Quart. J. geol. Soc. Lond.*, **7**, 25–30 (1849)
78. De la Beche, H. T. *Researches in theoretical geology.* 1834. London: Chas. Knight
79. De la Beche, H. T., 'On the formations of the rocks of South Wales and South-Western England'. *Mem. Geol. Survey, U.K.*, **1**, 1–296 (1846)

80. Diller, J. S., 'The educational series of rock specimens'. *Bull. U.S. geol. Surv.*, **150**, (1898)

81. Dorsey, G. E., 'The origin of the color of red beds'. *J. Geol.*, **34**, 131–143 (1926)

82. Droste, J. B., 'Clay mineralogy of lower Tertiary continental deposits of the San Juan Basin, Colorado'. *Trans. Ill. Acad. Sci.*, **47**, 126–128 (1955)

83. Dunbar, C. O. and Rodgers, John. *Principles of stratigraphy.* 1957. New York: John Wiley and Sons

84. Dunham, K. C., 'Red coloration in desert formations of Permian and Triassic age in Britain'. *Int. Geol. Cong., 19th, Algeria (1952), C. R. sect. VII, f.* **VII,** 25–32 (1953)

85. Du Toit, A. L., 'The Stormberg formation in the Cape Colony'. *Geol. Mag.*, **43**, 36–38 (1906)

86. Du Toit, A. L. *The Geology of South Africa.* 1926. Edinburgh: Oliver & Boyd

87. Du Toit, A. L., 'The climatic setting of the vertebrate fauna of the Karroo system and its significance'. *Sp. Pub. Roy. Soc. S. Afr., Rbt. Broom Comm. vol.*, 113–125 (1948)

88. Earley, J. W. *et al.*, 'A regularly interstratified montmorillonite-chlorite'. *Amer. Min.*, **41**, 258–267 (1956)

89. Edwards, A. B., 'The petrology of the bauxites of Tasmania'. *Mineral Inv., Commonwealth Sci. and Ind. Res. Org.*, Geol. Dept. Univ. Melbourne, 26 p. (1955)

90. Edwards, J. D., 'Studies of some early Tertiary red conglomerates of central Mexico'. *Prof. Pap. U.S. geol. Surv.*, **264H**, 153–183 (1955)

91. Efremov, J. A., 'The Gondwana System of India and the vertebrate life history in the late Palæozoic'. *Palaeont. Soc. India*, **2**, 24–28 (1957)

92. Eichhoff, H. J. and Reineck, H. E., 'Sekundäre verfärbungen durch herauslösen von hämatit aus gesteinen'. *Neues Jb. Miner. Mh.*, **11–12**, 315–324 (1953)

93. Emerson, B. K., 'Geology of Hampshire County, Massachusetts' (pp. 10–22), in *Gazetteer of Hampshire County Massachusetts* (W. B. Gray). 1888. Syracuse, New York

94. Evans, J. W., 'Devonian' (pp. 128–153), in *Handbook of the Geology of Great Britain* (Evans and Stubblefield, ed.), 1929

95. Eyles, V. A., 'The composition and origin of the Antrim laterites and bauxites'. *Mem. geol. Surv. Northern Ireland* (1952)

96. Falke, Horst, 'Leithorizonte, Leitfolgen und Leitgruppen im pfälzischen Unterrotliegenden'. *Neues Jb. Geol.*, **99**, 298–354 (1954)

97. Fenneman, N. M., 'Geology of the Boulder District, Colorado'. *Bull. U.S. geol. Surv.*, **265**, 9–101 (1905)

98. Fisher, D. W., 'Lithology, paleoecology, and paleontology of the Vernon shale (late Silurian) in the type area'. *Bull. N.Y. St. Mus.*, **364** (1957)

99. Fleming, John, 'On the occurrence of the scales of vertebrated animals in the Old Red Sandstone of Fifeshire'. *Edinb. J. nat. geogr. Sci.*, **3**, 81–86 (1831)

100. Flett, J. S., 'The climatological problem of the Old Red Continent; 1. Climatic evidence presented by Old Red Sandstone rocks'. *Int. Geol. Cong., 17th U.S.S.R.*, 1937, *Rpt. 17th sess.*, **6**, 159–166 (1940)

101. Fox, C. S., 'The climates of Gondwanaland . . .'. *Int. Geol. Cong., 17th U.S.S.R.*, 1937, *Rpt. 17th sess.*, **6**, 187–208 (1940)

102. Frass, E., 'Die Bildung des germanischen Trias, eine petrogenetische Studie'. *Jh. Ver. vaterl. Naturk. Württemb.*, **55**, 37–100 (1899)

103. Fripiat, J. J., Gastuche, M. C. and Couvreur, J., 'Complexes of kaolinite with ferric oxides'. *Bull. Acad. Belg. Cl. Sci.*, **39**, 890–900 (1953)

104. Geikie, Archibold, 'On the Old Red Sandstone of western Europe'. *Trans. roy. Soc. Edinb.*, **28**, 345–452 (1879)

105. Gheith, M. A., 'Differential thermal analysis of certain iron oxides and oxide hydrates'. *Amer. J. Sci.*, **250**, 677–695 (1952)

106. Gheith, M. A., 'Stability relations of ferric oxides and their hydrates'. *Int. Geol. Cong., 19th, Algeria, C. R., sect. 10, f.* **10**, 79–80 (1953)

107. Gheith, M. A., 'Iron oxide minerals'. *Abst. Proc. geol. Soc. Egypt*, **1**, 30–32 (1955)

108. Gignoux, Maurice. *Stratigraphic Geology* (French Ed., 1950). 1955. San Francisco: Freeman and Co.

109. Gladpovsky, A. K. and Sharovo, A. K., 'Magnetit i maghemit v melovykh osodochnykh bokstakh . . .'. *Voprosy Geol. Azii (Akad. Nauk S.S.R.)*, **2**, 239–244 (1955)

110. Godwin-Austen, R. A. C., 'On the valley of the English Channel'. *Quart. J. geol. Soc. Lond.*, **6**, 69–97 (1850)

111. Godwin-Austen, R. A. C., 'On the possible extension of the Coal-Measures beneath the southeastern part of England'. *Quart. J. geol. Soc. Lond.*, **12**, 38–73 (1856)

112. Goodchild, J. G., 'Desert conditions in Britain'. *Trans. Edinb. geol. Soc.*, **7**, 203–222 (1897)

113. Gosselet, J. *Esquisse géologique du nord de France . . . ; Terrains secondaires.* 1881. Lille

114. Grabau, A. W. *Principles of Stratigraphy.* 1913. New York: A. G. Seiler

115. Graham, G. W., 'Note on red colouration and climatic influence in Sudan'. *Geol. Mag.*, **63**, 280–282 (1926)

116. Green, A. H., 'The geology of coal' (pp. 1–72), in *Coal, Its History and Uses* (T. E. Thorpe, ed.). 1878. London: Macmillan and Co.

117. Gregory, J. W., 'The Pre-Cambrian or Pre-Palaeozoic of Scotland' (p. 28–42), in *Handbook of the Geology of Great Britain* (Evans and Stubblefield, ed.). 1929

118. Griffin, G. M. and Ingram, R. L., 'Clay minerals of the Neuse River estuary'. *J. sediment Petrol.*, **25**, 194–200 (1955)

119. Grim, R. E., 'The depositional environment of red and green shales'. *J. sediment Petrol.*, **21**, 226–232 (1951)

120. Grim, R. E. *Clay Mineralogy.* 1953. New York: McGraw-Hill Book Co.

121. Grim, R. E., 'Concept of diagenesis in argillaceous sediments'. *Bull. Amer. Ass. Petrol. Geol.*, **42**, 246–253 (1958)

122. Grim, R. E., Bradley, W. F. and White, W. A., 'Petrology of the Paleozoic shales of Illinois'. *Rep. Invest. Ill. geol. Surv.*, **203**, 35 p. (1957)

123. Hager, D. S., 'Factors affecting the color of sedimentary rocks'. *Bull. Amer. Ass. Petrol. Geol.*, **12**, 901–938 (1928)

124. Hagerman, T. H., 'Granulometric studies in northern Argentine'. *Geogr. Ann., Stockh.*, **18**, 125–212 (1936)

125. Hallimond, A. F., 'Iron ores: bedded ores of England and Wales . . .'. *Spec. Rep. Min. Resour. G.B.*, **29**, 139 p. (1925)

126. Hamdi, H. and Iberg, R., 'Zur Kenntnis der alluvialen Tone des Nils'. *Z. PflErnähr. Düng.*, **67**, 193–197 (1954)

127. Harder, E. C., 'Iron-depositing bacteria and their geologic relations'. *Prof. Pap. U.S. Geol. Surv.* **113**, 89 p. (1919)

128. Harder, E. C., 'Stratigraphy and origin of bauxite deposits'. *Bull. geol. Soc. Amer.*, **60**, 887–907 (1949)

129. Hardon, H. J. and Favejee, J. C. L., 'Qualitative X-ray analysis of the clay fraction of the principal soil types of Java'. Mineral. Onderz. aan Kleien en Kleiminer.; *Meded. LandbHoogesch. Gent.*, **43**, 55–59 (1939)

130. Harrison, J. B., 'The katamorphism of igneous rocks under humid tropical conditions'. *Imp. Bur. Soil Sci., Roth. Exp. Sta.*, 79 p. (1933)

131. Harshbarger, J. W., Repenning, C. A. and Irwin, J. H., 'Stratigraphy of the uppermost Triassic and the Jurassic rocks of the Navajo country'. *Prof. Pap. U.S. geol. Surv.*, **291** (1957)

132. Haughton, S. H., 'The fauna and stratigraphy of the Stormberg series'. *Ann. S. Afr. Mus.*, **12**, 323–497 (1924)

133. Haughton, S. H., 'Beaufort series' (pp. 133–137), and 'Stormberg series' (pp. 137–140); in The Union of South Africa (Rogers, *et al.*). *Handbuch der regionalen Geologie*. 1929. Heidelberg: Carl Winters

134. Heard, A. and Davies, R., 'The Old Red Sandstone of the Cardiff district'. *Quart. J. geol. Soc. Lond.*, **80**, 489–515 (1924)

135. Henderson, Junius, 'The foothills formations of north central Colorado'. *Rep. geol. Surv. Colo., 1908*, 145–188 (1909)

136. Henderson, Junius, 'The foothill formations of north central Colorado'. *Bull. geol. Surv. Colo.*, **19**, 58–98 (1920)

137. Henin, Stephane and Le Borgne, Eugene, 'Causes des propriétés magnétiques de certains sols'. *C. R. Acad. Sci., Paris*, **236**, 736–738 (1953)

138. Henning, K. L., 'Die Red Beds. Ein Beitrag zur Geschichte der bunten Sandsteine'. *Geol. Rdsch.*, **4**, 228–244 (1913)

139. Hitchcock, C. H., 'Glacial drift', in *Geology of New Hampshire*, v. **III**, pt. 3, 177–338 (1878)

140. Hitchcock, Edward. *Report on the geology, mineralogy, botany, and zoology of Massachusetts*. 1833. Amherst, Mass.

141. Hofer, L. J. E. and Weller, Sol, 'The nature of the iron compounds in red and yellow sandstone'. *Science*, **106**, 470 (1947)

142. Honeyborne, D. B., 'The clay minerals in the Keuper marl'. *Clay Min. Bull.*, **1**, 150–155 (1951)

143. Hooks, W. G. and Ingram, R. L., 'The clay minerals and the iron oxide minerals of the Triassic "red beds" of the Durham basin, North Carolina'. *Amer. J. Sci.*, **253**, 19–25 (1955)

144. Horwood, A. R., 'The origin of the British Trias'. *Geol. Mag.*, **47**, 460–463 (1910)

145. Huddleston, W. H., 'On the geological history of iron ores'. *Proc. Geol. Ass., Lond.*, **11**, 104–144 (1889)

146. Huffmann, H., 'Mineralogische Untersuchungen an fünf Bodenprofilen über Basalt, Muschelkalk und Buntsandstein'. *Heidelberg. Beitr. Min.*, **4**, 67–88 (1954)

147. Ijzerman, R. *Outline of the geology and petrology of Surinam*. 1931. The Hague: Martinus Nyhoff

148. Imlay, R. W., 'Paleoecology of Jurassic seas in the western interior of the United States'. *Mem. geol. Soc. Amer.*, **67, 2**, 469–504 (1957)

149. Irving, E., 'The origin of the paleomagnetism of the Torridonian sandstones of north-west Scotland'. *Phil. Trans.*, **250**A, 100–110 (1957)

150. Irving, E., 'Rock magnetism: a new approach to some paleogeographic problems'. *Phil. Mag. Suppl.*, **6**, 194–218 (1957)

151. James, Henry, 'Remarks on the variegated appearance of the New and Old Red Sandstone systems'. *Phil. Mag., 3rd ser.*, **23**, 1–3 (1843)

152. Jones, O. T., 'The geological evolution of Wales and adjacent regions'. *Quart. J. geol. Soc. Lond.*, **111**, 323–351 (1956)

153. Julien, A. A., 'On the geological action of the humic acids'. *Proc. Amer. Ass. Adv. Sci.* (1879), 311–410 (1880)

132   F. B. VAN HOUTEN

154. Katzer, Fr. *Grundzüge der Geologie des unteren Amazonasgebietes.* 1903. Leipzig: Max Weg. Verlag
155. Keeling, P. S., 'Sepiolite at a locality in the Keuper marl of the Midlands'. *Miner. Mag.*, **31**, 328–332 (1956)
156. Keller, W. D., 'Experimental work on red bed bleaching'. *Amer. J. Sci.*, **18**, 65–70 (1929)
157. Keller, W. D., 'Illite and montmorillonite in green sedimentary rocks'. *J. sediment. Petrol.*, **23**, 3–9 (1953)
158. Keller, W. D., 'Clay minerals in the type section of the Morrison formation'. *J. sediment. Petrol.*, **23**, 93–105 (1953)
159. Keller, W. D., 'Glauconitic mica in the Morrison formation in Colorado' (pp. 120–128), in *Clays and Clay Minerals*, Nat. Acad. Sci., Nat. Res. Council, **566**, 1958
160. Keller, W. D., 'Argillation and direct bauxitization in terms of concentrations of hydrogen and metal cations at surface of hydrolyzing aluminium silicates'. *Bull. Amer. Ass. Petrol. Geol.*, **42**, 233–245 (1958)
161. Kerr, W. C. *Report of the geological survey of North Carolina, I.* 1875. Raleigh, N.C.: J. Turner
162. King, L. C., 'Basic palaeogeography of Gondwanaland during the late Paleozoic and Mesozoic eras'. *Quart. J. geol. Soc. Lond.*, **114**, 47–70 (1958)
163. King, P. B., 'Sierra Diablo foothills', in *Geology and Mineral deposits of Pre-Cambrian rocks of the Van Horn area, Texas.* Univ. Texas Publ. No. **5301**, 71–121 (1953)
164. Knowlton, F. H., 'Evolution of geologic climates'. *Bull. geol. Soc. Amer.*, **30**, 499–565 (1919)
165. Koken, E., 'Ist der Buntsandstein eine Wüstenbildung?' *Jh. Ver. vaterl. Naturk. Württemb.*, **61**, lxxvi–lxxvii (1905)
166. Koster, Erhard, 'Aufbau und Sedimentationsrhythmen der Kågerödsformation in der Bohrung Klappe in nordwestlichen Schonen'. *Geol. Fören. Stockh. Förh.*, **78**, 463–502 (1956)
167. Köster, H. M., 'Beitrag zur Kenntnis indischer Laterite'. *Heidelberg. Beitr. Min.*, **5**, 23–64 (1955)
168. Krishnan, M. S., 'Geological history of Ragasthan and its relation to present-day conditions'. *Bull. nat. Inst. Sci., India*, **1**, 19–31 (1952). (*Proc. of Symp. on the Ragputana Desert*)
169. Krynine, P. D., 'Arkose deposits in the humid tropics'. *Amer. J. Sci.*, **29**, 353–363 (1935)
170. Krynine, P. D., 'Geomorphology and sedimentation in the humid tropics'. *Amer. J. Sci.*, **32**, 297–306 (1936)
171. Krynine, P. D., 'Petrology and genesis of the Siwalik series'. *Amer. J. Sci.*, **34**, 422–466 (1937)
172. Krynine, P. D., 'The origin of red beds'. *Trans. N.Y. Acad. Sci.*, **2**, 60–68 (1949)
173. Krynine, P. D., 'Petrology, stratigraphy, and origin of the Triassic sedimentary rocks of Connecticut'. *Bull. Conn. geol. nat. Hist. Surv.*, **73** (1950)
174. Kubiena, W. L., 'Uber die Braunlehmrelikte des Atakor'. *Erdkunde*, **9**, 115–132 (1955)
175. Kulp, J. L. and Trites, A. L., Jr., 'Differential thermal analysis of natural hydrous ferric oxides'. *Amer. Min.*, **36**, 23–44 (1951)
176. Kummel, B., 'Paleoecology of lower Triassic formations of southeastern Idaho and adjacent areas'. *Mem. geol. Soc. Amer.*, **67**, **2**, 437–468 (1957)

177. Lamborn, R. E., Austin, C. R. and Schaaf, D., 'Shales and surface clays of Ohio'. *Bull. geol. Surv. Ohio*, **39** (1938)
178. Lee, J. S. and Lee, Y. Y., 'Sinian glaciation of China'. *Int. Geol. Cong., 17th, U.S.S.R.*, 1937, *Rpt. 17th sess.*, **6**, 33–40 (1940)
179. Lee, W. T., 'Early Mesozoic physiography of the southern Rocky Mountains'. *Smithson. misc. Coll.*, **69** (1918)
180. Lippi-Boncambri, C., Mackenzie, R. C. and Mitchell, W. A., 'The mineralogy of some soils from central Italy'. *Clay Min. Bull.*, **2**, 280–288 (1955)
181. Lippmann, F., 'Über einen Keuperton von Zaiserweiher bei Maulbronn'. *Heidelberg. Beitr. Min.*, **4**, 130–134 (1954)
182. Lippmann, F., 'Clay minerals from the Röt member of the Triassic near Göttingen, Germany'. *J. sediment. Petrol.*, **26**, 125–139 (1956)
183. Lomas, Joseph, 'Desert conditions and the origin of the British Trias'. *Geol. Mag.*, **44**, 511–514, 554–563 (1907)
184. Lomas, Joseph, 'Desert formations, with reference to the origin of the Trias'. *Trans. Leicester lit. phil. Soc.*, **13**, 105–110 (1909)
185. Loomis, F. B., 'Origin of the Wasatch deposits'. *Amer. J. Sci.*, **23**, 356–364 (1907)
186. Lyell, Charles. *Principles of Geology*, 2 vols. (5th ed.). 1837. Philadelphia: J. Kay Jr. and Bros.
187. Lyell, Charles. *Elements of Geology*. 1838. London: John Murray
188. MacCarthy, G. R., 'Colors produced by iron in minerals and the sediments'. *Amer. J. Sci.*, **12**, 17–36 (1926)
189. MacCarthy, G. R., 'Iron-stained sands and clays'. *J. Geol.*, **34**, 352–360 (1926)
190. Mackenzie, R. C., 'The oxides of iron, aluminum, and manganese' (pp. 299–328), in *The Differential Thermal Investigation of Clays*. 1957. Miner. Soc. London
191. Mackenzie, R. C., 'The illite in some Old Red Sandstone soils and sediments'. *Miner. Mag.*, **31**, 681–689 (1957)
192. Mackie, Wm., 'The feldspars present in sedimentary rocks . . .'. *Trans. Edinb. geol. Soc.*, **7**, 443–468 (1899)
193. MacNair, Peter, 'The physical conditions under which the Deuterozoic rocks of Scotland were deposited. Pt. 1. The Old Red Sandstone'. *Trans. geol. Soc. Glasg.*, **17**, 105–145 (1922)
194. MacNair, Peter and Reid, James, 'On the physical conditions under which the Old Red Sandstone of Scotland was deposited'. *Geol. Mag.*, **33**, 106–116 (1896)
195. Mantell, G. A., 'Description of the *Telerpeton elginense* . . .'. *Quart. J. geol. Soc. Lond.*, **8**, 100–108 (1852)
196. Mather, W. W. *Geology of New York; Pt. 5, comprising the geology of the Ist geological district*. 1843. Albany, N.Y.
197. Maw, George, 'On the deposition of iron in variegated strata'. *Quart. J. geol. Soc. Lond.*, **24**, 351–400 (1868)
198. McKay, A. W., 'The red sandstone of Nova Scotia'. *Rep. Brit. Ass.*, **XXXV**, 66–67 (1866)
199. McKee, E. D., 'The environment and history of the Toroweap and Kaibab formations of northern Arizona and southern Utah'. *Publ. Carneg. Instn*, **492** (1938)
200. McKee, E. D., 'Stratigraphy and history of the Moenkopi formation of Triassic age'. *Mem. geol. Soc. Amer.*, **61** (1954)
201. Medlicott, H. B. and Blanford, W. T. *A manual of the geology of India, I.* 1879. Calcutta: Govt. Print. Off.
202. Mencher, Ely, 'Catskill facies of New York State'. *Bull. geol. Soc. Amer.*, **50**, 1761–1794 (1939)

203. Merrill, W. M. and Winar, R. M., 'Molas and associated formations in San Juan Basin–Needle Mountains Area, southwestern Colorado'. *Bull. Amer. Ass. Petrol. Geol.*, **42**, 2107–2132 (1958)

204. Meyerhoff, H. A. and Collins, R. F., 'Mississippian–Pennsylvanian contact in western South Dakota' (abst.). *Proc. geol. Soc. Amer.*, **1934**, 94–95 (1935)

205. Miller, D. N. and Folk, R. L., 'Occurrence of detrital magnetite and ilmenite in red sediments; new approach to significance of redbeds'. *Bull. Amer. Ass. Petrol. Geol.*, **39**, 338–345 (1955)

206. Miller, Hugh. *Old Red Sandstone* (1906 edn.). 1841. London: J. M. Dent and Sons, Ltd.

207. Miller, W. J., 'Origin of color in the Vernon shale'. *Bull. N.Y. St. Mus.*, **140**, 150–156 (1910)

208. Millot, Georges, 'The principal sedimentary facies and their characteristic clays'. *Clay Min. Bull.*, **1**, 235–237 (1952)

209. Milne, I. H. and Earley, J. W., 'Effect of source and environment on clay minerals'. *Amer. Ass. Petrol. Geol.*, **42**, 328–338 (1958)

210. Mitchell, B. D. and Mitchell, W. A., 'The clay mineralogy of Ayrshire soils and their parent rocks'. *Clay Min. Bull.*, **3**, 91–97 (1956)

211. Moberly, Ralph, 'Mesozoic Morrison, Cloverly . . . Bighorn Basin, Wyoming and Montana'. *Bull. geol. Soc. Amer.*, **71**, 1137–1176 (1960)

212. Mohr, E. C. J. and Van Baren, F. A. *Tropical Soils.* 1954. London: Interscience Publ. Ltd.

213. Moody, G. T., 'The cause of variegation in Keuper marls and in other calcareous rocks'. *Quart. J. geol. Soc. Lond.*, **61**, 431–439 (1905)

214. Mook, C. C., 'Study of the Morrison formation'. *Ann. N.Y. Acad. Sci.*, **27**, 39–191 (1916)

215. Moore, C. C., 'The chemical examination of sandstones from Prenton Hill and Bidston Hill'. *Proc. Lpool. geol. Soc.*, **8**, 241–269 (1899)

216. Munoz Taboadela, M., 'The clay mineralogy of some soils from Spain and from Rio Muni (West Africa)'. *J. Soil. Sci.*, **4**, 48–55 (1953)

217. Murchison, R. I. *The Silurian System*, Pt. 1. 1839. London: John Murray

218. Neumayr, Melchior. *Erdgeschichte, I* (2nd edn.). 1890. Leipzig: Verlag des Bibliogr. Inst.

219. Newton, Henry, 'Geology of the Black Hills' (pp. 1–222), in *Report on the Geology and Resources of the Black Hills of Dakota*, U.S. Geogr. and Geol. Survey Rocky Mountain Region, 1880

220. Newberry, J. S., 'The fauna and flora of the Trias of New Jersey and the Connecticut Valley'. *Ann. N.Y. Acad. Sci.*, **6**, 124–128 (1887)

221. Norin, Erik, 'The lithological character of the Permian sediments of the Angara series in central Shansi, north China'. *Geol. Fören. Stockh. Förh.*, **46**, 19–55 (1924)

222. Norin, Erik, 'An Algonkian continental sedimentary formation in western Shansi'. *Bull. geol. Soc. China*, **3**, 55–71 (1924)

223. Nyun, M. A. and McCaleb, S. B., 'The reddish brown lateritic soils of the North Carolina piedmont region . . .'. *Soil Sci.*, **80**, 27–40 (1955)

224. Oldham, R. D., 'A comparison of the Permian breccias of the Midlands with the upper Carboniferous glacial deposits of India and Australia'. *Quart. J. geol. Soc. Lond.*, **50**, 463–470 (1894)

225. Osborne, G. D., 'A review of some aspects of the stratigraphy, structure and physiography of the Sydney Basin'. *Proc. Linn. Soc., N.S.W.*, **73**, 4–37 (1948)

226. Palache, Charles, Berman, Harry and Frondel, Clifford. *The System of Mineralogy*, 7th edn., I. 1944. New York: John Wiley and Sons
227. Peach, B. N. *et al.*, 'Report on recent work of the Geological Survey . . .'. *Quart. J. geol. Soc. Lond.*, **44**, 378–441 (1888)
228. Penck, Albrecht, 'Geomorphologische Probleme aus Nordwest Schottland'. *Z. Ges. Erdk. Berl.*, **32**, 146–191 (1897)
229. Pepper, J. F., Dewitt, Wallace and Demarest, D. F., 'Geology of the Bedford shale and Berea sandstone in the Appalachian Basin'. *Prof. Pap. U.S. geol. Surv.*, **259**, 111 p. (1954)
230. Percival, J. G. *Report on the geology of the state of Connecticut.* 1842. New Haven, Conn.: Osborn and Baldwin
231. Pettijohn, F. J. *Sedimentary Rocks* (2nd edn.). 1957. New York: Harper and Bros.
232. Phillippi, Emil, 'Über die Bildungsweise der buntgefärbten klastischen Gesteine der continentalen Trias'. *Neues Jb. Min. Geol. Paläont. Centralb.*, **1901**, 463–469 (1901)
233. Pirsson, L. V. *Rocks and Minerals.* 1913. New York: John Wiley
234. Plice, M. J., 'Factors affecting soil color (progress report)'. *Proc. Okla. Acad. Sci.*, **23**, 49–51 (1943)
235. Posnjak, Eugen and Merwin, H. E., 'The hydrate ferric oxides'. *Amer. J. Sci.*, **47**, 311–348 (1919)
236. Ramsay, A. C., 'On the occurrence of angular, subangular, polished, and striated fragments and boulders in the Permian breccia of Shropshire . . .'. *Quart. J. geol. Soc. Lond.*, **11**, 185–205 (1855)
237. Ramsay, A. C., 'On the physical relations of the New Red Marl . . .'. *Quart. J. geol. Soc. Lond.*, **27**, 185–199 (1871)
238. Ramsay, A. C., 'On the red rocks of England of older date than the Trias'. *Quart. J. geol. Soc. Lond.*, **27**, 241–256 (1871)
239. Raymond, P. E., 'The significance of red color in sediments'. *Amer. J. Sci.*, **13**, 234–351 (1927)
240. Raymond, P. E., 'The pigment in black and red sediments'. *Amer. J. Sci.*, **240**, 658–669 (1942)
241. Reade, T. M., 'The New Red Sandstone and the physiography of the Triassic period'. *Naturalist, Lond.*, April, 108–111 (1889)
242. Reed, R. D., 'Sespe formation, California'. *Bull. Amer. Ass. Petrol. Geol.*, **13**, 487–507 (1929)
243. Reeside, J. B., 'Triassic-Jurassic "red beds" of the Rocky Mountain region', a discussion. *J. Geol.*, **37**, 47–63 (1929)
244. Reeves, Frank, 'Geology of the Cement oil field, Caddo County, Oklahoma'. *Bull. U.S. geol. Surv.*, **726**, 41–85 (1921)
245. Reineck, H. E., 'Zur Petrogenese der Waderner Schichten am N-Flügel der Nahemulde'. *Neues Jb. Geol. Abh.*, **100**, 289–323 (1955)
246. Reinemund, J. A., 'Geology of the Deep River coal field, North Carolina'. *Prof. Pap. U.S. geol. Surv.*, **246**, 159 p. (1955)
247. Riba, O., 'Sur la type sédimentation du Tertiare continental de la partie ouest du bassin de L'ebre'. *Geol. Rdsch.*, **43**, 363–370 (1955)
248. Richardson, G. B., 'The upper red beds of the Black Hills'. *J. Geol.*, **11**, 365–393 (1903)
249. Richardson, Lindsdale, 'Trias' (pp. 319–340), in *Handbook of the Geology of Great Britain* (Evans and Stubblefield, ed.). 1929
250. Richey, J. E. *et al.*, 'The Geology of North Ayrshire'. *Mem. geol. Surv., Scotland* (1930)

251. Riviere, André, 'Sur l'origine des argiles sédimentaires'. *Int. Geol. Cong.*, *19th*, *Algeria* (1952), Fasc. **18**, 177–180 (1953)
252. Robb, G. L., 'Red bed coloration'. *J. sediment. Petrol.*, **19**, 99–103 (1949)
253. Robertson, Thomas, 'The origin of the Etruria marl'. *Quart. J. geol. Soc. Lond.*, **87**, 13–26 (1931)
254. Rogers, A. W. *An introduction to the geology of Cape Colony*. 1905. London: Longmans Green
255. Rogers, H. D. *Description of the geology of the state of New Jersey*. 1840. Philadelphia
256. Russell, I. C., 'On the physical history of the Triassic formation of New Jersey and the Connecticut Valley'. *Ann. N.Y. Acad. Sci.*, **1**, 220–254 (1878)
257. Russell, I. C., 'Subaerial decay of rocks and the origin of the red color of certain formations'. *Bull. U.S. geol. Surv.*, **52** (1889)
258. Russell, I. C., 'The Newark system'. *Bull. U.S. geol. Surv.*, **85** (1892)
259. Salomon, W. *Grundzüge der Geologie, II.* 1926. Stuttgart: Schweitzerbart Verlag
260. Scheffer, F., Welte, E. and Ludwieg, F., 'Zur Frage der Eisenoxydhydrate im Boden'. *Chem. d. Erde*, **19**, 51–64 (1957)
261. Schmalz, R. F., 'Thermodynamic calculations relating to the origin of red beds (abst.)'. *Bull. geol. Soc. Amer.*, **69**, 1639–1640 (1958)
262. Schultz, L. G., 'Clay studies'. *U.S. geol. Surv.*, *TEI* 590, 124–126 (1955)
263. Schulz, Eugen, 'Geognostische Übersicht der Bergreviere Arnsberg, Brilon, und Olpe . . .'. *Festg. an die D. Geol. Gesell.*, (1887)
264. Schwarzbach, Martin. *Das Klima der Vorzeit*. 1950. Stuttgart: F. Enke
265. Schweitzer, P., 'Notes on felsites of the Palisade Range'. *Proc. Lyceum Nat. Hist.*, ser. I–II (1870–74), 244–252 (1871)
266. Scrivenor, J. B., 'The New Red sandstone of south Devonshire'. *Geol. Mag.*, **85**, 317–332 (1948)
267. Seward, A. C. *Plant life through the ages*. 1931. New York: Macmillan
268. Shaler, N. S., 'Description of quarries and quarry regions', in *Report on the Building Stones of the United States . . . 1880*, Census Off., Dpt. Int., 107–279, 1884
269. Shaler, N. S. and Davis, W. M. *Illustrations of the earth's surface; glaciers*. 1881. Boston
270. Sherlock, R. L., 'Red rocks as indicators of past climates'. *Proc. Trans., Southeastern Natur. and Antiq.*, **46**, 38–53 (1941)
271. Sherlock, R. L. *The Permo-Triassic formations*. 1947. London: Hutchinson's Sci. and Tech. Pub.
272. Sherman, G. D., 'The genesis and morphology of the alumina-rich lateritic clays' (pp. 154–161), in *Problems of clay and laterite genesis*, Amer. Inst. Min. Metall. Eng., 1952
273. Shotton, F. W., 'Some aspects of the New Red Desert in Britain'. *Lpool. Manchr. Geol. J.*, **1**, 450–465 (1956)
274. Sinclair, W. J. and Granger, Walter, 'Eocene and Oligocene of the Wind River and Bighorn basins'. *Bull. Amer. Mus. nat. Hist.*, **30**, 83–117 (1911)
275. Sioli, Harold, 'Sedimentation im Amazonasgebiet'. *Geol. Rdsch.*, **45**, 608–633 (1957)
276. Smith, F. G. and Kidd, D. J., 'Hematite–goethite relations in neutral and alkaline solutions under pressure'. *Amer. Min.*, **34**, 403–412 (1949)
277. Spring, W., 'Sur les matières colorantes, à base de fer . . .'. *Rec. Trav. chim. Pays-Bas*, **17**, 202–211 (1898)

278. Stavrou, A., 'Untersuchungen über die magnetischen Eigenschaften der griechischen Roterde'. *Beitr. Geophys.*, **66**, 214–255 (1957)
279. Stehli, F. G., 'Possible Permian climatic zonation and its implication'. *Amer. J. Sci.*, **255**, 607–618 (1957)
280. Steinwehr, H. E., 'Über das Pigment roter Gesteine'. *Neues Jb. Geol.*, **99**, 355–360 (1954)
281. Stephen, I. and MacEwan, D. M. C., 'Swelling chlorite'. *Geotechnique, Lond.*, **2**, 82–83 (1950)
282. Stevenson, I. M., 'Truro map-area, Colchester and Hants counties, Nova Scotia'. *Mem. geol. Surv. Can.*, **297** (1958)
283. Strand, Trygve, 'Fossil climates as indicated by Eocambrian and Paleozoic deposits in Norway'. *Int. Geol. Cong., 17th, U.S.S.R., 1937, Rpt. 17th sess.*, **6**, 11–20 (1940)
284. Süssmilch, C. A. *An introduction to the geology of New South Wales* (3rd edn.). 1922. Sydney: Angus and Robertson
285. Swineford, Ada, 'Petrography of upper Permian rocks in south-central Kansas'. *Bull. Kans. geol. Surv.*, **111** (1955)
286. Tank, R. W., 'Clay mineralogy of Morrison formation . . .'. *Bull. Amer. Ass. Petrol. Geol.*, **40**, 871–878 (1956)
287. Tester, A. C., 'Mississippian-Pennsylvanian contact in the Rocky Mountain region'. *Amer. Ass. Petrol. Geol., Program. Ann. Meet*, 63 (1959)
288. Thomas, H. D., 'Phosphoria and Dinwoody tongues in lower Chugwater of central and southeastern Wyoming'. *Bull. Amer. Ass. Petrol. Geol.*, **18**, 1655–1692 (1934)
289. Thomas, H. H., 'A contribution to the petrography of the New Red Sandstone in the west of England'. *Quart. J. geol. Soc. Lond.*, **65**, 229–244 (1909)
290. Tieje, A. J., 'The red beds of the Front Range in Colorado: a study in sedimentation'. *J. Geol.*, **31**, 192–207 (1923)
291. Tomlinson, C. W., 'A study of the conditions of origin of the Permo-Carboniferous and Triassic red beds of the western United States'. *J. Geol.*, **24**, 153–179, 238–253 (1916)
292. Tricart, J., 'Aspects sedimentologiques du delta du Senegal'. *Geol. Rdsch.*, **43**, 384–397 (1955)
293. Troedsson, Gustaf, 'Bidrag till kännedomen om Kågerödsformation i Skane'. *Geol. Fören. Stockh. Förh.*, **64**, 289–328 (1942)
294. Trotter, F. M., 'Reddened beds of Carboniferous age in northwest England and their origin'. *Proc. York. geol. (polyt.) Soc.*, **29**, 1–20 (1953)
295. Tunell, George and Posnjak, Eugen, 'The stability relations of goethite and hematite'. *Econ. Geol.*, **26**, 337–343 (1931)
296. Vail, C. E., 'Lithologic evidence of climatic pulsation'. *Science*, **46**, 90–93 (1917)
297. Valeton, Ida, 'Petrographie des süddeutschen Hauptbuntsandsteins'. *Heidelberg. Beitr. Min.*, **3**, 335–379 (1953)
298. Valeton, Ida, 'Lateritische Verwitterungsböden zur Zeit der jungkimmerischen Gebirgsbildung im nördlichen Harzvorland'. *Geol. Jber.*, **73**, 149–164 (1957)
299. Van der Gracht, W. A. J. M., 'Permo-Carboniferous Orogeny in south-central United States'. *Amer. Ass. Petrol. Geol.*, **15**, 991–1057 (1931)
300. Van der Marel, H. W., 'Gamma ferric oxide in sediments'. *J. sediment. Petrol.*, **21**, 12–21 (1951)
301. Van der Merwe, C. R. and Heystek, H., 'Clay minerals of South African soil groups: I. Laterites and related soils'. *Soil Sci.*, **74**, 383–401 (1952)

K

302. Van der Merwe, C. R. and Heystek, H., 'Clay minerals in the South African soil groups: III. Soils of the desert and adjoining semiarid regions'. *Soil Sci.*, **80**, 479–494 (1955)

303. Van Hise, R. C. and Leith, C. K., 'The geology of the Lake Superior region'. *Monogr. U.S. geol. Surv.*, **52**, 641 p. (1911)

304. Van Houten, F. B., 'Origin of red-banded early Cenozoic deposits in Rocky Mountain region'. *Bull. Amer. Ass. Petrol. Geol.*, **32**, 2083–2126 (1948)

305. Van Houten, F. B., 'Clay minerals in sedimentary rocks and derived soils'. *Amer. J. Sci.*, **251**, 61–82 (1953)

306. Van Kersen, J. F., 'Bauxite deposits in Suriname and Demerara (British Guiana)'. *Leid. geol. Meded.*, **21**, 249–375 (1956)

307. Vanuxem, Lardner. *Geology of New York: Part III, comprising the survey of the 3rd Geological District.* 1842. Albany, N.Y.

308. Versey, H. C., 'Permian' (pp. 299–311), in *Handbook of the Geology of Great Britain* (Evans and Stubblefield, ed.). 1929

309. Visser, K. J. L., 'The structural evolution of the Union'. *Proc. geol. Soc. S. Afr.*, **60**, xiv–xlix (1957)

310. Vivaldi, J. L. M. and MacEwan, D. M. C., 'Triassic chlorites from the Jura and the Catalan coastal range'. *Clay Min. Bull.*, **3**, 177–183 (1957)

311. Von Richthofen, F. F. *Führer für Forschungsreisende.* 1886. Berlin: Rbt. Oppenheimer

312. Wadia, D. N. *Geology of India.* 1919. London: Macmillan and Co.

313. Wahlstrom, E. E., 'Pre-Fountain and recent weathering on Flagstaff Mountain near Boulder, Colorado'. *Bull. geol. Soc. Amer.*, **59**, 1173–1189 (1948)

314. Walther, Johannes. *Geschichte der Erde und des Lebens.* 1908. Leipzig: Veit and Co.

315. Walther, Johannes, 'Über algonkische Sedimente'. *Z. dtsch. geol. Ges.*, **61**, 283–305 (1909)

316. Waters, A. C., 'John Day formation west of its type locality (abst.)'. *Bull. geol. Soc. Amer.*, **65**, 1320 (1954)

317. Watson, D. M. S., 'The Beaufort beds of the Karroo system of South Africa'. *Geol. Mag.*, **50**, 388–393 (1913)

318. Watts, W. W. *Geology of the ancient rocks of Charnwood forest, Leicestershire.* 1947. Leicester: Edgar Bachus

319. Weaver, C. E., 'A lath-shaped non-expanded dioctahedral 2 : 1 clay mineral'. *Amer. Min.*, **38**, 279–289 (1953)

320. Weaver, C. E., 'A discussion of the origin of clay minerals in sedimentary rocks' (pp. 159–173), in *Clays and Clay Minerals*, Nat. Acad. Sci., Nat. Res. Council, Publ. 566, 1958

321. Weaver, C. E., 'Origin and significance of clay minerals in sedimentary rocks'. *Bull. Amer. Ass. Petrol. Geol.*, **42**, 254–271 (1958)

322. Weeks, A. D., 'Mineralogical study of some Jurassic and Cretaceous claystones and siltstones from western Colorado and eastern Utah'. *U.S. geol. Surv.*, TEI **285**, 22 p. (1953)

323. Weller, J. M., 'Outline of Chinese geology'. *Bull. Amer. Ass. Petrol. Geol.*, **28**, 1417–1429 (1944)

324. Welo, L. A. and Baudisch, Oscar, 'Relationships among the oxide hydrates and oxides of iron and some of their properties'. *Chem. Rev.*, **15**, 45–97 (1934)

325. White, David, 'The upper Paleozoic floras, their succession and range'. *J. Geol.*, **17**, 320–341 (1909)

326. White, David, 'Flora of the Hermit shale, Grand Canyon, Arizona'. *Publ. Carneg. Instn*, **405**, 221 p. (1929)

327. White, David, 'Some features of the early Permian flora of America'. *Int. Geol. Cong.*, *16th, United States*, 1933, *Rept. v. 1*, 679–689 (1936)

328. Wilfarth, M., 'Die Sedimentationsprobleme in der Germanischen Senke zur Perm- und Trias-zeit'. *Geol. Rdsch.*, **24**, 349–377 (1933)

329. Willis, Bailey, 'Paleozoic Appalachia or the history of Maryland during Paleozoic time'. *Maryland geol. Surv.*, **4**, 23–93 (1902)

330. Wills, L. J., 'On the fossiliferous lower Keuper rocks of Worcestershire'. *Proc. Geol. Ass., Lond.*, **21**, 249–331 (1910)

331. Wills, L. J. *The physiographical evolution of Britain.* 1929. London: Edward Arnold and Co.

332. Wilson, H. E., 'The petrography of the Old Red Sandstone rocks of the north of Ireland'. *Proc. R. Irish Acad.*, **55**, 283–320 (1953)

333. Woodworth, J. B., 'Geology of the Narragansett Basin, pt. II'. *Monogr. U.S. geol. Surv.*, **33**, 99–214 (1899)

334. Young, J. W., 'On the chemistry of some Carboniferous and Old Red Sandstones'. *Trans. geol. Soc. Glasg.*, **2**, 198–209 (1867)

VI

Geological Evidence of Cold Climate *

R. F. FLINT

I. Introduction

The broad inferences as to cold climates of the past, drawn from the geological record, are based on two kinds of evidence. These are fossils, occurring at localities where similar organisms do not live today, and physical features of the rocks, occurring at places where such features are not now being formed. Both kinds of evidence are established through use of the principle of uniformity of process: the fossils because their nearest living relatives occupy environments that are comparatively cold or because the isotopic composition of their shells implies sea-water temperatures that are relatively low; the physical features because we find similar things being

* Critical discussion of the manuscript by J. E. Sanders and A. L. Washburn is gratefully acknowledged.

fashioned today or in the very recent past, by glaciers, floating ice, ground frost and other agencies that demand a cold climate for their activity. In cold-climate sediments of Pleistocene age the two kinds of evidence occur closely associated. Examples are tundra plants such as *Dryas octopetala* and land mammals such as the woolly mammoth (*Mammuthus primigenius*) and woolly rhinoceros (*Coelodonta antiquitatis*) occurring in close relation to glacial drift. Their association strengthens the inference of cold climate that is derived independently from each.

The evidence from fossils is discussed elsewhere in this book; the present chapter deals only with physical features. Most of the physical evidence of former cold climates that is well exposed to view and that has been described in the literature pertains to the Pleistocene epoch. Detailed discussions of it are readily available.[2, 7, 24] No comparable summaries of the far more ancient, pre-Pleistocene cold periods exist, although a partial summary was published by Coleman (reference 3, pp. 77–241). The object of the present discussion is to select and evaluate the particular sorts of evidence of cold climate that are likely to be preserved in strata far older than Pleistocene, in an attempt to shed light on cold climates of ancient times.

As used in this chapter an ancient 'cold climate' is defined as a climate colder than today's in the area of the evidence under consideration. As will appear hereafter, there is little reliable physical evidence of cold climate apart from features that demonstrate the former presence of glaciers; although other evidence exists, that of glaciation is preponderant, and underlies the bulk of the present discussion.

Glacier ice implies, in the area of its accumulation, a sustained mean annual temperature of no more than 0°C, usually accompanied by notably cold summers. Once formed, however, large glaciers of the ice-sheet type influence the climate above them. Hence evidence of glaciation at any place does not necessarily imply a *secular* climate cold enough and moist enough to create a glacier, as long as it cannot be excluded that the glacier formed first elsewhere, and then invaded the place in question, in part through the operation of factors that favour glacier self-extension.

Lest it seem to be implied that low temperature alone is the only climatic parameter indicated by former glaciers, we should note that today's glaciers are best developed where precipitation also is relatively abundant. Parts of Siberia, Alaska and Tibet experience very low temperatures, yet receive so little precipitation that glaciers neither exist there today, nor did they exist at any time during the Pleistocene glacial ages. Hence the glacial evidence of cold climate is also evidence of a climate sufficiently moist to maintain glaciers.

Also needed is a clear distinction between extensive ice sheets, such as in Pleistocene times invaded broad areas of low altitude even down to sea-level, and the smaller glaciers that occupy highland areas discontinuously. Owing to the atmospheric-temperature lapse rate of about 0·6°C/100 m, glaciers can occupy highlands the bases of which experience continual warm-tropical temperatures. An example is the existing ice-cap on New Guinea, standing

4000 to 5000 m above the tropical-rain forest belt but separated from it in horizontal measurement by only a very few tens of kilometres. By analogy, the occurrence of evidence of glaciation in ancient rocks need not in itself imply *secular* temperatures lower than those encountered today in equatorial high altitudes, for the glaciation may have been local, and solely the result of the presence of very high land standing in a moist environment. Earth movement and erosion may have altered topography and altitudes to such an extent that the former highlands of origin have disappeared. Hence inference as to the secular climate of the time must be drawn with great caution. The more extensive and the more nearly continuous the features indicating ancient glaciation, the more likely it is that secular temperatures were relatively low; i.e. that the secular climate was cold by our definition.

II. Evidence of Former Glaciation

II.1 *Abraded Bedrock Surfaces*

One of the earliest groups of features recorded in the literature of science as evidence of glaciation consists of surfaces of bedrock abraded by drift-shod ice. In detail the features include high polish, striations both fine and coarse, and grooves some of which exceed 25 m in depth and 1 km in length. Also included are small fractures and gouges, generally crescentic in form, occurring with striations and polish on a single surface of bedrock.

Striations and polish have long been recognized also as characteristic of many fault interfaces. Such slickensided surfaces must be eliminated (if none of the surfaces are internal rather than external and if independent evidence of faulting is negative) before glacial origin can be established.

Further, striations and even small grooves can be made by any flowing or floating heavy mass. Icebergs and pans of sea ice and river ice have been observed to scratch rocks submerged beneath shallow water, and mass movements such as snow avalanches, landslides, mudflows and *nuées ardentes* also have been shown to scratch or groove their floors. It is necessary, therefore, to establish glacial origin through the identification of associated features that are unequivocally glacial. The most reliable of these are stoss-and-lee forms and tillite, both described hereafter. Actually, glaciated rock surfaces are virtually always accompanied by till or tillite. If a surface is not so accompanied, it should be regarded with suspicion at least until the alternative origins mentioned have been eliminated.

Even without unequivocal associations, glacial origin becomes more probable with increasing areal extent of the striated surfaces, as all but one of the alternative agencies are likely to be local. The exception is floating ice. However, surfaces abraded by this agency are likely to have short and randomly oriented scratches and to be overlain by marine or lacustrine sediments; yet like glaciated surfaces they imply cold climate.

II.2 *Streamline Topographic Forms*

In many areas the abrasion of bedrock surfaces by glaciers has resulted in the modelling of smooth boss-like forms through streamline flowage of the glacier with its abrasive bed load. Commonly these swell-like bosses are unsymmetrical, ending distally or downstream in small cliffs or hackly surfaces caused by glacial quarrying. Such stoss-and-lee forms are reliable indicators of direction of flow of the ice that fashioned them. Boss-like forms with minute striation detail are widely preserved in the region of the Dwyka (Karroo) glaciation in southern Africa, mainly because the glacier ice left them covered with sediment that constituted a continuous cap or seal up to the time of their recent exposure by erosion. Some of the bosses are so well exposed that their stoss-and-lee form is clearly visible.

In addition to streamline forms small closed basins occur in the bedrock surface underlying the Dwyka tillite (reference 5, p. 91). These are similar to basins in bedrock surfaces recently glaciated and constitute further evidence of Dwyka glaciation.

II.3 *Till and Tillite*

The glacier-deposited, non-sorted sediment known as till, containing a wide range of grain sizes and a usually small proportion of stones having abraded facets, striations, or both, is characteristic of wide areas uncovered by the shrinkage of existing glaciers and of the great former glaciers as well. Being largely the product of mechanical disaggregation of fresh rocks, till is likely to consist mainly of fresh mineral chips. In its consolidated form (tillite) it has been identified in rocks of great age.

Obviously tillite is a prime indicator of ancient cold climate, but before a sedimentary rock can be accorded this distinction, its glacial origin must be established beyond doubt. Non-sorted sedimentary rocks began to be identified as tillites in the 19th century, when the most widely recognized non-sorted sediments consisted of till. This was before the diversity of origin of non-sorted sediments became fully appreciated. It is not surprising, therefore, that some such identifications are in doubt, and that some supposed tillites have been reappraised and divested of their glacial labels.[20,14]

The principal characteristics of till are as follows:*

A. *Grain Size*

The possible range of grain size is tremendous, extending from clay particles to boulders, some of which are of such enormous diameter that they have been mistaken for bedrock. In most tills fine grain sizes greatly predominate over pebbles and larger particles, although such size distribution is not universal. Of course the range of grain size is small in tills derived from rocks that do not yield particles of many sizes.

* See the checklist in reference 14, pp. 142–145.

B. *Sorting*

The sediment as a whole possesses almost no size sorting and is commonly chaotic in this respect. Therefore there is rarely any stratification, even within a fine-grained matrix in which coarser particles are imbedded.

C. *Shapes of Particles*

Constituent coarse particles are not rounded (although rounded particles, glacially derived from older sediments such as glacial outwash, may be present). Pebbles and cobbles include some that have subflat facets produced by glacial abrasion. Edges separating adjacent facets are somewhat rounded. Some pebbles and cobbles tend to approach a pentagonal, 'flat-iron' shape dominated by a conspicuous basal facet, commonly curved near the point of the flat-iron.

D. *Striations on Particles*

The surfaces (particularly facets) of a small proportion (commonly less than 5 per cent) of pebbles and cobbles possess striations, usually subparallel though in some cases oriented at random.[23]

E. *Fabric*

Some tills possess a fabric consisting of a tendency of the pebble- and cobble-size particles to lie with their long axes paralleling the direction of flow of the glacier.[11] No fabric measurements have been reported from any tillite.

F. *Lithology*

Lithological composition can be highly variable from one area to another, and can be strongly heterogeneous even in a single exposure, depending on the number of kinds of rocks that crop out in the upstream direction. Some elements can have travelled far, having been derived apparently from sources hundred of kilometers distant. Constituent minerals are likely to include many that are not decomposed. This fresh condition results from the predominantly mechanical means (mechanical weathering, glacial erosion) whereby the particles are released from parent rocks, as well as from short distance and rate of transport to the place of deposition. Of course fresh condition of components does not in itself establish glacial origin, for it is well known that fresh sediments originate in other ways. In subtropical Southern Rhodesia, for example, sediments that are both feldspathic and angular are forming today under a warm, strongly seasonal climate. The processes involved include disaggregation of granitic rocks by rapid weathering, and rapid transportation by flash floods through short distances to sites of deposition.

Fig. 1. Detail of exposure of Dwyka Tillite overlying striated and polished Venters-dorp Diabase. Nooitgedacht, Cape Province, South Africa. (Photo R. F. Flint.)

Fig. 2. Glacially-made ridges in Dwyka Tillite. Harrisdale, Cape Province, South Africa. Notebook is 9 in. long. (Photo R. F. Flint.)

G. *Boulder pavements*

Some tills include a flat-lying layer of boulders and cobbles, the upper surface of which bevels the stones. The bevel commonly carries parallel striations. These striated boulder pavements are lag concentrates resulting from removal of the fine matrix by wind or trickling water, after deglaciation of the locality. Thereafter renewed glaciation abraded the concentrate, which was very likely frozen fast in its matrix. No process other than glaciation is known to fashion concentrations of coarse fragments having these peculiar characteristics. Boulder pavements have been reported (reference 5, p. 91) from the Dwyka Tillite in South Africa.

H. *Thickness and lateral extent*

Tills range in thickness from a few centimetres to a hundred metres or more; thickness of tillite in South Africa is reported to exceed 600 m in places. Rather commonly the thickness of a till sheet varies abruptly within short distances. Lateral extent of an individual till body can vary from a hundred metres or less, to hundreds of kilometres.

I. *Underlying floor*

Some tills and tillites directly overlie a surface or floor of bedrock that is striated and/or polished (Fig. 1) and that may also have been sculptured by abrasion into swell-like bosses.

J. *Form of upper surface*

The upper surfaces of bodies of till possess widely varying forms, many of which consist of constructional features. Among these are: (*a*) streamline molded forms consisting of parallel grooves and ridges, like the marks in soil made by a blunt rake, with relief of from less than one metre to a hundred metres or more; (*b*) ground moraine, a non-linear topographic pattern of broad low hummocks and shallow basins with random ground plan and low relief; and (*c*) end moraine, a topographic pattern of long swells or ridges and related basins, in plan transverse to the direction of glacier flow, and commonly with considerable relief.

In the study of tillites topography is commonly neglected because in ancient tillites, as indeed in tills of early Pleistocene age, initial constructional topography has been destroyed by erosion. However, if from the moment of deglaciation erosion is prevented, even the details of a constructional till surface can be preserved.

A striking example is exposed near Harrisdale, Cape Province, South Africa, about 18 miles north-west of Kimberley.* Through an area of several acres is exposed a polished and striated floor, with very little relief, cut on

* The writer visited the locality in August 1957, in company with Dr. H. B. S. Cooke of the University of the Witwatersrand.

the Ventersdorp Diabase. It is characterized by numerous parallel striations oriented north-east–south-west, a regional trend. Directly overlying the floor are large patches of Dwyka Tillite 1 to 3 ft thick. The tillite consists of pebbles, cobbles, and boulders up to 30 in. in diameter, chiefly diabase, set in a matrix of finer particles apparently also chiefly diabase. The tillite thins to a feather edge around the margin of each patch, and its upper surface is itself striated. The striations are parallel with, and some of them continue unbroken into, the striations on the diabase exposed between the patches of tillite. The till is conspicuously ridged (Fig. 2), each ridge being 1 to 4 ft high and 2 to 15 ft wide. The ridges parallel the striations.

Evidently the till was lodged upon the diabase surface from the base of a moving glacier. That the basal drift was scanty is suggested by the thinness of the tillite. Apparently the ridges were made by a raking or moulding process during the time of movement, probably short, when the striations were engraved on bedrock and tillite. Closely similar features occur in drift made and exposed within recent time (see, for example, reference 7, p. 71).

Around the edges of the exposure, diabase and tillite pass beneath gray argillite. The argillite consists of flat-lying laminae broadly paralleling the surface of the underlying tillite and diabase. The laminae are paired in couplets averaging $\frac{1}{8}$ in. thick. Each couplet consists of a light-gray silty lamina and a thinner, dark-gray, finer-grained lamina, the coarser member grading up into the finer. The aspect of the argillite is much like that of the varved sediments of the late-Pleistocene sequence in Sweden.

The presence of the argillite, which is of wide extent, affords a reasonable explanation of the preservation of even the minute details of the constructional topography of the tillite. Evidently, during deglaciation of the district the terminus of the Dwyka glacier stood in lake water. As the glacier shrank, water gradually replaced ice over each part of the district, which therefore did not emerge from beneath the glacial lake until the bedrock and till had become buried beneath a blanket of lake-floor sediment. This blanket in turn was later covered by a great thickness of still younger sedimentary rocks, from which erosion has only recently succeeded in freeing the Harrisdale area.

The Dwyka Tillite in this district is satisfactorily established as a tillite on the basis of its internal characteristics alone. However, were it less typical internally, topographic features such as the ones described would alone justify its recognition as tillite as distinct from other non-sorted sedimentary rocks.

Of the ten characteristics enumerated above, (E), (F), (G) and (H) are not usually evident without detailed investigation, and (J) may have been entirely destroyed by post-glacial erosion of various kinds. In most instances a body of sediment possessing (A), (B), (C), (D) and (I) could be considered till or tillite with extremely high probability; (G) would raise the probability to virtual certainty. The tillite shown in Fig. 1 has (A), (B), (C), (D) and (I) at the locality illustrated, and at other localities has (G) as well. Probably it ranks as the most fully documented tillite as yet discovered.

II.4 *Till-like Sediments*

Sediments having various non-glacial origins can resemble till in that they can possess one or more of the characteristics of till. At one place or another such sediments have been mistaken for till. Most of them fall into the categories of conglomerates and pebbly mudstones. We can list (Table I) the more obvious classes, by agencies of sedimentation, noting the commonly expected characteristics of each class. Many of the characteristics are common to sediments of two or more different origins. Although useful as a checklist, such a list can not be a determinative table because owing to variability of the properties of most non-sorted sediments, most of the characteristics are not possessed by a single class exclusively. If an ancient lithified sediment of non-sorted character is suspected of being tillite, it must be examined with close attention to all its internal features, as well as its stratigraphic relation to underlying and overlying rocks. Alternative origins must be eliminated one by one, and positive identification as tillite should be made only on a basis of a combination of characteristics that render other origins extremely improbable.

II.5 *Stratified Glacial Drift*

A. *Outwash Sediments*

In many areas till of Pleistocene age is accompanied by bodies of outwash sediments in the form of sand and gravel carried away from the margins of a glacier by streams of melt-water. Outwash bodies are characterized by a preponderance of undecomposed constituents and by cut-and-fill stratification. As, however, these characteristics have been observed also in bodies of alluvium of non-glacial origin, they are not in themselves criteria of glacial conditions. The facets and striations on individual rock particles, relied on in the identification of till, are in outwash sediments rare or absent because of rapidity of attrition in pro-glacial streams.

The glacial origin of Pleistocene outwash is generally established on a basis of close physical relationship to bodies of till, but evidence of the relationship, both stratigraphic and morphological, is unlikely to survive long. The sites of outwash are valleys extremely vulnerable to erosion, as is testified to by the dissected state of outwash bodies of even quite recent origin. Ancient tillites are therefore unlikely to be accompanied by much sedimentary rock of outwash origin. Even where present, the outwash is likely to be identifiable independently of the tillite only in the rare instances where the stratigraphic relation between the two kinds of sediment is clearly exposed. Usually, therefore, the burden of proof of glacial origin is thrown back upon the tillite itself.

B. '*Varved clays*' and other Rhythmically Laminated Sediments

In Fennoscandia, north-eastern North America, and other parts of the world there are extensive bodies of fine-grained parallel-bedded sediments

Table 1. Characteristics of

Sediment	Common characteristics	Clasts			
		Composition	Provenance	Shape	Surface markings
Subaerial	Till	Any composition possible. Clast size related to c r u s h i n g strength of rock types	Mainly local; minor fraction exotic	Some with facets separated by rounded edges. A few 'flat-irons'	Striations and polish on many
	Sliderock / Landslide debris / Earthflow sediments / Solifluction sediments	Any composition possible	Local	Predominantly angular	Striations exceptiona on soft-rock clasts
	Mudflow sediments, including flowtill / Flash-flood alluvium / Fan alluvium		Confined to drainage basin	Predominantly worn	
Subaqueous	Slumped debris		Inherited	Inherited	Inherited
	Glacial-marine drift, including deposits from shelf ice, bergs, and sea ice; sea-floor till; subaqueous sediments bulldozed by tidewater glaciers and floating ice; in part modified by slumping and sliding		Resembles that of related till	Some with facets separated by rounded edges	Some with striations
Subaerial or subaqueous	Volcanic breccia	Volcanic	Local	Angular; not faceted	
	Fault breccia	Any composition possible	Local	Angular; slicken-sided clasts faceted	Slickensides may resemble glacial striations and/or polish, but may include internal as well as external ones
	Collapse breccia	Any composition possible; commonly carbonate rocks	Local	Angular; some may have solution surfaces	Solution markings

d Till-like Sediments

Stratification	Fossil content	Colour	Thickness, extent, and shape of body	Stratigraphic relationships
None, apart from thin lenses and transported bodies of stratified sediment. May possess distinctive fabric	None, apart from rare, broken, transported individuals	Inherited; mostly light coloured	Broad blankets, tongues; may be discontinuous. Thickness rarely exceeds 100 m	Underlying floor commonly polished, with striations and/or crescentic marks
			Tongues, blankets; may be thick	On, or near bases of, slopes
			Commonly tongues; relatively thin	
			Tongues and fan forms; may be thin	
Distorted or completely destroyed	If present, may include mixture from several depth zones	Mainly dark coloured	Local masses; thickness variable up to > 500 m	May be interstratified with fine-grained marine or lacustrine sediments
Non-stratified to stratified, with or without graded beds and/or distortion	May be present, broken and unbroken	Colour of matrix governed mainly by depth conditions of normal marine sediment. Colour of glacial fraction inherited	Broad blankets. Thickness may exceed 300 m	Commonly associated with till in landward direction
May be crudely stratified; more commonly not stratified			Local, irregular bodies	Related to volcanic vents
			Body narrow, thickness rarely greater than 15 m	May be associated with slickensided surfaces resembling glaciated floors
			Local, irregular bodies, mostly thin	May overlie solution remnants of soluble rocks

characterized by rhythmically paired laminae. These rhythmites are generally known in the literature as 'varved clays'. Their age is Pleistocene, and
their stratigraphic and topographic relations to bodies of till support the
widely held view that they accumulated in short-lived glacier-fed lakes. The
exact mechanism of sedimentation is still under discussion. The chief characteristic of 'varved clays' (which in most areas include more silt than clay) is
the presence of alternating laminae of relatively coarse and relatively fine
particles, constituting pairs or couplets. Each couplet has been thought to
represent an annual cycle marked by seasonal variations. In some couplets
the coarser component is itself laminated on a smaller scale, with repeated
changes of grain size.

The theory of annual rhythm finds some support in ^{14}C dates. Probably
it is valid for some 'varved clays' although not for all. The theory, however,
is not closely pertinent to the present discussion, which is concerned only
with the value of such sediments as indicators of glaciation. The obvious
relation between Pleistocene 'varved clays' and glaciation, coupled with
some laboratory evidence that low water temperature tends to favour this
type of stratification, has led to acceptance of pre-Pleistocene rhythmites as
evidence of ancient glaciation. Where close examination discloses detailed
resemblances between an ancient rhythmite and a Pleistocene 'varved clay'
(see for example reference 17, with a good discussion of the conditions of
sedimentation; see also reference 16), such acceptance may be valid, but the
mere presence of rhythmically laminated fine-grained sedimentary rocks
does not in itself establish glacial origin. Rhythmites, with an annual period
supported by substantial evidence but unrelated to the presence of glaciers,
are known. Most such sediments contain organic matter. Examples include
recent lacustrine sediments in the Alps [21] and the Green River Formation of
Eocene age in Colorado, Utah and Wyoming.[1]

The Pleistocene 'varved clays' of obviously glacial origin are nearly devoid
of organic matter (apart from small amounts of fossil pollen grains and a few
other fossils), are at least in part the result of mechanical settling rather than
chemical or biochemical precipitation (although the matter is still under
discussion, see reference 6), and are related directly or indirectly to till. Where
pre-Pleistocene lithified sediments of similar character occur with tillite
there is a strong probability that they are glacial. Whether in the absence
of tillite they can be considered glacial is not yet established, as this question
demands more thorough study than most such rocks have received.

II.6 *Structures Made by Glacial Movement*

Local structures occurring in stratified sediments and partly consolidated
strata have been attributed to deformation by the thrust and drag of glaciers
passing over them. Many such features of Pleistocene age form low ridges,
somewhat resembling end moraines, transverse to the direction of glacier
movement. Although conspicuous while they constitute part of the land
surface, the ridges are unlikely to be preserved long. The accompanying

structures, on the other hand, have a better chance of survival. Most of these are small unsymmetrical folds, and reverse faults, confined to shallow depths. Some are overlain by till; others are not. It is doubtful whether, in the absence of till or other evidence of glaciation, the glacial origin of such a structure preserved in ancient rocks would be clearly evident. The most nearly similar structures are those caused by subaqueous slumping and sliding, and these, of course, possess no inherent climatic significance.

II.7 *Altitude of Glacial Features*

Today glaciers occur in places where atmospheric temperatures are low—in high latitudes and at high altitudes. In East Africa, South America and New Guinea glaciers exist even at the equator. Therefore the mere presence of evidence of glaciation at some stratigraphic position in the geological column does not necessarily imply that sea-level temperatures at the time of glaciation were substantially less than those of today, for altitudes higher than those of today might have made glaciation possible. If, however, it can be shown that glaciation occurred at low altitude and in low or middle latitude, the implication that the climate then differed markedly from today's becomes strong. Hence evidence of altitude of ancient glaciation should be sought.

Evidence of ancient altitude is likely to be elusive. In high mountains not only the glacial drift itself, but also the conspicuous erosional features that constitute the effects of glaciers and attendant frost-wedging activity are so vulnerable to destruction that their preservation is not to be expected. Despite this fact, evidence of altitude is in rare instances preserved. The topography of the floor beneath the Dwyka Tillite in South Africa, and the overlap of younger strata upon the tillite, indicated to Du Toit (reference 4, p. 192) that at the time of the Dwyka glaciation the highest summits reached altitudes of 3000 to possibly 5000 ft.

On the other hand low altitude is recorded by interbedding of drift with marine sediments, indicating that the related glacier ice reached tide-water; and extensive glacial-marine sediments (see Table I) imply the former widespread presence of ice shelves and bergs. Such evidence establishes former low temperatures at low altitude. An example from pre-Pleistocene strata is found in South-west Africa, where the Dwyka Tillite grades by facies change and overlap into sediments containing marine fossils (reference 4, pp. 213–214, 216). The implied difference in mean annual sea-level temperature at the margin of the glacier, as compared with that of today, is of the order of 10–15°C.*

Apart from altitude, the areal extent of tillite and related glacial features affords a basis for determining whether ancient glaciers were local valley glaciers or extensive ice sheets. On such evidence it is quite clear that the Dwyka glaciation was primarily the work of ice sheets.

* Calculated from assumed analogy with temperatures at the ice-sheet margin at New York at the time of the Pleistocene Wisconsin maximum as deduced by Manley.[13]

III. Non-Glacial Evidence of Cold Climate

III.1 *Features Made by Freezing and Thawing of the Ground*

A. *Solifluction Sediments*

There has grown up a large literature on features known or supposed to be caused by differential movements of rock particles in unconsolidated sediment, as a result of freezing and thawing of a shallow zone beneath the ground surface. Most such features are insufficiently well known to permit the isolation and evaluation of the various factors involved in their origin; they include frost-wedged debris, solifluction sediments, involutions and ice-wedge pseudomorphs. Being surface features they are unlikely to survive as features of ancient rocks. Perhaps the most likely to survive, because of their widespread occurrence in regions of cold climate today, are solifluction sediments. These develop prominently on sloping terrain where summer thawing fails to penetrate the full depth of frozen ground. Hence the thawed materials at the surface become saturated with thaw water, which cannot escape vertically downwards by percolation. The result is rapid downslope flowage of thin blankets—commonly less than 1 m thick—of pasty mush. Solifluction sediments are little sorted or not sorted at all, and in this respect resemble till. Locally, at least, they differ from till in that they possess a fabric in which the long axes of some pebbles and cobbles have an appreciable dip instead of being flat lying. Presumably the dip is related to the angle of slope on which the sediment was deposited, but this fabric needs investigation before a criterion could be derived from it. Sediments formed in this manner imply a climate marked by annual freezing throughout a long winter season, or by perennially frozen ground. However, similar sediments can form in other ways (Table I), so that it may be difficult, and in places impossible, to identify the process of origin.

B. *Involutions*

In some localities alternate freezing and thawing engenders involutions of sorted or stratified layers of sediment immediately beneath the surface. The involutions are limited to shallow depths and consist of irregular, generally unsystematic folds and complex contortions.* The actual mechanisms involved are not fully understood, and freeze-and-thaw origin is inferred in part through association with glacial features. Confusion of freeze-and-thaw contortion with structures made by glacier movement is possible, although the climatic implications of the two are similar. Confusion with structures resulting from subaqueous slumping (see reference 10, pp. 5, 20–22; reference 12, pp. 14–24) is also possible; this is more serious, as the latter structures imply no particular kind of climate. At any rate the likelihood of preservation of such structures in ancient rocks is slight.

* See illustrations in Schafer[18]; Schwarzbach[19] (p. 40).

C. *Ice-wedge Pseudomorphs*

Freeze-and-thaw also causes ice-wedge pseudomorphs. These result from the filling from above, during thawing, of wedge-shaped cracks caused earlier by shrinkage of frozen ground during winter spells of intense cold. They are essentially clastic dikes, as much as several metres in length, that pinch out downwards. Apparently they imply perennially frozen ground with occasional sustained winter temperatures of −10°C or lower. Features having a similar appearance in cross-section can originate through quite different processes.[25] Hence linear continuity in plan should be present if ice-wedge origin is to be accepted. Although ice-wedge pseudomorphs are capable of being preserved, none of pre-Pleistocene age has been reported.

III.2 *Rafted Cobbles and Boulders in Alluvium*

Erratic cobbles and boulders occur imbedded in the modern alluvium of large Arctic streams and in the Pleistocene alluvium of some streams in middle latitudes. Many such erratics are striated. They are not, however, of glacial origin, as they occur in drainage basins no parts of which have been glaciated. They are ascribed[22] to rafting, via pans of river ice, down streams that are, or formerly were, subject to winter freezing.

Erratic-bearing sediments, whether alluvium or other, are preserved in pre-Pleistocene strata. But as rafts other than ice, such as floating trees, can transport rock fragments of large diameter, the climatic implication of any group of erratics must depend on the evidence they furnish as to the kind of raft that transported them. The presence of striations affords fairly good evidence of ice. Absence of these marks affords no basis for climatic inference, despite suggestions such as that erratic boulders in Cretaceous marine strata indicate ice rafts (reference 8, p. 351).

Rafted cobbles in lacustrine and marine rocks of late Carboniferous age have been reported from South Africa by Du Toit,[4] who attributed them to iceberg transportion. The interpretation is undoubtedly correct, but it is established primarily on the stratigraphic relation of the rocks to the Dwyka Tillite, and not on inherent features of the erratics themselves, of which no feature alone seems to compel the concept of glacial origin.

III.3 *Colours of Sediments*

The opinion is expressed occasionally, that sediments formed under cold climates are likely to be light coloured. However, the geological record seems to show no obvious positive correlation between colour and cold climate. For example, pale colours are abundant in terrestrial strata of early and middle Cenozoic age in central and western North America; yet the related fossils record temperate climates. There appears to be little relation between colour and cold climate except for the negative statement that red beds are not likely to have accumulated under frigid conditions. Indeed the

L

colours of sediments are controlled by such a variety of factors that a single one—low temperature—could hardly be expected to exercise a controlling influence.

IV. Summary

(1) An ancient cold climate is defined for convenience in discussion as a climate colder than that of today in the area being considered.

(2) Physical evidence of ancient, pre-Pleistocene cold climate consists mainly of features of former glaciation.

(3) The most reliable and apparently the most widespread evidence of ancient glaciation is tillite. As sedimentary rocks of several other origins, some of them without climatic significance, resemble tillite, thorough identification is essential. Five criteria, if possessed by a rock, indicate with high probability that the rock is a tillite. A number of rocks identified in the literature as tillites are of non-glacial origin.

(4) Rhythmically laminated sedimentary rocks, similar to Pleistocene 'varved clays', constitute acceptable auxiliary, though not conclusive, evidence of glaciation.

(5) The altitude of formation of ancient glacial features should be determined if possible, because in middle or low latitudes glaciation at low altitude is a more reliable indicator of secular cold climate than is high-altitude glaciation.

(6) Expectable evidence of cold climate, other than glacial features, includes rafted erratics and features made by freeze-and-thaw in the ground. The former have been reliably reported as occurring in ancient rocks; as yet the latter have been reported but rarely.

(7) There appears to be no positive correlation between the colour of a sedimentary rock and its origin in a cold climate.

References

1. Bradley, W. H. *Prof. Pap. U.S. geol. Surv.*, **158**, 87 (1929)
2. Charlesworth, J. K. *The Quaternary Era, with special reference to its glaciation.* 1957. London: Arnold
3. Coleman, A. P. *Ice Ages: recent and ancient.* 1926. New York: Macmillan
4. Du Toit, A. L. *Trans. geol. Soc. S. Afr.*, **24**, 188 (1922)
5. Du Toit, A. L. *Compt. rend. XV Internat. Geol. Cong. S. Africa*, **2**, 90 (1929)
6. Eden, W. J. *Amer. J. Sci.*, **253**, 659 (1955)
7. Flint, R. F. *Glacial and Pleistocene Geology.* 1957. New York: Wiley
8. Gregory, J. W. *Compt. rend. X Internat. Geol. Congr. Mexico*, **1**, 407 (1907)
9. Hartshorn, J. H. *Bull. geol. Soc. Amer.*, **69**, 477 (1958)
10. Heim, A. *Geol. Rdsch.*, **15**, 1 (1924)
11. Holmes, C. D. *Bull. geol. Soc. Amer.*, **52**, 1299 (1941)
12. Kuenen, Ph. H. *Verh. Akad. Wet. Amst.*, **20**, 1 (1953)
13. Manley, G. *Amer. J. Sci.*, **253**, 256 (1955)
14. Newell, N. D. *Bull. geol. Soc. Amer.*, **68**, 1569 (1957)

15. Sayles, R. W. *Mem. Mus. comp. Zool. Harv.*, **56**, 141 (1914)
16. Sayles, R. W. *Proc. nat. Acad. Sci., Wash.*, **2**, 167 (1916)
17. Sayles, R. W. *Mem. Mus. comp. Zool. Harv.*, **47**, no. 1 (1919)
18. Schafer, J. P. *J. Geol.*, **57**, 154 (1949)
19. Schwarzbach, M. *Das Klima der Vorzeit*. 1950. Stuttgart: Enke
20. Van Houten, F. B. *Bull. geol. Soc. Amer.*, **68**, 383 (1957)
21. Welten, M. *Veröff. geobot. Inst. Rübel*, **21** (1944)
22. Wentworth, C. K. *Bull. geol. Soc. Amer.*, **39**, 941 (1928)
23. Wentworth, C. K. *J. sediment. Petrol.*, **6**, 85 (1936)
24. Woldstedt, P. *Das Eiszeitalter. Grundlinien einer Geologie des Quartärs. 1. Die allgemeinen Erscheinungen des Eiszeitalters*, 1954. *2. Europa, Vorderasien und Nordafrika im Eiszeitalter*, 1958. Stuttgart: Enke
25. Yehle, L. A. *Amer. J. Sci.*, **252**, 532 (1954)

VII

The Application of Geophysics to Palaeoclimatology

A. E. M. Nairn and N. Thorley *

I. The Measurement of Palaeotemperatures

I.1 *Introduction*

Modern climatology derives from a large number of observations on rainfall, wind speed, temperature, large-scale movements of ocean currents and atmospheric pressure. Much of this information is taken regularly over small intervals of time and processed mathematically in order to predict short-term weather conditions, and high altitude meteorological measurements have been used for long-term weather forecasting. In view of this wealth of physical information required daily by the meteorologist, and which eventually makes up the data for world climate, it is not surprising that studies of palaeoclimatology have been almost completely qualitative.

It is sometimes possible to differentiate between ancient tropical, subtropical, temperate and Arctic conditions and to trace the changing patterns of land and sea formations over geological time, but there has hitherto been little possibility of estimating average annual rainfalls, regional temperatures, ocean salinity, humidity and pressure of the atmosphere in various geological epochs; for example, it is difficult to compare quantitatively the details of ancient and present-day tropical climates, and it is highly improbable that comparative studies of these topics will ever be more than qualitative. How-

---

* The palaeotemperature section was written by N. Thorley, the palaeomagnetic section by A. E. M. Nairn.

ever, some geological data can be treated by physical and quantitative methods. Examples of this are palaeomagnetic studies (see Section II), work on wind directions (Chapter III) and, even more striking, the measurement of palaeotemperatures by the determination of the abundance ratio of the oxygen isotopes on the mass spectrometer. This method is limited to marine temperatures and depends on the fact that the ratio of ^{18}O to ^{16}O in calcium carbonate taken from a marine fossil shell is temperature dependent. It is therefore a measurement which can lead to a determination of the temperature of the water from which the carbonate shell was originally deposited during the life-time of the animal. The possibility of using such an isotopic temperature scale is due to the small differences in chemical properties between isotopes of the same chemical element.

Thirty years ago isotopes of the same element were regarded as having exactly the same chemical properties due to their identical atomic numbers, and hence could only be separated by physical methods, the purpose for which mass spectrographs were originally used. The modern use of radioactive isotopes in 'labelled' compounds as tracers in biological, chemical and metallurgical investigations depends essentially on the similarity of chemical properties.

In the early 1930s intensive studies of the chemical properties of isotopic substances, both theoretical and experimental, led to the successful fractionation of the lighter isotopes by non-physical methods and this in turn led to a more detailed study of natural abundances. It was soon found that the natural relative abundances of the common elements, taken from either land or sea, were not constant over the earth nor with geological time, and these differences have been attributed largely to isotopic fractionation.

The causes of the small chemical differences between isotopes of the same element are thermodynamic in nature and can only be described in terms of quantum statistics. It is proposed to deal in turn with the theoretical aspect of the problem of palaeotemperatures based on quantum statistics, then with the actual difficulties of measuring palaeotemperatures and the conditions for their reliability, and with the practical difficulties of the actual abundance ratio determination on the mass spectrometer. Finally the published results will be presented and reviewed.

I.2 *Isotope Exchange Equilibria*

Differences in properties between isotopes of the same element are due to small differences in molecular or atomic energy states. The theoretical problem is therefore a statistical one, and in particular requires the methods of quantum statistics. Molecular energy states are made up of: (*a*) translational states proportional to the isotopic mass of each nucleus; (*b*) rotational states depending on the moments of inertia of the molecules; (*c*) electronic states which are independent of isotopic masses; and (*d*) vibrational states depending on isotopic masses and affecting the zero-point energy of the molecules.

In comparing isotopes of the same element, only the vibrational states need be considered, as the other energy states are negligible at room temperatures, and these small energy differences are greatest for isotopes of low mass. Any property which can be broadly interpreted in terms of the kinetic theory can be used to distinguish between isotopes of the same element if experimental methods of detection are sensitive enough. Thus small differences of vapour pressure or of thermal diffusion are detectable. In calculating vapour pressure at a given temperature it is necessary to know all the possible energy levels of the molecules, and how they are filled, both for the solid and vapour phases. When equilibrium is reached between two or more phases there must also be equilibrium between the energy levels of the phases concerned. Generally speaking, any condition of equilibrium can be described if we know the details of the occupied energy levels of all the participants.

The expression which can be used in dealing with problems in quantum statistics is the 'partition function' Q, given by

$$Q = \sum_i e^{-E_i/kT}$$

where the summation is taken over all the energy states of the molecule and $E_i =$ the energy of the ith state, $k =$ Boltzmann's constant, and $T =$ absolute temperature.

In each state the value of E_i depends on the zero from which energy is measured. The partition function is connected with the probability of finding a molecule in a given energy state, and a property of partition functions is that the equilibrium between two phases is proportional to the ratio of their partition functions. The data required for the theoretical calculation of the energy states are obtained from molecular spectroscopic data, much of which has been accumulated in connection with problems of molecular structure.

In some cases these spectroscopic data are sparse or unreliable and the corresponding statistical calculations are not exact, but in many examples of exchange equilibria the calculations are as accurate as the experimental observations.

Chemical reactions are often reactions of exchange equilibria and the isotopes concerned arrange themselves in the different compounds so that the free energy of the whole system is a minimum. Using an illustration due to Emiliani[18] consider the exchange reaction

$$CO_2 + H_2O \rightleftharpoons H_2CO_3 \tag{1}$$

in which the two main isotopes of oxygen are ^{18}O and ^{16}O with an abundance ratio of 1 : 500. Exchange possibilities are:

$$C\,^{18}O_2 + H_2\,^{16}O \rightleftharpoons H_2\,C\,^{18}O_2^{16}O$$
or
$$C\,^{16}O_2 + H_2\,^{18}O \rightleftharpoons H_2\,C\,^{16}O_2^{18}O$$
or
$$C\,^{16}O\,^{18}O + H_2\,^{16}O \rightleftharpoons H_2\,C\,^{16}O_2^{18}O$$
or
$$C\,^{16}O\,^{18}O + H_2\,^{18}O \rightleftharpoons H_2\,C\,^{18}O_2^{16}O$$

It can be seen that the ^{18}O and ^{16}O isotopes on the right hand side can go into either the CO_2 molecule or the H_2O molecule on returning to the original state. If the rearrangements were governed by pure chance then the probability of ^{18}O entering the CO_2 molecule is exactly $2:1$, but in practice it is slightly greater than $2:1$ because the total energy of the vibrational states for the molecules $(C\ ^{18}O\ ^{16}O + H_2\ ^{16}O)$ is less than that of the molecules $(C\ ^{16}O_2 + H_2\ ^{18}O)$. Therefore the ^{18}O shows a preference for the carbon dioxide molecule, and the $^{18}O : ^{16}O$ ratio is slightly greater in CO_2 than in H_2O when they are in equilibrium.

Treating this more generally, an exchange reaction can be written

$$aXY_1 + bZY_2 \rightleftharpoons aXY_2 + bZY_1$$

when X, Y, Z are participating atoms of which Y has the two isotopes Y_1 and Y_2, and a, b are the numbers of molecules involved. The equilibrium constant is given by:

$$K = \frac{(Q_{XY_2})^a (Q_{ZY_1})^b}{(Q_{XY_1})^a (Q_{ZY_2})^b} = \frac{\{Q_{XY_2}/Q_{XY_1}\}^a}{\{Q_{ZY_2}/Q_{ZY_1}\}^b}$$

i.e. by the ratios of the partition functions of the isotopic molecules. For a given chemical compound with two possible forms such as XY_1 and XY_2 it is known that the ratio of their partition functions depends on their molecular weights, moments of inertia, quantum energy states and temperature. All this information is required, and for some reactions is available, before values of K can be calculated. The equilibrium constant is temperature dependent, as can be seen from the expression for the partition function, and it is also the ratio of the abundance in one compound to the abundance in the other. Experimentally, by the Law of Mass Action, we have

$$K = \frac{\{[XY_2]/[XY_1]\}^a}{\{[ZY_2]/[ZY_1]\}^b}$$

and this can also be regarded as the fractionation or enrichment factor for the reaction. In most cases $K \sim 1$ and when K is slightly greater than 1 the abundance ratio of $Y_2 : Y_1$ of the XY molecules will be greater than that of the ZY molecules and there will be a preferential concentration of Y_2 in XY. Hence an experimental determination of the abundance ratios in the two compounds will give the equilibrium constant. This will be nearer to 1 as the temperature increases, e.g. for the CO_2–H_2O isotopic equilibrium $K(0°C) = 1·045$ and $K(25°C) = 1·039$.[18]

I.3 *The Carbonate–Water Equilibrium*

The investigation of marine fossils is concerned with the precipitation of calcium carbonate in equilibrium with sea-water, and the fractionation factor is then the ratio of the oxygen isotopes in the total carbonate ion to the ratio in water. The general equations can be reduced to one reaction, viz:

$$H_2\ ^{18}O + \tfrac{1}{3} C\ ^{16}O_3^= \rightleftharpoons H_2\ ^{16}O + \tfrac{1}{3} C\ ^{18}O_3^=$$

for which

$$K = \frac{[H_2{}^{16}O][C\,{}^{18}O_3{}^=]^{\frac{1}{3}}}{[H_2{}^{18}O][C\,{}^{16}O_3{}^=]^{\frac{1}{3}}}$$

$$= \frac{\{[C\,{}^{18}O_3{}^=]/[C\,{}^{16}O_3{}^=]\}^{\frac{1}{3}}}{[H_2\,{}^{18}O_3]/[H_2\,{}^{16}O]}$$

Using spectroscopic data for the fractionation between the carbonate ion in the calcite lattice and in aqueous solution the following approximate values of K have been calculated at various temperatures.[50] These are shown in Table I below.

Table I

Fractionation Factors for CO_3 (aq)–H_2O(l) Equilibrium

Temperature	0°C	8°C	17°C	25°C
K-value	1·0176	1·0162	1·0149	1·0138

These figures are not absolutely correct because of lack of precision in some of the spectroscopic data. However, they do show a temperature coefficient of K of about 4 parts per thousand per 25°C, i.e. 0·016 per cent K per °C. This value varies slightly, depending on the details of the calculation, but in general it can be seen that if an experimental value of K is to be used to estimate the temperature of the reaction to an accuracy of 1°C the accuracy in K must be 0·016 per cent. Hence the $^{18}O : {}^{16}O$ abundance must be capable of being measured with an accuracy of 0·01 per cent. This calls for the highest possible precision in mass spectrometry.

Calculation therefore shows that there is a simple relation between oxygen abundances and the temperature of the equilibrium reaction. Assuming that the isotopic composition of ancient and present-day marine waters is the same, or is known, it is possible to set up an empirical equation by measuring the abundances in shells deposited in controlled temperature conditions and hence use the calibration to measure palaeotemperatures.

I.4 *Measuring Palaeotemperatures with an Accuracy of* $\pm 1°C$

Oxygen abundances in the carbonate ion must be measured to 0·01 per cent if a temperature is to be given to 0·5°C. These abundances are measured on the mass spectrometer and this instrument is not usually capable of giving this high order of accuracy. However, particular attention has been paid to this problem in the Nier-type mass spectrometer described by McKinney *et al.*[51] In the method finally adopted the value of K is measured as a difference between the sample and a standard:

$$\delta = \left[\frac{R_{sample} - R_{standard}}{R_{standard}} \right] 1000$$

where R means $^{18}O/^{16}O$ ratio, and δ is then the parts per thousand difference in R between the sample and the standard. In the determination of δ the sample and the standard are examined by the mass spectrometer repeatedly in quick succession. The standard used [75] is the CO_2 gas extracted from a pulverized specimen of '*Belemnitella Americana*' from the South Carolina Upper Cretaceous Peedee formation. The accuracy of the instrument is such that the standard deviation quoted for about 100 analyses over a period of 2 years is 0·10 per thousand, or 0·4°C.[18] It appears then that the McKinney mass spectrometer is capable of giving the 1°C accuracy in temperature measurement.

From the equation for K it is obvious that the δ value will depend on the oxygen abundance ratio in the original marine water as well as on temperature, and if the empirical δ–T correlation is to be reliable it must be assumed that the isotopic composition of marine waters has remained constant throughout geological time or that it is known sufficiently accurately. The empirical equation for δ can be written [26] as:

$$T = 16\cdot5 - 4\cdot3\ (\delta - \alpha) + 0\cdot14\ (\delta - \alpha)^2$$

in °C. Here δ = measured difference for the carbonate sample and α is the correction to be applied if the oxygen abundance in the water has changed, i.e.

$$\alpha = \left[\frac{R - R_{\text{Mean}}}{R_{\text{Mean}}} \right] 1000$$

where R refers to water of ancient composition applicable to the shell being examined, and R_{Mean} refers to present day marine waters of average composition. Values of α can be estimated by applying geographical corrections and knowing whether the shell was deposited in glacial or non-glacial times. The range of δ is about -4 to $+1$ for a temperature range of 0–30°C and the average value of α is about 0·5, all expressed in parts per mil.

A further difficulty is in the choice of suitable fossil shells. It is obvious that the sample must retain its original isotopic composition and there are many physical processes which are based on kinetics which would destroy this, including solid state diffusion and growth by recrystallization. It is known, for instance, that aragonite shells lose their record because of recrystallization. Reliable material for examination must therefore be calcite showing no recrystallization or secondary growth. Belemnite guards appear to give the best results but work has also been done on Inoceramus and on a number of Ostreidae.[47] In all cases the test of reliability must be repeatability within the accuracy of the experiment. Pelagic foraminifera have been used to estimate surface Pleistocene temperatures, and benthonic foraminifera for ocean bottom temperatures.[18]

I.5 *The McKinney–Nier Mass Spectrometer*

In order to obtain the necessary precision McKinney et al.[51] modified an existing Nier 60° 6-in. radius mass spectrometer to give greater sensitivity along the following lines. The ancillary electronic equipment was redesigned to give a very high degree of stability, the usual electrometer valve amplifier in the double-collector balancing circuit was replaced by a vibrating reed electrometer which also reduced the residual noise of the system, and a gas feed system was designed which enabled the standard and sample gases to be introduced and analysed in rapid succession. Instruments of this type have been used satisfactorily for about 10 years.

The method adopted is to collect $C\ ^{18}O\ ^{16}O$ and $C\ ^{16}O\ ^{16}O$ carbon dioxide gas ions on the two collector plates simultaneously, amplify the mass 46 ions by means of the vibrating reed electrometer and the mass 44 by means of the normal electrometer valve d.c. amplifier, and balance the two voltages to give a null reading on a recording potentiometer. By taking a number of successive displays of the standard and sample gas the mean difference gives the appropriate value of δ. Over a large number of readings an error of $\pm 1\,°C$ in a measured temperature represents confidence limits of $\pm 2 \times$ standard deviation.

I.6 *Establishing the Temperature Scale*

The possibility of measuring palaeotemperatures by the oxygen isotope method was first suggested by Urey[73] in an important theoretical paper on the thermodynamic properties of isotopic compounds. At that time mass spectrometers were only available with accuracies of about ± 0.1 per cent in the abundance ratios required, and the estimated accuracy in palaeotemperatures was no better than $\pm 5\,°C$. This paper extended a large number of calculations by Urey and Grieff[74] using the available spectroscopic data. Isotope fractionation of oxygen was shown theoretically to be temperature dependent and therefore there should be detectable differences in the $^{18}O : ^{16}O$ ratio in the carbonate–water, sulphate–water and phosphate–water systems in equilibrium.

McCrea[50] studied the isotopic exchange equilibrium in the carbonate–water system in particular and his calculations gave the results for K as listed in Table I. These calculations can be taken as typical although not absolutely precise, due to uncertainty in some of the experimental data from spectroscopic measurements.

McCrea also paid considerable attention to the preparation of the carbon dioxide in the experimental verification of this theory. He studied the growth of inorganic calcium carbonate from aqueous solutions and also perfected a method whereby the isotopic composition of the inorganic carbonates produced at a given temperature was the same as that of organically produced carbonates taken from animals depositing in known marine waters at the same temperature. The final equation submitted by McCrea was

$$T = 16.0 - 5.1(7)\ (\delta - \alpha) + 0.09(2)\ (\delta - \alpha)^2 \text{ in } °C$$

where α is the isotopic composition of the water relative to the average marine water taken.

It is important to note that this equation refers to calcite precipitated chemically and not organically. This raises the question of possible bio-chemical exchange effects in the living animal which would be absent in any straightforward chemical precipitation experiments. In order to check this possible difference, an empirical organic temperature scale was set up by Epstein, Buchsbaum, Lowenstam and Urey[23] using only carefully selected marine animals kept in thermostatically controlled temperature baths in various laboratories. The shells were notched periodically and when the damage had been repaired by the animal the new shell was scraped away and analysed in the mass spectrometer. Certain organisms gave unsatisfactory results but after applying the water correction (deviation from mean water composition) the rest gave the following empirical temperature equation:

$$T = 14 \cdot 8 - 5 \cdot 41 \, \delta \text{ in } °C$$

This compared favourably with McCrea's result for inorganic carbonate quoted above, showing that the biochemical effect was small. This was found to be even less important in the revised equation given by the same group,[26] viz:

$$T = 16 \cdot 5 - 4 \cdot 3 \, \delta + 0 \cdot 14 \, \delta^2 \text{ in } °C$$

where δ has here been corrected for water analysis. The standard deviation is $0 \cdot 4°C$.[18] This equation agrees well with that of McCrea, above.

This final temperature equation can now be accepted as applying to all suitably chosen marine shells. It must be used carefully, however, because it depends on a knowledge of the δ-value of the marine waters in which the present-day or fossil shell has lived. The work on present-day or living organisms growing in controlled conditions and in various known marine waters shows that the latter is by no means constant isotopically, and errors of the order of 3–4°C may be introduced into a final temperature assessment. Epstein and Mayeda[24] have shown that the variation in the content of natural waters varies sufficiently to make this the greatest uncertainty in palaeo-temperature determination.

A further important factor is the effect of environment of different species. Epstein and Lowenstam[25] have studied the development of calcareous skeletal material in Bermuda waters and found that marine animals behave differently in this respect. Some species grow shell only at certain periods, i.e. during a portion of the local temperature range rather than throughout the full range. It was concluded that each species would give its own 'temperature' of the same water and if a local temperature cycle is to be determined with any reliability it is necessary to make comparative seasonal variation studies of a number of different species. Thus the record given by the analysis of a complete shell will be the average surface-water temperature within its growth temperature range and may not be the true annual mean temperature.

It is apparent that the whole position of palaeotemperatures will have to be reassessed when a method of obtaining the oxygen isotope content of the original marine waters has been found. Alternatively, if this can be eliminated by experiment the palaeotemperatures reported will have less probable error.

It may be possible to do this with a non-carbonate reaction, e.g. the sulphate–water equilibrium has been suggested:

$$H_2{}^{18}O_l + \tfrac{1}{4}S{}^{16}O_4{}^{=} \rightleftharpoons H_2{}^{16}O_l + \tfrac{1}{4}S{}^{18}O_4{}^{=}$$

$$K = \frac{\{[S{}^{18}O_4{}^{=}]/[S{}^{16}O_4{}^{=}]\}^{\frac{1}{4}}}{[H_2{}^{18}O_l]/[H_2{}^{16}O_l]}$$

where $K_{0°C} = 1\cdot0204$, $K_{25°C} = 1\cdot0157$, and $\Delta K = 0\cdot002$ per degree centigrade approximately.

Unfortunately animals do not deposit sulphate readily and another suggestion has been made, *viz*: the phosphate–water equilibrium. This is

$$H_2{}^{18}O_l + \tfrac{1}{4}P{}^{16}O_4{}^{\equiv} \rightleftharpoons H_2{}^{16}O_l + \tfrac{1}{4}P{}^{18}O_4{}^{\equiv}$$

where $K_{0°C} = 1\cdot0104$, $K_{25°C} = 1\cdot0087$ and $\Delta K = 0\cdot0007$ per degree centigrade approximately.

This change is very small and is also complicated by the fact that the phosphate ion can only exchange with water through a series of biological reactions. Nevertheless it seems necessary to pursue one or other of these two alternatives in an effort to solve the problem of the isotopic constitution of ancient marine water.

I.7 *Review of Results*

A. *Cretaceous Palaeotemperatures*

One of the more interesting applications of the ^{18}O method for temperature measurement is contained in a paper by Urey, Lowenstam, Epstein and McKinney[75] dealing with Upper Cretaceous temperatures. After much consideration these authors showed that the belemnites were the most likely animals to give true temperature indications. A one-inch diameter disc was cut from an Oxford Clay Jurassic belemnite showing well-defined growth rings, and polished to 3 mm thickness. Samples of the carbonate were removed from selected places across a diameter and analysed for ^{18}O variation. The results showed a cyclical variation along the radius and a rough correlation with the seasons assuming that no large-scale migration took place. The animal recorded three summers and four winters after the carbonate had been deposited sufficiently heavily to be analysed. It cannot be deduced from this that the animal deposited continuously throughout its whole life-span, but at least it deposited rhythmically. Assuming that the average deposit in summer is greater than that in winter, the animal must have lived for about 4 years in warmer water during its youth, living in cooler water in its old age. The peak-trough maximum variation is about 6°C and the average temperature is about 17·6°C. Even allowing for the approximate nature of the results these results are quite remarkable. The average temperature of six other English belemnites quoted by the authors in the same paper is 18·6°C.

Three belemnites from Denmark, all from the Upper Cretaceous, were also measured and these averaged 13·3°C; while those from a similar stratigraphical position in South Eastern U.S.A. gave an average temperature of 15·7°C. It is thought that, considering the differences in latitude, *viz*: 33–41°N for North American specimens and 52–56°N for the European specimens, the differences in temperature are not very pronounced, and would indicate that the belemnites were not tropical animals but preferred the cooler waters of the North.

At this stage one must emphasize that it is dangerous to deduce too much from these measurements. Thus, if the chosen belemnite lived roughly in the same place all its life then the temperature variations reported are truly seasonal, even if there is error in the absolute value of the temperatures. Alternatively, if the animal migrated in order to keep its environment temperature constant there are two possibilities.

(1) If it travelled to water of the same isotopic composition at each migration then the temperature variations are still real but not so marked as they would be if the animal had stayed put.

(2) If it migrated to water of a different isotopic composition then it must have gone into brackish or fresh water or travelled huge distances in the sea. This seems improbable, but if true it renders the experimental palaeotemperatures meaningless.

Finally, the migration might be such as to give a real temperature cycle but with a peak to peak period which is *not* one year, so that the animal does not display seasonal changes but merely maximum and minimum temperatures at unknown time intervals. In addition, the problem of the lack of knowledge of the isotopic composition of the original water still remains and until it is solved some of the quoted results should be treated qualitatively. There is also the possibility of a threshold temperature below which there is no record. But if this is not very high, and if there is a true difference in the temperature tolerance of growth for all the measured specimens, the results under discussion show a possible uniformity in temperature in the zone stretching from Denmark to the Mississippi during the Maestrichian. The indication is that this zone was subtropical. Possibly the temperature of the Northern waters was maintained largely by ocean mixing from the equatorial regions, due perhaps to the separation of North and South America, or perhaps due to unknown currents in the Tethys sea.

Lowenstam and Epstein [47] have conducted a further comprehensive investigation into palaeotemperatures of the Post Aptian Cretaceous using belemnite guards, Inoceramus, brachiopods, oyster fragments, chalks, etc., collected from Western Europe, South Eastern U.S.A., Japan, Australia, India and Algeria. Results showed a rise in temperature from the Cenomanian to the Coniacian and decreasing in the Maestrichian. This change is particularly well shown by the belemnites. During the maximum temperature of this period, 20°C, the marginal subtropical belt extended northward to the present day north temperate belt and then receded southwards. Such conclusions depend largely on the careful selection of material for isotopic analysis.

B. Tertiary to Recent Palaeotemperatures

An exhaustive study of more recent times was begun by Emiliani and Epstein [22] who first investigated the temperature variation of the Lower Pleistocene of Southern California. Temperature oscillations were found, due largely to marine currents and local tectonics. One main cold and one main warm period were indicated.

Many marine studies of the Pleistocene have been made from the analysis of deep-sea cores. The present-day temperature in the Gulf of Mexico ranges between 22°C and 29°C and Emiliani [16] has shown that the corrected palaeotemperatures of selected pelagic foraminifera is about 27·5°C. Results of equatorial waters are particularly valuable since the seasonal variation of temperature is relatively small, and the palaeotemperatures must therefore be close to the yearly mean. Emiliani [17] also presents data on benthonic foraminifera of Pliocene, Miocene and Oligocene age in three deep-sea sediment cores from the equatorial Pacific. The evaluated results indicate a progressive temperature drop of about 8°C during the 30 million years from the Upper Oligocene to the present. This agrees well with other geological estimates. The deep-sea water of the open ocean basins should mix with the surface waters nearer the poles and the uncertainty in the isotopic composition of such waters is believed to be small. These results must therefore be considered fairly reliable. A further study [16] of the depth habitat of pelagic foraminifera, as indicated by different species, and the comparison of isotopically derived temperatures and the known ocean temperature–depth relationship, shows a definite depth stratification of different species in surface waters. This is due to different biological reactions to changes in temperature and density of the water.

Having established the suitability of certain species of pelagic foraminifera for palaeotemperature measurements, Emiliani extended his work to a thorough investigation of Pleistocene temperatures [18] as given by some Atlantic, Caribbean and Pacific deep-sea cores. Measured temperatures are essentially surface temperatures and the results gave interesting periodic phenomena in the Atlantic and the Caribbean, showing that these equatorial waters underwent periodic temperature fluctuations with a peak to trough amplitude of about 6°C and a frequency of about 45 000 years. The temperature differences of the Pacific cores were not so well defined due to increased mixing. The Caribbean core reported in this paper showed seven complete temperature cycles and radiocarbon dating suggested that the earliest minimum (280 000 years ago) corresponded to the first major glaciation period and in more recent times the temperature measurements forecast a new ice age in about 10 000 years. The last maximum was 6000 years ago.

Using benthonic foraminifera Emiliani[18] showed that the Pleistocene temperatures of the Pacific bottom waters did not change very much during the glacial and interglacial periods up to the present. Further, the temperatures were somewhat lower in the eastern Atlantic equatorial waters due to the influx of a large quantity of marine ice in the North Atlantic. In the Pacific the temperature of the interglacial periods was only about 0·8°C greater than the glacial.

Satisfactory correlation between times of temperature minima and times of insolation minima in high northern latitudes was found, and Emiliani concluded that the contrast of world climates during the Pleistocene was by insolation in northern latitudes with a lag of about 5000 years before the full temperature changes were recorded. This demonstrates that the exact correlation between insolation and continental events needs reconsidering and that latitude and insolation must be taken together when studying the frequency of glacial epochs.

In the Tertiary, Emiliani has investigated the Oligocene and Miocene temperatures of some equatorial and subtropical Atlantic sections.[19] The temperatures reported are more uniform than the Pleistocene temperatures first measured, presumably due to the lack of extreme insolation effects and to a sea–land pattern favouring uniform sea temperatures. There was no significant difference between Oligocene temperatures and present-day temperatures but two of the Miocene cores showed a record of about 5°C lower than the others. Until these low Miocene temperatures have been confirmed any explanation must be regarded as speculative.

More recently Emiliani[21] has discussed a middle N. Atlantic deep-sea core of Pleistocene age and has shown that the temperatures are closely similar to those of equatorial Atlantic, Caribbean and Mediterranean waters previously measured. The smoothed curve for this core is shown in Fig. 1, in which the temperature fluctuations are quite apparent. There is satisfactory age correlation to stage 8 after which there is some doubt in this core owing to uneven sedimentation effects at this stage. This is inferred from the change of pattern after stage 8, although it must be pointed out that it is still periodic. Also, the ages assigned can be in error by as much as 20 per cent. The generalized curve, going back some 300 000 years, is based on combined deep-sea core observations and is shown in Fig. 2. There is also some agreement with continental temperature variations inferred from other geological data. It was shown that the temperature of the bottom water of the equatorial Atlantic followed the oscillations of surface temperature but with a smaller amplitude and lag of a few thousand years. The top section of the core gave a temperature of 18°C and since the present-day variation at this point is from 18·0°C in February to 25·5°C in August it is inferred that the species used, *Globigerina inflata*, grows in the surface mainly in the winter months, or at some depth of average temperature 18°C during the summer. It is difficult to produce strong evidence in favour of either of these possibilities, but analysis of modern species tends to show that surface temperatures are more likely.

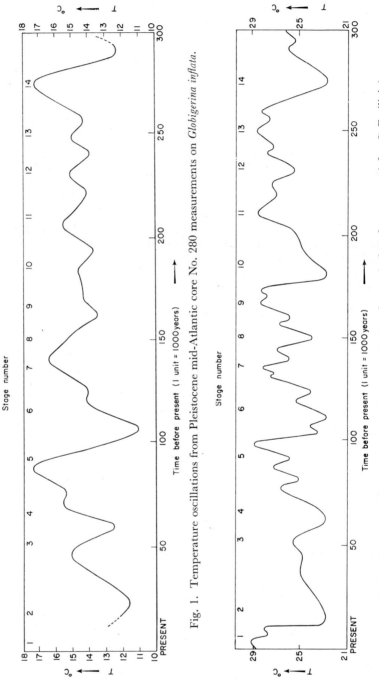

Fig. 1. Temperature oscillations from Pleistocene mid-Atlantic core No. 280 measurements on *Globigerina inflata*.

Fig. 2. Generalized Pleistocene temperature oscillations for tropical surface waters (after C. Emiliain).

A number of bottom-water temperature measurements show that the Pacific Ocean bottom water changed little between glacial and interglacial times but the Atlantic changed by about 4°C, possibly due to change in isotopic composition of the bottom water rather than a pure temperature change. Emiliani[20] has attempted to summarize the various methods of studying deep-sea cores and the results obtained for temperature and distribution of foraminifera species. Some of the difficulties of glacial and interglacial dating of differences were resolved, e.g. the dating of the last glacial period has been brought some 2000 years nearer the present so that the last rise in temperature started 13 000 years ago.

The work of Emiliani has shown the possibility of correlation between primary temperature oscillations, as revealed isotopically, and glacial and interglacial events for selected species of foraminifera, and Wiseman[79] has reported that secondary oscillations, as revealed by carbonate chemical analysis, can be obtained from areas remote from deep sea troughs, e.g. top of a sea-knoll. This 'fine structure' of the record is not revealed by the temperature measurements and the secondary oscillations can be correlated with climatic changes in Europe and North America.

A paper by Yalkowsky[80] is a timely warning of some of the dangers of interpretation of deep-sea core results. Taking the published palaeotemperatures of a certain core, Yalkowsky analysed the cores spectroscopically for several elements as well as carrying out carbonate analyses. Data are presented which tend to indicate that no correlation exists between carbonate content and palaeotemperatures for this particular core. No others have been investigated.

This shows the danger of over-estimating the usefulness of the measurements of the deep-sea cores, and the recent measurements on various correlations show that it is not safe to rely on one set of physical measurements from which to draw climatic conclusions. It may be necessary to treat the whole sets of published data statistically in an effort to find the most significant sets of data.

I.8 Summary and Conclusions

It has been shown that on theoretical grounds a determination of the $^{18}O : {}^{16}O$ ratio in suitably deposited carbonate shells of marine animals can lead to an estimate of palaeotemperatures. The expected differences from a standard ratio are so small that very precise mass spectrometric techniques are required, and these experimental difficulties have been discussed, together with the difficulties of selecting reliable experimental material. The principal danger in this method is the lack of knowledge of the $^{18}O : {}^{16}O$ ratio of the sea water in which the animal deposited its carbonate shell. Bearing this in mind certain results have been reviewed and it is suggested that they are sufficiently interesting to make the method worth pursuing.

If the various assumptions concerning the ancient waters are correct the published results show seasonal temperature fluctuations in Cretaceous times with a maximum of about 20°C in the Coniacian, cooling to about 16°C in

M

the Maestrichian. These figures are based on many measurements on fossils of this age. A single Middle Oligocene temperature is quoted as 28·3°C and Lower-Middle Miocene temperatures of 24·1°C and 22·8°C suggesting a progressive cooling through the Tertiary. These temperatures showed little periodicity but in the Pleistocene definite periodic oscillations of temperature were found corresponding to the glacial and interglacial ages. The range of these temperature variations was very roughly 20–30°C. There is no correlation with carbonate content.

It must be stressed that in no case are there sufficient data to enable thoroughly sound conclusions to be drawn. In comparing the isotopic temperatures of different geological ages a knowledge of the isotopic constitution of the ancient waters is more essential than it is when dealing with a single age. Also, all comparisons should be made with specimens taken from the same geographical position. Finally, the same species should be used throughout wherever possible.

If isotopic palaeotemperatures are ever measured with a negligible error a world-wide survey of suitable fossil shells could enable rough climate (temperature) zones to be drawn for various geological epochs. At present no observations on pre-Jurassic temperatures have been made, but if these were available they would be independent of the more usual geological observations and, along with results such as those described in this section, they would make a valuable contribution to the determination of palaeo-climates.

II. The Application of Palaeomagnetism to Palaeoclimatology

II.1 *Introduction*

Palaeomagnetism, the branch of geophysics concerned with the study of the geomagnetic field of the past, spans geological and historical time until near the end of the 16th century when, with the advent of Gilbert's work, modern geomagnetism can be said to have commenced. The study of the geomagnetic field of remote epochs is made possible by the determination of the directions of permanent magnetization in rocks, for the permanent magnetization of certain rocks is believed to be a record of the direction of the earth's magnetic field at the time of the rocks' formation. The outcome of research on such rocks has been to show that the earth's magnetic field has frequently reversed its polarity and that the mean magnetic poles in pre-Miocene times differed significantly from the present geographical pole. Interest in continental drift and polar wandering has been renewed by the latter conclusion taken in conjunction with an assumption about the long-term nature of the geomagnetic field. The assumption that, by averaging over a sufficiently long period, secular variation is eliminated and the mean magnetic poles coincide with the geographical poles, is in accord with theories of the earth's magnetic field.

By the same token, palaeomagnetism can also be applied to palaeoclimatology. From the mean magnetic declination and inclination not only can the ancient pole position be calculated but also the ancient latitude and orientation of sampling sites. Since it is inconceivable that climatic belts can have been other than generalized latitudinal zones, inferences of climatic significance can be drawn. There are obvious limitations since the width of the climatic zones is unknown, to which must be added the variable effects of land–sea distribution and a host of other factors. The unique advantage of palaeomagnetism is that inferences can be drawn not only from unfossiliferous sedimentary beds and lava flows, but also from intrusive rocks which only reached the surface during the course of erosion long ages after their emplacement, although recent research by Kawai in Japan throws doubt on the value of results obtained from igneous rocks originally emplaced in depths.

It is obvious that any successful application of palaeomagnetism must depend upon being able to show that the assumptions which are made, whether explicit or implicit, are fully justified. These assumptions, of three main kinds, about the long-term nature of the geomagnetic field, the origin of the permanent magnetization of rocks, and their magnetic stability, will be considered successively; they have also been discussed to a greater or lesser degree by Runcorn,[69, 71] Nagata,[53] Blackett,[2] Irving,[36] Collinson and Nairn.[8]

II.2 *The Geocentric Axial Dipole Assumption*

The geomagnetic field is conveniently described in terms of the magnetic elements (see Fig. 3) and of these declination (D), inclination (I), total field intensity (F) and the horizontal component (H) are particularly important

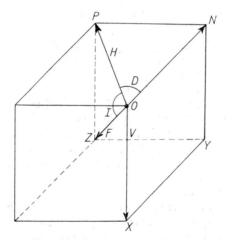

Fig. 3. Diagram showing the inter-relations of the magnetic elements. If $ONYX$ represents the geographic meridional plane and OZ represents the total field intensity F in size and direction, then $OPZX$ is the plane of the magnetic meridian where OP represents the horizontal magnetic component H and OX represents the vertical component V. Angle NOP is the angle of declination D, and POZ the angle of inclination I.

for the present purpose. The angle between the direction in which a horizontally swinging compass needle comes to rest and the geograhical or true north is known as the angle of declination (D). The compass points in the direction of the horizontal field component (H), the vertical plane in which it lies being the local magnetic meridian. A compass needle pivoted about a horizontal axis at right angles to the magnetic meridian, sets at an angle to the horizontal, the angle of inclination (I) and points the direction in which total field is operating. This angle varies from $90°$ at the dip, or magnetic poles, to zero at the magnetic equator. The total intensity (F) can be resolved into horizontal (H) and vertical (V) components, H being zero at the dip poles and a maximum at the magnetic equator. The inter-relationships of the magnetic elements can be expressed diagrammatically, or in simple trigonometrical terms.

Distribution charts of the magnetic elements have been drawn; those showing lines of equal declination are isogonic charts, whilst isoclinic charts show lines of equal dip. However, continuous readings in magnetic observatories show that the earth's magnetic field is always changing both in intensity and direction, and by comparing mean values for successive years, thereby eliminating transient fluctuations, it becomes clear amongst other things that both the declination and inclination undergo a steady change or secular variation. This change, usually not at a constant rate, may be considerable over a long period of time although available evidence suggests that it does not continue indefinitely in one direction. The well-known record of the direction of the magnetic force at London from the late 16th century illustrates the point (see Fig. 4), and similar results are known from other observatories. In palaeomagnetism it is believed that if mean values for successive years were averaged over a long period of the order of a few thousand years, secular variation would be eliminated, and that the mean field over this period would approximate to a geocentric axial dipole. If this were so, that is if the magnetic field were comparable to the field which would be produced by a bar magnet at the centre of, and aligned along, the rotational axis of the earth, it would then follow that the mean direction of the horizonal component (H) would always coincide with a geographical meridian, and the inclination (I) would be a function of the latitude (λ), the relationship being $\tan \lambda = \frac{1}{2} \tan I$ (Plate I). In other words the mean magnetic poles would coincide with the poles of the rotational axis, that is the geographical poles.

Chevallier[5] was able to show that the declinations and inclinations of the historically dated lava flows of Mount Etna fit within the limits of experimental error, and may be used to extrapolate backwards in time, the secular variation curve known from the Naples observatory. Farther back in time an increasing number of measurements have been made on archaeologically dated remains, principally the baked clay or brick walls of old kilns. Usually the kiln can be assigned to a particular century so that it is possible to obtain a series of spot determinations going back into Roman times (Fig. 4). This work, sometimes called archaeomagnetism, shows that secular variation has

Plate I. The relationship of magnetic inclination to latitude. The magnet at the centre of the globe produces the axial dipole field, while the small compass needles mounted at the sides illustrate how the inclination depends on the latitude.

Plate II. The inclinations which would be recorded at different latitudes if the geographical poles were coincident with the mean European pole position in Permian times, derived from palaeomagnetic data.

followed substantially the same pattern over the last two thousand years.[9] The pattern can be traced even farther back by means of varved clays, the seasonally banded deposits particularly well developed in post-glacial times. Griffiths[30] working on recent, dated, Swedish varves considered that the varved clay results paralleled the known secular variation curve, although errors in inclination attributable to hydrodynamic conditions[46] were possible. A long series of New England varved clays were studied by Johnson, Murphy and Torreson[41] who concluded '. . . that the declination remained substantially constant on the average, with excursions of the order of ±30° . . . consistent with the measurements [of declination] made at London, Boston and Baltimore during the last few hundred years. The average value

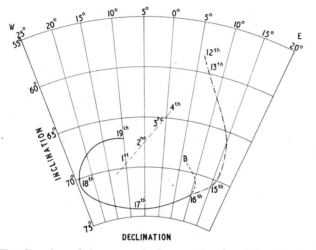

Fig. 4. The direction of the magnetic force at London (after Bauer, Cook and Belshé). Bauer's extrapolation from Rome shown by broken line B. Earlier results from 1st–4th centuries and 12th–16th centuries based on archaeological results and broken lines through these points are only tentative.

of declination over the 5000 years is +10° from the present declination, which is about −15° in New England.' These conclusions were extended to cover about one million years by the inclusion of results from deep-sea cores from the Pacific. Thus Johnson, Murphy and Torreson were the first to produce some evidence to show that secular variation in declination may be eliminated by averaging over a long period, although they included no information on inclination. The importance of the 5° difference of the mean direction from true north cannot be gauged in the absence of any estimate of significance of the mean. Since that time, however, the results of a host of palaeomagnetic investigations have been published on Miocene and post-Miocene rocks from Australia,[38] Japan,[42] North America,[65,4] Iceland[33,34] and Mull.[3,76] In all these cases there is no significant difference[27] between their calculated mean pole position and the geographical pole. This is equally true whether the rocks are normally or reversely magnetized, the latter indicating that during parts of the Tertiary the earth's magnetic field reversed its polarity many times.

This evidence is felt to be adequate justification for the belief that the earth's mean magnetic field does indeed approximate to a geocentric axial dipole. Consequently when in stable rocks the ancient pole, calculated from the mean declination and inclination of a geological formation, differs significantly from the present pole, then the geographical co-ordinates of the site from which the samples were obtained cannot have been the same as at the present day. Once rocks older than Miocene are considered, this is found to be the case and not only do the pole positions calculated from the mean declination and inclination begin to differ significantly from the present geographical poles, but additionally, significant differences appear between the pole positions of coeval rocks from different continents. This fact is well illustrated by the Eocene extrusives rocks of Northern Ireland,[35] Victoria [38] and India.[6] However, consistent results are obtained over areas of continental extent, for example from the European Permian [62, 66, 72] and the Triassic rocks of North America.[15]

It will be clear that palaeomagnetic studies are of a statistical nature. The deviation of individual results from the mean direction of magnetization is determined not only by experimental errors but also by secular variation. Sampling must therefore be carried out over a time scale long by comparison with the secular variation. Most, if not all, rock formations represent a sufficient period of time to satisfy this condition. The statistics in general use were developed by Fisher [27] and elaborated by other workers.[70, 77]

II.3 *The Origin of the Permanent Magnetization in Rocks*

The permanent magnetism of rocks is due to their content of accessory amounts of ferromagnetic minerals, as much as a few per cent in certain igneous rocks but often less than half of one per cent in many sediments. The ferromagnetic minerals are predominantly the anhydrous ferric oxides, magnetite (Fe_3O_4) and haematite (α-Fe_2O_3) and their mutual solid solutions with titanium.[32-34, 49] There is a strongly magnetic oxide maghemite (γ-Fe_2O_3) detected in certain rocks [53] which is metastable [32, 78] and whose contribution to the permanent magnetic moment is therefore suspect. Although the magnetic sulphide, pyrrhotite, has been found [2] it does not appear to make a significant contribution to rock magnetism.

It has been demonstrated experimentally [31, 48, 52] that on cooling from high temperatures an igneous rock acquires a magnetic moment, termed thermoremanent, which is aligned in the direction of the ambient field. The critical temperature about which this moment is acquired, known as the Curie point temperature, varies according to the composition of the ferromagnetic minerals involved. The intensity of the thermo-remanent moment is normally proportional to the ambient field intensity where this does not exceed a few tens of oersteds. The physics of the process has been studied by Nagata [53] and Runcorn.[69, 71] A few rocks have been found in which the thermo-remanent magnetization is in the opposite direction to the ambient field, but these appear to be exceptional.[54-56]

Sedimentary rocks can be magnetized by the orientation during the course of deposition of detrital magnetic particles under the influence of the earth's magnetic field. These magnetic particles probably acquired a thermo-remanent magnetic moment in the source rock. Sedimentation experiments with redispersed varved clays[41, 46] or disaggregated sandstones have demonstrated such an alignment, although King[46] has shown that the direction may be affected by hydrodynamic conditions, and Irving[37] states that orientation can continue until the water content of the sediment is reduced by compaction. The experiments also showed a systematic error in inclination.[30]*

Chemical magnetization, in which the ferromagnetic material is the product of a chemical reaction, can affect sediments and a number of special cases are known.[14, 49, 59] A widespread phenomenon is the occurrence of red oxide cement, and coating of individual grains in sedimentary rocks. The significance of its contribution to the magnetic moment is still the subject of discussion. Creer[10] has given reasons for believing that the red cementing material may be responsible for the secondary component of magnetization in certain Keuper marl samples. On the other hand, the progressive removal of this red coating (by acid leaching) assumed to surround all grains, leads to a progressive drop in intensity of magnetization without a change in direction until the red colour has vanished. This suggests that the red material is related to the primary permanent magnetization. Domain theory provides a possible explanation, in terms of grain size, of both cases.[10] The method whereby this red oxide cement or grain coating was acquired is also still disputed (see, however, Chapter V).

Unaltered, coeval sediments and lavas from the same region give essentially the same declinations and inclinations. Such a result predicted from experimental work and most frequently used as evidence in favour of the reversal of the earth's magnetic field, has an important bearing on the inclination error of sediments. The first comparisons were of Permian rocks where no significant differences in inclination were reported. As the inclinations found are very low, this is not surprising, and since then Belshé[1] has reported lower inclinations in Carboniferous sediments when compared with lavas. Thus while both sediments and lavas can accurately record the declination of the time of their formation, the inclination recorded in sediments may be of the order of 10^8 too low[46] (not borne out by recent work†).

II.4 *The Stability of Magnetization*

From its inception the original declination and inclination of any unmetamorphosed rock has been subjected to the action of a weak magnetic field

---

* Since this article was written a more detailed account has been published by Griffiths, D. H., King, R. F., Rees, A. I., Wright, A. E. *Proc. roy. Soc.*, **256**A, 359 (1960).

† Opdyke. Personal communication.

(the earth's field) and possible slight heating as a consequence of burial. It has been shown[53] that a weak magnetic field can build up a secondary magnetization known as an isothermal remanent magnetization (IRM). This means, in the case of the earth, that an isothermal remanent magnetization could have been built up only since the last reversal of the magnetic field, for field reversals have a demagnetizing effect, each reversal tending to erase the IRM built up during the preceding period. Japanese workers[53] have proved that a partial thermo-remanent magnetization (PTRM) can be built up by a magnetic field as weak as the earth's over temperature ranges such as might be experienced by rocks on deep burial. The direction of the secondary IRM and PTRM generally differs from the original magnetization of the rock and the consequence is that the direction of magnetization measured—if the original is not entirely masked—lies somewhere between the true original direction and the dipole field of the site. Fortunately, by the application of a series of laboratory and field tests, rocks which possess such secondary components can be eliminated as well as rocks which are inherently unstable. In certain cases it is even possible to remove this secondary component without destroying the original magnetization.

The field tests, which make use of field relations to examine stability, were first described by Graham[28] and extensively applied and augmented by Irving and Runcorn.[40] They are basically of two kinds, the conglomerate and the fold tests. Since an unstable magnetic component tends to become aligned in the direction of the ambient field, the random magnetic orientation in a conglomerate of pebbles derived from a known formation is evidence of the magnetic stability of the latter since the conglomerate was formed. The inference of stability in pre-conglomerate time is obvious, but only in the case of an intra-formational conglomerate can the inference be more nearly justified. A similar argument can be applied to samples taken from opposite limbs of a fold. If consistent results are obtained by 'unfolding' the beds, that is by referring the magnetic directions to the bedding planes rather than to the field position, stability since deformation is indicated. The examination of intra-formational slump bedding,[40] like the intra-formational conglomerate test, narrows the time range over which stability can only be inferred, to the point where the stability can be reasonably assumed proven. In contrast to the essentially geological field tests, in laboratory testing the physical properties of the rock are examined. If it can be shown that the magnetization of a rock remains constant over a range of applied magnetic fields and temperatures greater than might be reasonably expected in the course of its geological history, then stability can be inferred. The inference must be qualified, however, as laboratory tests cannot simulate the long-term effects of slight heating and weak fields. The effects of weak fields in building up an isothermal remanent magnetization have been studied by Creer[10] and Nagata.[53] One of the chief methods of testing used is that of demagnetization, either by alternating fields[10,53] or by a steady field in the direction opposite to the polarization of the rock.[41] In many instances it can be shown that the directions of magnetization remain essentially unaltered

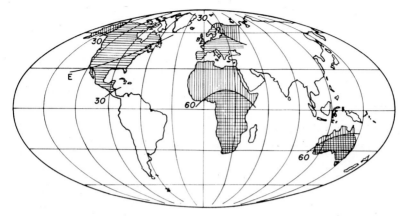

Fig. 5. The equator and latitudes 30° and 60° during Carboniferous times predicted from palaeomagnetic results in Europe, N. America, Africa and Australia.

as the intensity of remanent magnetization diminishes, and Creer[10,11] has demonstrated that in at least some unstable rocks the secondary component can be removed without affecting the original, stable component. The other main method consists of heating and then cooling specimens in an inert atmosphere and zero magnetic field. The agreement of magnetic measurements before and after the experiment is regarded as evidence of stability. This method has been much used by Roche[66] who heated specimens up to 300°C.

II.5 *Conclusions*

Experience has shown that the lithologies most suitable for palaeomagnetic work are the bright coloured, predominantly continental deposits, and the

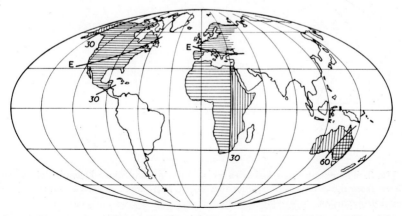

Fig. 6. The equator and latitudes 30° and 60° during Permian times predicted from palaeomagnetic results in Europe, N. America, Africa and Australia.

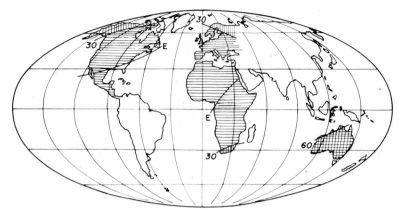

Fig. 7. The equator and latitudes 30° and 60° during Triassic times predicted from
palaeomagnetic results in Europe, N. America, Africa and Australia.

basic and intermediate extrusive and hypabyssal rocks. Even in these
categories many rocks are found to be magnetically unstable. The drab
coloured deposits, pale deltaic sandstones,[59] and grey to black and green
shales are usually associated with very low intensities of magnetization and
instability. If rocks fulfill the stability tests and can be shown to be unmetamorphosed, undeformed and relatively little disturbed, it is reasonable to
suppose that they form a record of the earth's magnetic field in past epochs.
    The first series of results spanning the geological column were obtained
from British and North American rocks.[12,13,67]*   These showed that the
departure of the mean pole position of each preceding geological epoch from

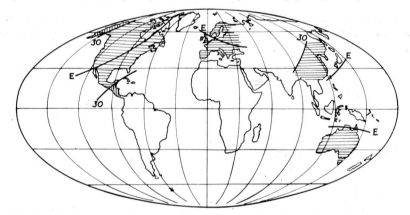

Fig. 8. The equator and latitudes 30° and 60° during Siluro-Devonian times predicted from palaeomagnetic studies of Chinese and North American Silurian rocks
and European and Australian Devonian rocks.

    * Since this article was written a much more detailed study has been published, by
Collinson, D. W. and Runcorn, S. K., *Bull. geol. Soc. Amer.*, 71, 915 (1960).

the present pole increased in a consistent manner. On the basis of the geocentric axial dipole representing the true nature of the magnetic field over such lengths of time, the only possible interpretation is in terms of changes of latitude and orientation of both Britain and North America with respect to the pole (Plate II). In climatic terms these areas may have passed through different climatic zones in the course of geological time, and their latitude and orientation at any given time can be found. Recent work on rocks from Australia,[39] India,[6, 7] South America[11] and Central and South Africa[29, 58, 60] confirms these findings, and further suggests differential movement between the various continents.[36, 61, 68]

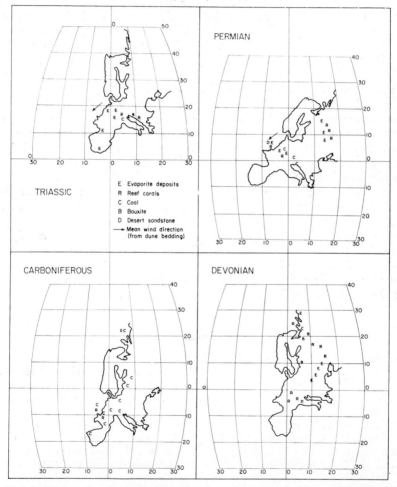

Fig. 9. Europe in the latitude and orientation suggested by palaeomagnetic results from rocks of Devonian, Carboniferous, Permian and Triassic. Plotted on the maps are geological data of climatic significance.

In general, with the exception of Irving,[36] very little regard has been paid to the palaeoclimatological aspects of palaeomagnetism, and apart from one comparative study,[64] the information is not generally presented in a form conducive to climatic interpretation. Further, insufficient stress has been given to the restriction of the validity of palaeomagnetic results to the continental mass from which they were obtained (see however references 36, 61). To overcome this difficulty the palaeomagnetic contribution to palaeoclimates is summarized by means of a series of sketch-maps (Fig. 5, 6, 7 and 8) in which the equator, 30° and 60° latitudes are drawn extending to the boundaries of the continent from which the data were obtained. (For the sake of clarity, zones lying between the poles and latitude 60° are crosshatched, zones between 30° and 60° are denoted by vertical ruling while horizontal ruling is found in the equatorial region.) They cover a time range from the Silurian to the Triassic, these being the only periods for which results from several continents are available. This method of presenting the climatic inferences drawn from palaeomagnetism is independent of any assumptions of continental drift and polar wandering, although it is clearly impossible to reconcile the result with present land distributions. The maps, however, may be a useful basis for further research and form a preliminary framework to which other climatic data may be related. An alternative method is to plot the regions involved in their correct longitudes and orientations according to the palaeomagnetic evidence. This cannot be done for more than a single area without involving assumptions about relative position. It does illustrate, however, the good agreement between palaeoclimatic and palaeomagnetic evidence, of which Europe is a good example (Fig. 9).*

At this stage of research when so little is known of considerable portions of the geological column in so many parts of the world, the maps can only be regarded as tentative. Eventually it is to be hoped that mosaics can be produced from which it will be possible to reassemble continuous climatic belts for the different geological epochs, and in so doing inevitably light will be shed on the vexed problem of crustal movements.

References

1. Belshé, J. C. *Advances in Physics*, **6**, 187 (1957)
2. Blackett, P. M. S. *Lectures in Rock Magnetism.* 1956. Jerusalem: Weizmann Science Press of Israel
3. Bruckshaw, J. M. and Vincenz, S. A. *Mon. Not. R. astr. Soc. geophys. Suppl.*, **6**, 579 (1954)
4. Campbell, C. D. and Runcorn, S. K. *J. geophys. Res.*, **61**, 449 (1956)
5. Chevallier, R. *Ann. Phys., Paris*, **4**, 5 (1925)
6. Clegg, J. A., Deutsch, E. R. and Griffiths, D. H. *Phil. Mag.*, **1**, 419 (1956)
7. Clegg, J. A., Radakrishnamurty, C. and Sahasrabudhe, P. W. *Nature, Lond.*, **181**, 830 (1958)
8. Collinson, D. W. and Nairn, A. E. M. *Bull. Overseas geol min. Res.*, **7**, 381 (1959)

* Data provided by N. D. Opdyke.

9. Cook, R. M. and Belshé, J. C. *Antiquity*, **32**, 167 (1958)
10. Creer, K. M. *Phil. Trans.*, **250**A, 130 (1957)
11. Creer, K. M. *Ann. géophys*, **14**, 373 (1958)
12. Creer, K. M., Irving, E. and Runcorn, S. K. *J. Geomagn. Geoelect., Kyoto*, **6**, 163 (1954)
13. Creer, K. M., Irving, E. and Runcorn, S. K. *Phil. Trans.*, **250**A, 144 (1957)
14. Doell, R. R. *Trans. Amer. geophys. Un.*, **37**, 156 (1956)
15. Du Bois, P. M., Irving, E., Opdyke, N. D., Runcorn, S. K. and Banks, M. R,. *Nature, Lond.*, **180**, 1186 (1957)
16. Emiliani, C. *Amer. J. Sci.*, **252**, 149 (1954)
17. Emiliani, C. *Science*, **119**, 853 (1954)
18. Emiliani, C. *J. Geol.*, **63**, 538 (1955)
19. Emiliani, C. *J. Geol.*, **64**, 281 (1956)
20. Emiliani, C. *Science*, **125**, 383 (1957)
21. Emiliani, C. *J. Geol.*, **66**, 264 (1958)
22. Emiliani, C. and Epstein, S. *J. Geol.*, **61**, 171 (1953)
23. Epstein, S., Buchsbaum, R., Lowenstam, H. A. and Urey, H. C. *Bull. geol. Soc. Amer.*, **62**, 417 (1951)
24. Epstein, S. and Mayeda, T. R. *Geochim. et cosmoch. Acta*, **4**, 213 (1953)
25. Epstein, S. and Lowenstam, H. A. *J. Geol.*, **61**, 424 (1953)
26. Epstein, S., Buchsbaum, R., Lowenstam, H. A. and Urey, H. C. *Bull. geol. Soc. Amer.*, **64**, 1315 (1953)
27. Fisher, R. A. *Proc. roy. Soc.*, **217**A, 295 (1953)
28. Graham, J. W. *J. geophys. Res.*, **54**, 131 (1949)
29. Graham, K. W. T. and Hales, A. L. *Advances in Physics*, **6**, 149 (1957)
30. Griffiths, D. H. *Mon. Not. R. astr. Soc. geophys. Suppl.*, **7**, 103 (1955)
31. Herroun, E. F. and Hallimond, A. F. *Proc. phys. Soc., Lond.*, **55**, 214 (1943)
32. Hofer, L. J. E. and Weller, S. *Science*, **106**, 470 (1947)
33. Hospers, J. *Nature, Lond.*, **168**, 1111 (1951)
34. Hospers, J. *Nature, Lond.*, **173**, 1183 (1954)
35. Hospers, J. and Charlesworth, H. A. K. *Mon. Not. R. astr. Soc. geophys. Suppl.*, **7**, 32 (1954)
36. Irving, E. *Geofis. pur. appl.*, **33**, 23 (1956)
37. Irving, E. *Phil. Trans.*, **250**A, 100 (1957)
38. Irving, E. and Green, R. *Mon. Not. R. astr. Soc. geophys. Suppl.*, **7**, 347 (1957)
39. Irving, E. and Green, R. *Geophys. J.*, **1**, 64 (1958)
40. Irving, E. and Runcorn, S. K. *Phil. Trans.*, **250**A, 83 (1957)
41. Johnson, E. A., Murphy, T. and Torreson, O. W. *Terr. Magn. atmos. Elect.*, **53**, 349 (1948)
42. Kawai, N. *J. geophys. Res.*, **56**, 73 (1951)
43. Kawai, N. *Proc. imp. Acad. Japan*, **32**, 464 (1956)
44. Kawai, N., Kume, S. and Sasajima, S. *Proc. imp. Acad. Japan*, **32**, 459 (1956)
45. Kawai, N., Kume, S. and Yasukawa, K. *Proc. imp. Acad. Japan*, **32**, 455 (1956)
46. King, R. *Mon. Not. R. astr. Soc. geophys. Suppl.*, **7**, 115 (1955)
47. Lowenstam, H. A. and Epstein, S. *J. Geol.*, **62**, 207 (1954)
48. Manley, H. *Geofis. pur. appl.*, **27**, 105 (1954)
49. Martinez, J. D. and Howell, L. C. *Nature, Lond.*, **178**, 204 (1956)
50. McCrea, J. M. *J. chem. Phys.*, **18**, 849 (1950)
51. McKinney, C. R., McCrea, J. M., Epstein, S., Allen, H. A. and Urey, H. C. *Rev. sci. Instrum.*, **21**, 724 (1950)
52. Nagata, T. *Nature, Lond.*, **165**, 245 (1950)

53. Nagata, T. *Rock Magnetism*. 1953. Tokyo: Maruzen
54. Nagata, T. *Nature, Lond.*, **172**, 850 (1953)
55. Nagata, T., Akimoto, S. and Uyeda, S. *Proc. imp. Acad. Japan*, **27**, 643 (1951)
56. Nagata, T., Akimoto, S. and Uyeda, S. *Nature, Lond.*, **172**, 630 (1953)
57. Nairn, A. E. M. *Nature, Lond.*, **178**, 935 (1956)
58. Nairn, A. E. M. *Advances in Physics*, **6**, 162 (1957)
59. Nairn, A. E. M. *Mon. Not. R. astr. Soc. geophys. Suppl.*, **7**, 308 (1957)
60. Nairn, A. E. M. *Bull. Overseas geol. min. Res.*, **7**, 398 (1959)
61. Nairn, A. E. M., in Clegg, J. A., *Nature, Lond.*, **178**, 1085 (1956)
62. Nairn, A. E. M. *Bull. Soc. géol. Fr.*, **7**, 721 (1957)
63. Nicholls, G. *Advances in Physics*, **4**, 113 (1955)
64. Opdyke, N. D. and Runcorn, S. K. *Bull. geol. Soc. Amer.*, 71, 959 (1960)
65. Opdyke, N. D. and Runcorn, S. K. *Science*, **123** (1956)
66. Roche, A. *C.R. Acad. Sci., Paris*, **244**, 2952 (1957)
67. Runcorn, S. K. *Bull. geol. Soc. Amer.*, **67**, 301 (1956)
68. Runcorn, S. K. *Proc. Geol. Ass. Canada*, **8**, 77 (1956)
69. Runcorn, S. K. *Advances in Physics*, **4**, 244 (1955)
70. Runcorn, S. K. *Advances in Physics*, **6**, 169 (1957)
71. Runcorn, S. K., in J. Bartels, ed., *Handbuch der Physik*, Vol. 48. 1956. Berlin: Springer-Verlag; Heidelberg: Göttingen
72. Rutten, M. C., van Everdingen, R. O. and Zijderfeld, J. D. A. *Geol. en Mijnb.*, **19**, 193 (1957)
73. Urey, H. C. *J. chem. Soc.*, 562 (1947)
74. Urey, H. C. and Grieff, L. J. *J. Amer. chem. Soc.*, **57**, 321 (1935)
75. Urey, H. C., Lowenstam, H. A., Epstein, S. and McKinney, C. R. *Bull. geol. Soc. Amer.*, **62**, 399 (1951)
76. Vincenz, S. A. *Mon. Not. R. astr. Soc. geophys. Suppl.*, **6**, 590 (1954)
77. Watson, G. and Irving, E. *Mon. Not. R. astr. Soc. geophys. Suppl.*, **7**, 289 (1957)
78. Welo, L. A. and Baudisch, O. *Phil. Mag.*, **17**, 753 (1934)
79. Wiseman, J. D. H. *Nature, Lond.*, **182**, 153 (1958)
80. Yalkowsky, R. *J. Geol.*, **65**, 480 (1957)

VIII

Palaeozoological Evidence of Climate.

(1) Vertebrates

A. S. ROMER

I. Introduction

The attitude of vertebrate workers towards the study of past climates has tended to be a negative one. The evidence for the interpretation of past climates obtainable from vertebrate fossils and the vertebrate evolutionary story is, on the whole, much less important than that derived from sedimentary and palaeobotanical data. In consequence, the vertebrate palaeontologist generally accepts the conclusions reached by the geologists and botanists and attempts to fit the vertebrate story into their climatological picture.

But although the vertebrate evidence for climatic interpretation is much more modest in amount than that furnished by other fields, it is, nevertheless, seemingly significant at many points and should not be disregarded in any broad discussion of the nature of past climates.

Such evidence may be derived from any one of a variety of sources.

(1) Certain conclusions can be drawn from the geographical distribution of continental vertebrates in past faunas—this without necessarily considering the possible habits of the forms concerned. A broad latitudinal spread of extinct forms may suggest climatic conditions quite in contrast to the sharp north–south temperature gradients existing today; unfortunately, however, the distribution of fossil beds of any one age is usually too limited to afford satisfactory evidence on this basis. The limitation of an extinct fauna to specific continental regions implies barriers to migration. Such barriers may have been topographic—the presence of water gaps or impassible ranges. Climatic barriers, however, may be important factors—differences in rainfall or (of greater importance) temperature differences. Steaming swamps or

jungles, barren deserts, bitter cold or torrid heat, any one of these conditions may be as effective a barrier to vertebrate migration as a water gap.

(2) In many cases direct, if sometimes prosaic and frequently dubious, interpretations of past climates may be attempted on the assumption that given forms or groups of vertebrates lived in the past under the climatic conditions favoured by their living relatives. As noted later, such evidence is of very considerable value in the study of Pleistocene faunas (although even here caution must be exercised). But farther back in time, deductions of this sort are of lessened value. Our knowledge of recent vertebrates demonstrates that even within a genus there have often evolved adaptations to a variety of climates, and the possibilities of past variations in climatic adaptations increases both with the magnitude of the systematic category involved and with the remoteness in time of the period considered (cf. Colbert[4]). But despite the frailty of assumptions of this sort based on single forms, relative strength may be obtained by the consideration of whole faunas, particularly if they contain representatives of a variety of groups which have common climatic adaptations at the present time.

(3) Evidence may be obtained from consideration of structural or physio- logical characters present in the fossil forms concerned or their modern representatives. Evidence from the fossils is, in general, limited to skeletal features, but even so one may cite, for example, the fact that prevalence in a fauna of mammals with high-crowned teeth and slender limbs is strongly indicative of steppe conditions. Although there can be little positive know- ledge of the physiology of extinct forms, it is reasonable to assume that certain broad functional characteristics have been long-lived. For example, it is probable that lack of effective internal mechanisms for control of tempera- ture was as characteristic of most (although not all) extinct reptiles as it is of the surviving types,[1] and that, therefore, reasonable deductions as to past temperatures may be made on the basis of the presence or absence of reptile remains.

(4) Evidence from study of the circumstances under which a fossil verte- brate died and was entombed may be of interest with regard to climates. In such situations the sediments furnish most of the useful information, but the nature of the animal remains themselves is often suggestive. As an example, Watson[33] long ago pointed out that South African Permian pareiasaurs are almost always found right side up and completely articulated in mudstones, indicating that these individuals were bogged down and, hence, suggesting that in life (as in death) they were swamp dwellers. The frequent finding of fossils of a given species clustered in groups or even in great masses of in- dividuals invites speculation as to the reasons for such catastrophes (cf. Weigelt[35]). Storms, freezing or, in the case of aquatic animals, drought have been suggested in various instances.

(5) Less direct evidence, but evidence of far greater importance from many points of view, can be derived from a consideration of the broad picture of vertebrate history. In great measure the evolutionary story is one of con- tinuous adaptation to environment, and adaptation to climatic conditions

surely played no mean part. There are a number of major events in vertebrate history which it is difficult or impossible to interpret unless they occurred in 'response' to specific climatic situations. Among these, as discussed below, seasonal drought conditions appear to have been especially significant.

II. Seasonal Drought and the Evolution of Devonian Vertebrates

The climatic conditions associated with the deposition of red beds are discussed elsewhere in this volume. Whatever general conclusions may be arrived at—or not arrived at—regarding this problem, it seems certain that most red beds in which vertebrate remains are common were formed under climates of the type often termed 'tropical savanna', in which seasons of abundant rain alternate with seasons of drought. Evidence for this has been drawn from sediments and plants. The vertebrates themselves, however, furnish strong arguments for this conclusion as regards Palaeozoic red beds.

For the Devonian, in particular, the predominance of lung-bearing fishes in fresh-water deposits is especially significant. Gills were, of course, the primary breathing apparatus of primitive vertebrates. To be sure, gills appear to have originated primarily as food-straining devices, a function still present in lower chordates and even the larval lamprey today, and quite surely present in many if not all of the primitive ostracoderms of the Silurian and Devonian. Except, however, for secondary reversions, this primitive function has been abandoned by all adult fishes above the agnathous level; gills are the typical breathing organs in the fish world.

Lungs, in contrast, are the breathing structures of land vertebrates, which obtain their oxygen from the air. They are rare among living fishes. Today, only five genera of fish, living in tropical fresh water, have functional lungs. There are the three Dipnoi ('lungfishes' in popular terminology), including *Epiceratodus* of Australia, *Protopterus* of Africa and *Lepidosiren* of South America, and, in addition, *Polypterus* and *Calamoichthys*, two African genera which (as first demonstrated by Goodrich[11]) are aberrant relatives of the most primitive Actinopterygii.

It was at one time assumed that lungs arose late in fish history, and were developed only in forms related to the ancestry of tetrapods (lungs are absent in cyclostomes and recent shark-like fishes). In the vast majority of living bony fishes, the teleosts, there is found an air-bladder, a single dorsal outgrowth of the gut which generally operates as a hydrostatic organ, although in a few cases it functions to some extent in breathing. It was formerly assumed that the air-bladder was a more ancient structure than the paired ventral lungs, and that lungs arose by modification of the air-bladder. More recently, however, Goodrich[12] and others have demonstrated that it is more probable that the reverse is the case, and that if the two organs are actually homologous, the lung may be the older and more primitive structure.

Most (although not all) authorities agree that bony fishes pertain to three major groups, all of which were present in Devonian times, and were then

N

already clearly distinguishable. These three are: (1) the Dipnoi, or lung-fishes; (2) the Crossopterygii, ancestral to land vertebrates but now extinct except for the aberrant *Latimeria*; and (3) the Actinopterygii, ray-finned fishes which in their most highly developed phase, that of the teleosts, domi-nate the world of fishes today. The most ancient representatives of all three groups in Devonian times were almost all fresh-water forms. It is reasonable to believe that the Devonian lungfishes, like their descendants, had lungs. It is likewise generally agreed that the ancient crossopterygians, as ancestors of the land vertebrates, possessed lungs—a conclusion supported by the fact that the modern *Latimeria*, although living at a depth where lungs are useless, has vestiges of lung structure. And the evidence from *Polypterus* and *Cala-moichthys* strongly suggests that the most primitive actinopterygians also possessed lungs.

Thus, lungs were probably universal in all early bony fishes. But lungs, it seems, were not developed solely in the Osteichthyes, highest of fish classes. In Devonian fresh waters there were also present various placoderms (a class of armoured fishes now entirely extinct) and the last representatives of the archaic jawless group of the ostracoderms. In most cases we cannot, of course, determine whether lungs were present in these animals since our knowledge of them is almost entirely confined to the skeleton, and only in one fortunate instance is much of the soft anatomy known. *Bothriolepis* is an antiarch belonging to the placoderm group, and is one of the most common fishes of land Devonian deposits. As Denison[9] has shown, *Bothriolepis* has paired outpocketings of the pharynx which seem surely to be lungs. This suggests that, far from being confined to bony fishes, lungs may have been generally present—possibly even universally present—in early fresh-water vertebrates.

Perhaps the best known of all Devonian fresh-water vertebrate localities is 'Scaumenac Bay', a bluff lying between the villages of Miguasha and Fleurant, Quebec. A faunal list, such as that of Ørvig,[20] will include over a score of species. Actual collecting experience, however, shows that more than 95 per cent of all specimens recovered pertain to three forms only: *Bothriolepis*, *Scaumenacia* and *Eusthenopteron*, respectively an antiarch, a dipnoan and a crossopterygian, all three possessing, we are quite sure, functional lungs. This predominance of lung-bearers indicates that such structures were of major importance for life in Devonian fresh waters. The reason? It seems certain that they aided, as they do in fishes today, in survival under drought conditions.

All five living fishes which possess functional lungs—*Epiceratodus* in Australia, *Protopterus*, *Polypterus* and *Calamoichthys* in Africa, and *Lepidosiren* in South America—live in tropical areas subject to seasonal drought. When rainfall is abundant, gills are in general sufficient for obtaining necessary oxygen (although, in fact, the gills of *Protopterus* are so reduced that lungs are utilized the year round). In the season of drought, when streams dry up, the water of the remaining pools tends to become stagnant and deficient in oxygen. At such times lungs, giving the opportunity of obtaining atmo-spheric oxygen, are of the greatest importance in the survival of the individual. The dominance of lung-bearing fishes in the Devonian offers strong evidence that seasonal droughts were then widespread and intense.

Today, as noted, lung-bearing fishes are few in number; most fresh-water fishes are teleosts which have, instead, an air-bladder used little or not at all for breathing. Why this shift? Two reasons may be adduced. (1) It is probable that in the more recent geological periods 'tropical savanna' climatic regions have become more restricted in extent. (2) The lungless later actinopterygians have developed other methods of conquering drought conditions even if living in regions where such conditions exist. A number of teleosts have evolved moist chambers capable of absorbing atmospheric oxygen in, or in connection with, the gill chambers. More important is the fact that actinopterygians generally lay a much larger number of eggs than do dipnoans and, we may believe, crossopterygians. Much less emphasis need be placed on survival of the individual; the numerous progeny of few adults which may survive a drought can rapidly replenish the population.

A second major structural advance which appears to be correlated with drought conditions is the development of the land type of limb which, replacing the ancestral fish fin, made tetrapod life possible. This advance took place during the Devonian, for the ichthyostegid amphibians found at the end of that period had typical tetrapod appendages, despite the fact that they retained many other structural features of their crossopterygian relatives and ancestors.[15]

What was the underlying 'cause' which brought about the evolution of walking limbs and thus made possible the spectacular later evolution of amphibians, reptiles, birds and mammals? Not the pressure of enemies in the water, for the ancestral crossopterygians were dominant predaceous fishes. Not the search for food, for the older tetrapods were eaters of animal food, and there was, in the Devonian, precious little food of this sort on land.

Apparently the answer, first suggested by Watson[34] in regard to the Carboniferous embolomere amphibians and applied by Romer to the early amphibians in general (reference 24, pp. 52–53, etc.), is a seemingly paradoxical one—that tetrapod limbs were evolved as an adaptation not for living on land but, rather, so that their possessors could remain in their ancestral water habitat!

Many of the older amphibians were not land-dwellers. Their habitat, even if limbs were developed, was, like that of their crossopterygian cousins, fresh-water streams and lakes, where they preyed upon smaller fishes and invertebrates. Under normal conditions of rainfall, the amphibian had no advantage over his piscine relatives, and, indeed, was probably less adept at swimming. If a moderate drought occurred, the amphibian still had no advantage, for, with lungs, the crossopterygian could live in stagnant waters as well as he. But if drought became extreme, the utility of tetrapod limbs could at last become apparent. Two of the existing lungfish genera have evolved special means, by burrowing, of surviving if the waters of a stream or pond dry up. Presumably, however, such specialization was not present among Devonian fishes. If the water disappeared completely, the crossopterygian was stranded in the mud and, generally, doomed, while the ancestral amphibian could crawl—albeit, one expects, slowly and painfully in early stages—up or down the stream bed or overland, to search for a pool in which water still remained and in which he could resume his normal life.

Lungs and limbs are two major structural features which made the later development of tetrapod life possible. The evolution of these structures appears, however, not to have been due to any mysterious 'urge' towards higher things, but to their utility for survival in aquatic life under conditions of seasonal drought. Their development offers strong evidence for the wide-spread occurrence of climates of this type in the Upper Palaeozoic and specifically in the Devonian.

III. Vertebrates and Palaeozoic Temperatures

Although it is generally believed that for much of the Palaeozoic, tempera-tures were more equably distributed than at present, with a much gentler gradient between polar and tropical zones, vertebrates have relatively little evidence to contribute; for the simple reason that until close to the end of that era nearly all known fossil deposits lie in the present North Temperate belt and relatively little is known of pre-Permian vertebrate life in the present tropics or the Southern Hemisphere. However, certain finds of fresh-water fishes suggest that temperature gradients were not extreme, and the equatorial belt could be readily crossed. Australian Palaeozoic fresh-water fish faunas[14] are closely comparable to those of northern Europe. Still more conclusive is the fact that the antiarch *Bothriolepis*, abundant in the northern Devonian, is also reported from the Antarctic continent.[36]

The nature of deposits in the southern 'Gondwanaland' continental areas, including southern Africa, towards the close of the Palaeozoic affords impres-sive evidence of glaciation. Since it is in South Africa, in the late Palaeozoic and early Triassic, that the therapsids, ancestral to mammals, flourished most abundantly, it is often suggested that there may be a correlation between glaciation and the evolution of therapsids. Mammals have a series of mechanisms for internal temperature regulation which enable them to live under conditions of cold (or heat) in which 'lower' vertebrates cannot survive, and there is evidence suggesting that such mechanisms were developed to some degree in their therapsid ancestors; I have on various occasions pointed out that the development of a secondary palate in several therapsid lines is suggestive, and Brink[2] has noted other features possibly associated with incipient temperature regulation. It has been argued that the abundance of therapsids in the Permian of South Africa strengthens the conclusion from the sediments that cold climates existed there. Or (turning the argument in the other direction) that the evolution of temperature regulation in therapsids was 'stimulated' by the local climate.*

* I have elsewhere[26] pointed out that 'experiments' in the direction of thermal regulation are seen among the early Permian pelycosaurs ancestral to therapsids, as exhibited in the dorsal 'sails' of *Dimetrodon* and other genera.

A closer look at the geographical and chronological history of the therapsids, however, indicates that there is little positive evidence for this supposed correlation of glaciation and therapsid development. In Africa, glacial phenomena and therapsid occurrences are separated by a considerable time interval. Glaciation occurred during the time of deposition of the Dwyka beds, the exact age of which is still debatable but appears to have been close to the Carboniferous–Permian boundary. Following the Dwyka are the very thick Ecca beds, whose deposition may have taken all of early Permian time. Except at the very top, these beds are almost barren of any sort of animal life. It is only in the following *Tapinocephalus* beds of the Beaufort Series, in Middle Permian days, that the therapsid faunas appear in Africa. It is possible that their ancestors lived in the region earlier, but there is absolutely no proof that therapsids and glaciers at all approached one another in time.

Still further, there is no reason to believe that therapsids originated in Africa. On the contrary, the Pelycosauria, the more primitive synapsid order, from one family of which (Sphenacodontidae) the therapsids appear to have arisen, flourished in Europe and North America in late Carboniferous and early Permian days. In Russian beds which appear to have been deposited somewhat before the middle of the Permian are found forms transitional from pelycosaurs to therapsids and the most primitive members of the therapsids themselves. On present evidence one can more reasonably maintain that the group arose in the north, rather than half a world away in cold southern climates.

IV. Coal Swamps

Although climates with seasonal droughts seem to have continued to be widespread in late Palaeozoic and Triassic times, the Carboniferous gives evidence of the existence of a strongly contrasting type of climate then widespread in the Northern Hemisphere—that under which were laid down the deposits which form our major source of coal. One important factor in the development of the coal swamps was, of course, physiographic—the presence of large areas of flat lowland terrain capable of being turned into swampy areas. The second was climatic—conditions, obviously, of abundant rainfall. The vertebrates contribute evidence supporting (although support seems hardly needed) the conclusion that rainfall occurred at all seasons, in contrast to its presumed seasonal nature under red bed conditions.

A varied fish fauna is known from the coal deposits. Crossopterygians and dipnoans were present. But in contrast to the Devonian, actinopterygians, mostly rather small fishes of the palaeoniscoid group, are, in many deposits, overwhelmingly abundant. We cannot be sure, but it is likely that many if not all of these forms had already abandoned functional lungs and were, instead, possessed of air-bladders with little or no air-breathing potentiality. Actinopterygian abundance suggests year-round rainfall, the swamp waters thus remaining rich enough in oxygen so that no premium was placed on air-breathing.

A large fauna of tetrapods was present in the Carboniferous (the great majority of known forms coming from the latter part of the period). Our view of Carboniferous faunas is, of necessity, a biased one, since most of our knowledge is of the swamp dwellers of Europe and eastern and central North America, and we know little of forms dwelling at this time under different climatic conditions. One would, *a priori*, have expected that once vertebrates developed the ability to go ashore, progress in terrestrial life would have been rapid. This, however, was not true of the faunas found in the coal swamps. In these waters there appears to have been present an abundant supply of animal food for amphibians—palaeoniscoid 'minnows' and presumably, various small invertebrates. Why leave 'home'? In addition, the locomotor apparatus indicates that the climate was such that the seasonal 'urge' towards walking ashore because of drought conditions was absent here. In the absence of the threat of drought, limbs have little selective value for water dwellers. Of the labyrinthodonts (the group including all the largest and many more modestly proportioned amphibians of the times) a few Carboniferous forms had limbs which were stout if short; most, however, had quite small limbs which could not have been of much use on land and were probably used mainly for scuttling about in shallow water.[28] The remainder of the Carboniferous amphibians, mainly of small size, are generally included in the Lepospondyli. Here limbs were even less developed. In one group, the Microsauria, the body structure was usually rather like that of modern salamanders, but the limbs were small and weak, and no better than in most modern urodeles. In a second of these lepospondyl groups, the Nectridia, some genera developed enormous skulls which their tiny legs could not have lifted off the ground if out of water. In other nectridians, and in a third group of lepospondyls, the Aistopoda, limbs were further reduced or entirely absent, and progress of the long and slender body through the water was by a snakelike undulation. Thus, under typical Carboniferous climatic conditions, amphibian evolution did not 'advance'. In the happy humid paradise of the coal swamps, we find instead, degeneration as regards limbs, and a reversal of the trend toward potential continental life.

The coal swamps were, however, a fool's paradise in the long run. By the end of the Carboniferous, coal formation had, as far as we know, ceased over most of the world, and although similar conditions prevailed at various later times, the coal swamp amphibians were for the most part doomed. A fraction of the labyrinthodonts survived into the Permian and Triassic, but of the Carboniferous lepospondyl groups, only a very few forms survived into the early Permian, and there is at present absolutely no later trace of these forms (although some must have survived to give rise to the modern newts, salamanders and caecilians). Climatic change may be correlated with this major extinction.

V. Vertebrates and Seasonal Drought in the Late Palaeozoic and Triassic

Major deposition of red beds did not cease with the Devonian. Red beds as well as coal deposits were formed in the Carboniferous (although little is known of vertebrates from them). There are great areas of red beds of Permian age in Europe and North America, and in the late Triassic, fossiliferous red beds are widespread—in both western and eastern North America, in western and central Europe, in China and in South Africa. For most of these deposits there is considerable evidence from sediments and floras of seasonal aridity, and there are varied positive pieces of evidence to be gained from the vertebrate record itself.

Somewhat comparable to the Devonian story is that of fresh-water fish faunas in Permian and Triassic red beds. We know that by this time palaeoniscoids had become highly varied and, in certain deposits, extremely abundant, but in Permian red beds, such as those of Texas, they are quite rare. (It must, however, be pointed out that this relative rarity may be in part due to their usual small size and fragile structure, so that their remains are easily overlooked.) On the contrary, dipnoan and crossopterygian remains are common. In the lower part (Wichita group) of the Texas fossiliferous Permian, the common fishes (apart from the 'pleuracanth' fresh-water sharks) are the lungfish *Sagenodus* and the crossopterygian *Ectosteorhachis* ('*Megalichthys*'). Higher in the beds, *Sagenodus* and crossopterygians are absent, but a second lungfish, *Gnathorhiza*, is present in addition to the sharks. The lower Permian marks the end of typical crossopterygians (the coelacanths, increasingly adapted to a marine life, survived). Their extinction may be associated with the increasing rarity of red beds in later periods; except under drought conditions, the crossopterygians could not successfully compete with their ray-finned contemporaries.

The last major development in the geological record of 'tropical savanna' climates marked by worldwide red beds occurred in the late Triassic. There are numerous Triassic ray-finned fishes, but in general they are not abundant in typical red beds. An exception is the Newark series, of the eastern United States, where shoals of actinopterygians have been found at Durham (Conn.), and Sunderland (Mass.), and other localities; this correlated well with the fact that evidences of aridity in the Newark series are much less than in the case of red beds of the western part of the United States and of other continental areas. In these other districts, fish life is in general rarely found under typical red bed conditions; the only common finds being teeth of the dipnoan *Ceratodus*, predecessor of the living Australian lungfish, and well adapted to cope with seasonal drought.

As noted above, typical crossopterygians had become extinct before the close of the Permian, and after the Triassic finds of fossil lungfish are quite rare. The Triassic red beds just discussed are the last series of widespread beds of this sort, and opportunities for success of lung-bearing fishes in later geological periods were greatly reduced.

The modern lungfishes *Protopterus* and *Lepidosiren* have developed, in addition to the lung-breathing, a second adaptation for survival in the drought season. *Lepidosiren* digs a vertical cylindrical excavation in the bottom of the drying pool, curls his elongate and slender body into it, and thus buried in the muddy bottom, 'aestivates' until the coming of the rainy season. *Protopterus* has similar habits. *Epiceratodus* has no such adaptation, nor is it probable that the oldest, Devonian, dipnoans, with a relatively short and stout body, had this habit. To our surprise, Olson and the writer [29] found, a few years ago, positive evidence that this anti-drought adaptation was already developed in early Permian days. In the Clear Fork beds of Texas we found at several localities groups of vertical cylinders of clay with rounded bottoms—the cylinders being fortunately formed of a clay somewhat harder than that surrounding them, so that they could be clearly demarcated. A large fraction of such cylinders were 'empty'—that is, contained no bone. Others contained fish remains, and in a fair fraction were found teeth, plates and skeletons of the lungfish *Gnathorhiza*—a genus already suspected, on grounds of dentition, to be related to *Protopterus* and *Lepidosiren*.

The story seems clear and furnishes further testimony of seasonal drought. The deposits containing these cylinders were areas in which Permian lungfish dug burrows for aestivating. With the return of the waters, the burrows were filled with mud. In most cases, the lungfish emerged, and the 'petrified hole' contains no fish. A fraction of the aestivating fishes, however, failed to survive, and their remains had permanent burial in the pits that they had dug.

As noted earlier, the ancient lepospondyl groups of the coal swamps vanish from the record once the special conditions under which they had flourished disappeared. A fair number of labyrinthodont amphibians, however, survived into the Permian and Triassic. Certain of these, such as the dissorophids, had well-developed limbs and were, it is believed, quite competent to live much of their lives on land, with little need for bodies of water except for reproductive purposes. Other labyrinthodonts of the Permian and Triassic had small limbs, quite incompetent to support the animal outside the water. These would seem unlikely animals to be found in red bed climates, but it must not be forgotten that the tropical savanna type of climate is one in which rainfall is abundant for much of the year, and life would be good for water-dwelling labyrinthodonts if they could 'weather over' the drought season (usually comparatively short in described modern regions of this sort). As long as a modest percentage of the swamps and pools remained at such a time, all would be well. It would only be in times of exceptionally severe drought that a major catastrophe would take place. In some instances, the occurrence of a large number of fossil amphibians in a restricted area suggests an event of this sort.

One very clear case of catastrophic drought was discovered some years ago by a Museum of Comparative Zoology expedition in New Mexico. [25] Running completely through a small hill was a layer solidly packed with the remains of the metoposaurid stereospondylous labyrinthodont usually termed *Buettneria* (properly *Eupelor*). This was an animal of large size, with an enormous flattened head, a broad flat body and tiny legs which by no stretch of the imagination could be thought to have supported head and body on land. A slab removed intact and now exhibited in the museum contains in a few square metres more than a dozen skulls and numerous postcranial bones of this animal, all tightly massed together. Remains of several dozens of other individuals were excavated during the preparation of the block. A similar block has since been collected from the site for the United States National Museum. It is certain that the deposit contained many hundreds, and probably some thousands, of individuals of this amphibian.

The story seems reasonably clear. These remains represent the population of a large series of lagoons and swamps. Presumably the extent of such a series of habitable places would shrink considerably during a normal dry season. In this instance, however, it would seem that drought was exceptionally severe or prolonged; the water area in which metoposaurs could live became more and more restricted as pool after pool shrank and dried. Finally,.the entire population was concentrated into a single remaining pool, where this churning mass of amphibians came to its end.

It was noted earlier that drought conditions were responsible for the initiation in all probability of major features—lungs and limbs—without which the later evolution of tetrapods would have been impossible. It is highly probable that Palaeozoic seasonal droughts were responsible for a further major step in the rise of land animals, the evolution of the amniote egg, without which the land life above the amphibian level would have been impossible.

Although some modern amphibians, such as the toads, spend most of their lives far from the water, all the more familiar frogs, toads and newts of Northern Temperate regions are still bound to the water because of the nature of their developmental processes. Each spring the adults return to ponds and streams to mate and lay their eggs. In these ponds the young spend a considerable period as aquatic larvae before undergoing metamorphosis into adult form.

Proper land life was not achieved until the first reptiles developed the amniote type of egg, which can be laid on land and allows the young to emerge as miniature replicas of the adult, with the elimination of the aquatic larval stage. The picture of reptilian origins as often given (by the writer as well as many others) has been one in which it is assumed that the ancestors were advanced amphibians already competent to live on land and living there most of the time, but chained to the water by reproductive necessities. As the final event in progress toward proper terrestrial existence, it was thought, came the evolution of the amniote egg; the bonds were broken and the rapid evolution of true land animals—reptiles, birds and mammals—took place.

It now seems more probable that the actual sequence of events was the reverse of that once pictured; that it was the egg, not the adult, which first came ashore; and that seasonal drought may have been instrumental in the evolution of this developmental process, of such great importance for the later history of vertebrates.[27]

Palaeontological evidence appears to contradict the assumption that the ancestors of the reptiles were already land dwellers before the amniote egg made its appearance. Many of the oldest and most primitive fossil reptiles appear to have been amphibious, if not mainly aquatic, in habit, and even some of the pelycosaurs, already pointing the way toward mammals, were water-dwelling fish-eaters like their amphibian ancestors before them.

Why should these forms have developed an egg which is laid ashore if as adults they were in great measure water dwellers? A clue to the answer lies in the study of the reproductive habits of tropical amphibians today. Among them, the 'normal' procedure of laying eggs in the water is the exception, not the rule. The eggs may be laid near, but not in, the stream; in burrows, in cavities in tree trunks; they may be carried about by one parent or the other —laid in any place, it would seem, but in the water. The eggs, as in amniotes, frequently have a considerable yolk, partially or completely eliminating the necessity of feeding in a tadpole stage, and there are in some cases membranes developed about the embryos for protective or breathing purposes, in a fashion somewhat comparable to amniote structures.

Why this avoidance of the 'natural' mode of amphibian development? Two reasons appear to be operative. In modern anurans, these curious reproductive devices appear to be largely directed toward saving the eggs from being eaten; when laid in a tropical lagoon or stream, this 'amphibian caviar' is liable to be devoured by a variety of enemies ranging from insects to fellow vertebrates. In the late Palaeozoic, presumably such enemies were comparatively few; however, a factor which is present today but of lesser note may then have been of great importance. The larval, 'tadpole', stage is usually one of considerable duration. Under the relatively even distribution of rainfall throughout the year which is characteristic of many regions today, there is a reasonable expectancy that a pond in which eggs are laid will continue to hold water for the duration of the larval period. Not so under the savanna type of climate found in parts of the tropics today and prevalent in the widespread red bed areas of the late Palaeozoic. The drying of ponds and the consequent desiccation and death of the larvae would be a constant danger, and any adaptation which would eliminate the necessity of an aquatic larval stage would have a high selective value. Like the development of lungs and limbs, the evolution of the amniote egg was of the highest importance for the future of the vertebrates. But as in the case of lungs and limbs, the amniote egg was not a product of 'design', looking towards the future; it was a development of immediate value in the life of an aquatic vertebrate living under conditions of seasonal drought. Conversely, the development of this structure in late Palaeozoic days offers further evidence that such drought conditions were then widespread.

VI. Climate and Dinosaur Extinction

One of the most striking events in vertebrate history was the sudden extinction of the dinosaurs at the close of the Mesozoic era. In most Upper Cretaceous deposits the dinosaurs, whose career had begun in the late Triassic, are found to be in a most flourishing condition. To be sure, the distribution of the great amphibious sauropods was then somewhat restricted, and a few types characteristic of earlier phases are absent; but the Upper Cretaceous dinosaurs were numerous and varied, with carnivores large and small and with a host of duckbilled hadrosaurs and horned ceratopsians the most prominent and characteristic elements. There is some reduction in the variety of forms present in the Lance formation, the final phase of the Cretaceous in North America, but dinosaurs were still abundant and dominant. Then, in a moment—geologically speaking—the dinosaurs disappear and we enter the Age of Mammals.

The causes of dinosaur extinction have been discussed by numerous authors (most recently by Lapparent and Lavocat[16]), but no completely satisfactory answer has as yet been found, and very likely never will be found. Some of the numerous suggestions that have been made might reasonably account for a reduction of numbers or variety among dinosaurs, but hardly for rapid, total extinction. It will be noted that although many forms of life (including crocodilians and certain other reptiles) continued calmly on into the Tertiary, other important animal groups—pterosaurs, mosasaurs, ammonites, belemnites—were, like dinosaurs, wiped out at approximately this same time.

Not improbably the relations of dinosaurs to other living things of the period formed part of the picture of extinction, although the suggestion sometimes made that dinosaurs became extinct because mammals ate all their eggs is hardly to be considered seriously and (switching to the other extreme of the panorama of life) it is difficult to imagine an epidemic—whether of protozoan, bacterial or viral origin—which would selectively wipe out every dinosaur, large and small, and do no harm to most other reptiles, such as the crocodilians, closely related to the dinosaurs. To be sure, carnivorous dinosaurs would almost of necessity disappear if their herbivorous cousins were eliminated. But there is no satisfactory explanation from the biological angle for the extinction of the numerous herbivores. Among mammals there are various instances where extinction of herbivores occurred because of competition from other, more efficient, plant-eaters; but the herbivorous dinosaurs had no competitors. As regards the plant world, floral elements of Tertiary aspect were replacing typical Mesozoic forms in the Upper Cretaceous. However, this change in vegetation did not have any immediately disastrous effect on dinosaur life, for the known array of herbivorous dinosaurs is more varied in the late Cretaceous than ever before, and the highly developed dental batteries of the duck-billed dinosaurs show the ability of certain, at least, of the dinosaur groups to adapt themselves to changes in food supplies.

This change of floras is generally attributed to environmental changes which are known to have been under way during the Upper Cretaceous and it is reasonable to believe that the basic reasons for changes in the world's life—animal as well as vegetable—are to be sought in changes in the physical environment.

While there were, no doubt, highland dinosaur faunas, those with which we are familiar appear to have been in general inhabitants of warm lowland areas with a lush vegetation and with numerous streams, swamps and lagoons. Mook[18, 19] has studied in detail the earlier Morrison formation; conditions there, which he compares with those in the lowlands of eastern China, are quite probably typical of the habitats of most Jurassic and Cretaceous dinosaurs. Many of the dinosaurs were definitely water dwellers in part; the amphibious nature of the giant sauropods is accepted by all, and in the case of the hadrosaurs, most common of Upper Cretaceous forms, the webbed feet found in mummified specimens give ample proof that they too frequented the lagoons.

In America, a common 'popular' answer to the question of extinction is to say that 'the Rocky Mountains killed the dinosaurs'. It was during this period that there began the Laramide Revolution, in the course of which there occurred major elevations of land areas and the building of the Rocky Mountains and other mountain chains. With the rising of continental areas, it seems certain that there was a great diminution of low-level plains areas in which the swamps and lagoons favoured by dinosaurs could develop. Equally certainly there were accompanying changes in climates, although there is no evidence that such changes were sudden or truly revolutionary in nature. Rising land areas would cause changes in ocean currents and, in correlation, changes in the climates of the adjacent lands. The rise of mountain chains undoubtedly caused changes in wind patterns, with resulting climatic changes in adjoining continental areas. It is possible that lowered rainfall in specific areas may have contributed to reduction of favoured swamp-lagoon conditions.

Temperature as well as rainfall may have been concerned. Reptiles, lacking the temperature-regulating mechanisms found in mammals and birds, tend to vary in internal temperature in correlation with the temperature of their environment. Reptiles are, consequently, relatively rare today in temperate zones and absent in the Arctic. It has been suggested that a cooling of the earth's atmosphere at the end of the Mesozoic may have been important in dinosaur extinction. But there is no evidence of any marked diminution of temperatures at this stage of earth history; further, while the activity of a reptile decreases at low temperatures, there is no evidence that low temperatures will kill reptiles, as long as they are safely above freezing levels.

A converse of this theory, that of the heat-death of the dinosaurs, suggested by Cowles,[6] was adopted in the well-known moving picture, 'Fantasia', by Walt Disney. In this film, to the harsh accompaniment of Mussorgsky's 'Night on Bald Mountain', the last of the dinosaurs are seen staggering to their death across a hot and arid plain. This suggestion led to an interesting study by Colbert, Cowles and Bogert[5] on the effect of temperature changes on crocodilians—the closest living relatives of dinosaurs. To Colbert and Bogert the results do not appear to warrant the conclusion that over-heating was important in dinosaur extinction. Internal temperature changes take place more rapidly—and hence most dangerously—in small reptiles, in which the surface–volume ratio is high; in large animals, bodily heating takes place more slowly, and might be successfully countered by changes in posture or by seeking refuge in the shade or in water. It thus seems that if heat had caused any reptilian extinction, it should have been the small animals that died, not the larger ones. But small lizards continued untroubled into the Tertiary; it was the giant reptiles which disappeared. Cowles,[7] however, suggests that heat may have been effective in extinction in another fashion. In mammals, sperm formation does not occur if the gonads are at too high a temperature, and somewhat similar effects are seen in reptiles. Extinction due to reproductive failure may have been present in the picture.

Climatic changes may have been involved, then, in dinosaur extinction. But while such changes might have been contributory to a decline of dinosaurian life, they cannot—any more than suggested physiographic or biotic influences—give any reasonable explanation of the sudden extinction of this great series of reptiles. Conversely and, for present purposes, more to the point, the extinction of the dinosaurs fails to yield any concrete evidence concerning climatic change at the end of the Mesozoic.

VII. Vertebrates and Tertiary Climates

It is the general belief (based in great measure on palaeobotanical evidence) that in the early Tertiary the temperature gradients from poles to equator were much gentler than at present, with equable, relatively warm (but not tropical) conditions extending over much of the continental areas; and that, as the Tertiary progressed, these gradients became increasingly steep, to culminate in Pleistocene ice-age conditions. The story of Tertiary vertebrates is in no way in conflict with these beliefs. Although a certain amount of confirmatory evidence can be obtained from the fossil vertebrate record, it is much less in amount than that obtainable from palaeobotany.

In the case of plants, many of the genera in the early Tertiary floras are among those still existing today, and with restricted habitats; the assumption that early species had climatic preferences similar to those of modern representatives is not too far fetched. Quite different is the case with vertebrates, particularly the mammals which make up the bulk of the known Tertiary faunas. No species existing today are definitely known farther back than the Pleistocene; existing genera are no older than the very late Tertiary; few families can be traced back of the Oligocene; in the Eocene, and especially in the Paleocene, we are dealing in great measure with orders and sub-orders of mammals now entirely extinct. With the known evidence of major evolutionary development and diversification of mammals during the

Tertiary, an assumption that members of a family have always lived under the conditions favoured by their modern descendants is ridiculous; to dispute it, one need go no farther than reminding ourselves that the elephants and rhinoceroses, purely tropical today, had representatives inhabiting the cold tundras of the Pleistocene.

Were the Tertiary vertebrate faunas adequate to give a clear knowledge of all areas of a major continent at any given Tertiary stage, a study of the north–south distribution of mammals would give evidence as to whether or not zonal differences were present. Unhappily, this is not generally the case. In North America almost no Tertiary mammals are known except in the relatively narrow band between about 29°N and 50°N. This is hardly more than a third of the stretch between equator and poles and included today almost entirely in the temperate zone. In Europe, Tertiary fossil deposits are situated in what is today a similar climatic belt, although with both northern and southern boundaries some five degrees farther north. In Asia, the greater part of the known faunas are from a similar temperature zone, although we have a limited knowledge of vertebrates of more southerly regions. In South America, apart from recent discoveries in Colombia, we know almost nothing of the Tertiary except in temperate Argentina. African Tertiary faunas are too limited to give us much evidence; in Australia almost nothing is known of the Tertiary. In sum: nearly all of known Tertiary faunas are from areas which are today in the temperate zones; we have little from the present tropics, practically nothing from the Arctic. Mammals, hence, can tell us very little about the north–south distribution of temperatures in the Tertiary in any one continent.

Some evidence, however, can be gained from a study of intercontinental migrations. W. D. Matthew published in 1915 a now classical paper entitled 'Climate and Evolution'. Actually climate enters but little into his discussion, except for his thesis (strongly disputed by Darlington[8]) that the temperate zones (particularly in Eurasia) were the major areas in which vertebrate evolutionary progress occurred. His major contribution was a thorough discussion of the geographical distribution and migration routes of Tertiary mammals. He demonstrated that nearly all distributions of mammalian groups could be accounted for by assuming that during the entire Cenozoic the pattern of land area was essentially that present today, with the provisos that there was a connection between Siberia and Alaska at various times and that the isthmian connection between the Americas was absent during nearly the whole of the Tertiary. Matthew's conclusions have been strongly confirmed by Simpson (in various papers) and by other workers. It must be emphasized that assumptions, frequently made, that other connections between continents were present at one stage or another of the Tertiary, can be shown to confuse the general situation, rather than clarify it.

As noted earlier, although intercontinental migration barriers, or the lack of them, may be in part questions of topography, climate also enters the picture. It would be interesting to see whether the Tertiary tropics were capable of forming a major barrier to migration between inhabitants of northern and southern temperate regions. In the Pleistocene a surprisingly broad migration of northern forms into South America took place (aided, no doubt, by the presence over much of the route of high and relatively cool hill country). Of the Tertiary, little can be said in this respect, South America and Australia were cut off from the north by water barriers, and the African Tertiary record is too fragmentary to tell us much.*

One migration route, however, does furnish evidence of interest regarding Tertiary climates, that between New and Old Worlds via Siberia and Alaska. Comparative study of Eurasian and American faunas indicates that dry land existed here for much of the Tertiary.[31] Today the mean annual temperature at Behring Strait is about 20°F, with bitterly cold winters and cool summers. Were a land connection present there today, only the hardiest of northern animals could use it as a migration route. What of the past?

In the Lower Eocene the faunas of North America and Europe were remarkably similar, indicating a free exchange of faunas and the absence of any marked temperature barrier. Later in the Eocene, the two faunas diverge, but this divergence is generally and reasonably attributed to a breakdown for the time in the land connection rather than to temperature difficulties.

As the Tertiary progresses, however, there are increasing indications that climatic controls were entering the picture and that temperature gradients were becoming steeper. For example, the carnivore families Mustelidae (weasels and the like) and Viverridae (the civets and their relatives) have run parallel courses in many ways. Both include a wide diversity of forms of modest size, mainly forest dwellers. Both families appear in the Oligocene and have flourished ever since. But the mustelids are abundant in both Eurasia and North America, and there is every indication that there has been free interchange of mustelid forms between the two continents; on the other hand, the viverrids are exclusively Old World carnivores, and no member of the family was ever present in North America. The reason seems clearly to be found in the climatic preferences of the two groups. The mustelids are basically temperate zone forms, with various far northern representatives and few tropical ones; the viverrids, on the other hand, are almost purely tropical. The distribution pattern definitely suggests that already by mid-Tertiary times the Behring Strait pathway was already too cold for the passage of warm-weather lovers.

The assumption that increasingly sharp temperature gradients were present in the late Tertiary is strongly supported by the history of the advanced even-toed ungulates, the Pecora. Neglecting certain border-line and extinct forms these include four families: The Cervidae (deer), Giraffidae (giraffe and okapi), Bovidae (cattle, sheep, goats, antelopes) and Antilocapridae (American 'antelope'). All four families came into existence in the Miocene.

---

* It is of interest that the ungulate fauna of Africa today is of a type found in the Pliocene in at least the southern part of what are today temperate zones in Eurasia. But there is no guarantee that this Pliocene fauna was not also widespread in the Old World tropics at the time.

Cervids and giraffids are both browsers, but while the deer family is abundantly represented in both hemispheres, the giraffids (including various extinct genera as well as the two living forms) are confined to the Eastern Hemisphere. The contrast here exactly parallels that between mustelids and viverrids. The deer family is centred in the temperate zone, with few representatives in warm climates; the giraffids are found today only in the tropics, and their fossil representatives are known no farther north than India and the Aegean region.

The two further families—bovids and antilocaprids—are essentially grazers and for the most part plain dwellers. The bovids sprang into prominence in the Pliocene of the Old World and have remained abundant ever since in Eurasia and Africa. Of the antilocaprids, there survives only a single species, but in the Pliocene they proliferated on the western American plains in a fashion rather similar to the bovids on the other side of the world. Here, thus, are two highly developed groups of ungulates, related to one another but developing in parallel fashion in two distinct areas. No antilocaprid ever reached Eurasia. There is but one isolated record of any bovid having reached North America in the Pliocene, and even in the Pleistocene, apart from the circumpolar musk-oxen and a few 'strays', such as the saiga antelope, in Alaska, the only forms to make the crossing were the mountain sheep, mountain 'goat' and bison.

Why this nearly total lack of interchange? Obviously the presence of some barrier in the Siberian–Alaskan passage. One suggestion might be that the barrier was a physiographic one—the absence in the connecting area of plains or steppe areas suitable for the sustenance of most members of these groups. But this is contradicted by the very successful invasion of America by one typical plain-dwelling bovid type—the bison.

Temperature here again seems to be the answer. As regards the antilocaprid side of the picture we can say little. But as regards the bovids, the situation is clear. Most bovids are dwellers in warm climates. Only a relatively small percentage of the bovid species live in cool mountain climates, in temperate steppes and plains or under Arctic conditions. It is from such forms alone that the few bovid invaders of North America have been derived. The Behring Strait area offered a strong temperature block to late Tertiary migration of warmth-loving animals.

Were it not that their Tertiary fossil record is generally of a fragmentary nature, more reliance for climatic evidence might be placed on data gained from fossil reptiles and amphibians, than on mammals, since these forms, lacking the built-in temperature regulatory devices of birds and mammals, are more strictly controlled in distribution by external temperatures. The relative abundance of lizard remains in the earlier Tertiary rather far north in North America and Europe is certainly suggestive of a more northerly spread of mild climates than was the case later. The distribution of fossil crocodilians may well be significant. This is an ancient and conservative group, whose modern representatives are more exclusively tropical and subtropical in distribution than other lower tetrapods; even the alligator, most climatically venturesome of the group, does not go north of regions with a mean annual temperature of about 60°F in the southern United States and China. But in the early Tertiary, crocodilian remains are plentiful much farther north, and are found in Canada where currently mean temperatures are as much as 20° lower.

VIII. Mammals and Pleistocene Climates

It is only in the Pleistocene that evidence for climates derived from vertebrates becomes of major importance. It is the Mammalia which play the primary rôle. In addition to various forms now extinct, a very large proportion of living species of mammals were present in at least the later stages of the Pleistocene. Particularly in Europe numerous faunal assemblages characteristic of various areas and various Pleistocene stages have been collected and studied; numerous listings of such faunas may be found in such works as those of Osborn,[21, 22] Haug,[13] Charlesworth[3] and Zeuner,[37] as well as in monographs dealing with specific sites. Particularly useful in identification of climatic conditions are the rodents, which are present in considerable variety, particularly in cave deposits. There are generally accurate data as to the present climatic preferences and limitations for living mammalian species. Although it is reasonable to assume in the case of a modern species or a close relative that it lived under the same conditions in the Pleistocene as at present, a conclusion as to climate is suspect if one species alone were considered, for it is not impossible that Pleistocene vicissitudes might have had a strong selective influence on the climatic adaptations of one species or another. Strength, however, is given by considering a fauna as a whole. For example, in a cave near Schaffhausen on the German–Swiss border are found remains including *Arctomys marmota* (the marmot), *Myodes torquatus* (the snow lemming), *Alopex lagopus* (Arctic fox), *Gulo borealis* (wolverine), *Rangifer tarandus* (reindeer) and *Ovibos moschatus* (musk-ox). The European marmot is today restricted to the Alpine region, the other forms listed live at present in the cold north. Quite surely the fauna is indicative of a cold climate. No single animal on the list definitely proves the case. For example, it might be that in the Pleistocene the European marmot lived, as does its close relative, the American 'woodchuck', in milder temperate lowlands. Even for such a form as the musk-ox, one might argue that this member of an essentially warm-climate family (the Bovidae) had not yet in the Pleistocene shifted to its present northern life zone. No single form proves the case, but the conclusions drawn from the fauna as a whole are positive.

In similar fashion, a steppe type of climate in European areas is strongly suggested by the presence of such forms as the bobac (*Arctomys bobak*), the jerboa (*Allactaga jaculus*) and the saiga antelope (*Saiga tartarica*), now inhabiting the steppes of central Asia. Again, much warmer climates than those now found in western Europe are indicated by the presence in various sites of hippopotami, hyaenas and other forms with a range typically much farther south.

o

In various instances the situation is complicated by the presence of extinct forms. Frequently, however, we can arrive at definite conclusions regarding their climatic preferences by their faunal association with forms whose temperature range is known. If, for example, a given extinct animal is repeatedly present in assemblages including various surviving forms of boreal habits, we can confidently use the presence of this extinct mammal, even if found alone, as indicative of cold conditions. Thus even if we did not know of the hairy coat of the woolly mammoth (*Mammuthus primigenius*), we could confidently predict that any deposit in which it is found was formed under chilly conditions, because of the frequent presence of this species in faunal assemblages, such as that at Schaffhausen, containing many species living today in cold climates. In contrast, *M. meridionalis*, the southern mammoth, is in itself suggestive of milder climates because of its frequent association with species characteristically living at present in warm areas.

In such fashion there has been built up in Europe a mass of evidence from mammals which strengthens and further substantiates the evidence of Pleistocene climates obtainable from sediments and plants. The situation is not as far advanced in other areas. However, in North America such studies as Hibbert's work on rodent microfaunas and that on the Pleistocene succession in Nebraska by Schultz and his geological colleagues are advancing our knowledge greatly, and Chinese work in recent decades has contributed greatly to establishing the Pleistocene climatic story in eastern Asia.

If we compare the Recent mammalian fauna with that of the Pleistocene, we find that what has occurred in the passage from this older epoch to modern times is not so much evolutionary progress as impoverishment. All modern species appear to have been present in the later part of the Pleistocene and many at least appear to have come down to us essentially unchanged from earlier stages of the Ice Age. The faunal contrast between Pleistocene and Recent lies in the fact that the world over there were formerly present, in addition to those destined to survive, numerous forms now entirely extinct. In the Northern Hemisphere prominent Pleistocene forms which have since vanished include a variety of proboscidians (mastodons and mammoths of several sorts), sabre-toothed 'tigers', bears distinct from those of today, giant cervids, giant beaver and so on. In North America there were in addition ground sloths, glyptodonts and giant armadillos, all now extinct, and further, horses and camels, absent now in that continent although surviving elsewhere. In South America there has been a very considerable depopulation since the Pleistocene, with the disappearance of whole orders of native ungulates as well as numerous edentates; the African Pleistocene faunas included a large series of 'relict' types once present in Eurasia and now completely vanished; Australian caves have yielded a number of extinct marsupials, mainly of large size, and even extinct 'giant' monotremes. Worldwide, the present fauna is a depleted one. Presumably in some way significant is the fact that most of the extinct forms were of large size (Hooijer, particularly, has called attention to the fact that in many instances the immediate ancestors of living forms grew to larger sizes during the Pleistocene).

Can Pleistocene climatic conditions have been concerned with these extinctions? It is hard to believe that glaciation can have been responsible for faunal reductions in southern continents, where glacial phenomena were of little importance, and in the case of South America, invasion by North American rivals and predators is quite surely a major factor in the elimination of native elements. As regards the northern continents, however, it has been frequently argued, with seeming justice, that the vicissitudes of the Pleistocene were primarily responsible for faunal reduction.

Examination of the evidence indicates that this thesis cannot be maintained. In Europe a limited number of extinctions appear to have occurred well back in the Pleistocene, such forms including mastodons and sabretooths, but a number of animals now extinct continued on to sub-Recent times—late enough to be hunted or pictured by our Upper Palaeolithic ancestors not too many thousands of years ago. Presumably as ice-ages waxed and waned, there was considerable drift, north and south, from highlands to lowlands and back again, but much of the fauna continued untroubled throughout the Pleistocene.

The story was similar in North America. Oliver P. Hay, long a major American authority on the Pleistocene, had early in his career studied a fauna of early Pleistocene age, supposedly Aftonian, from the glaciated region of Iowa. This fauna included such forms as horses and camels which appeared to him not to be present in any deposits which could be correlated with later glacial or interglacial stages. He therefore concluded that of the Pleistocene forms now extinct, most disappeared at an early date, due to climatic tribulations, and that only a small percentage of such animals had continued into the later part of the Ice Age.

Scepticism as to the reality of this thesis arose in me through the discovery of the skull of a native camel—supposedly extinct, according to Hay, for half-a-million years—in such a fresh condition that shreds of dried meat still adhered to it. I therefore set about summarizing such evidence as was then available as to the chronology of American Pleistocene fossil finds. Obviously Hay's thesis of early major extinction was incorrect. I expected to find, instead, a story of gradual extinction. To my surprise, I came [23] to a conclusion the exact opposite of that of Hay—namely, that as far as the evidence went, it indicated that almost the entire Pleistocene fauna of North America had continued on, untroubled by climatic changes, throughout the Pleistocene, and only when the Ice Age drew to a close (if it has drawn to a close) did any major extinction occur. In the quarter century that has passed since this study, much new evidence has come to light, but my conclusions, I believe, still stand. The fauna found in the famous La Brea tar pits of California (summarized by Stock [32]) was thought by Hay to be no later than about the first interglacial stage; but actually it appears to be representative of the mammalian population inhabiting the western United States until not many thousands of years ago. Hay's erroneous beliefs were due to his mistaking ecological differences for chronological ones. His Iowa 'Aftonian' fauna was one from the eastern margin of the great plains; most later glacial and interglacial fossil finds are from areas in the forested regions of the north-east, where such animals as camels and horses would be rare at any time.

Climate thus appears to have had little influence on the striking impoverishment of the mammalian fauna since the Pleistocene. If so, to what is it due? The appearance and spread of *Homo sapiens* is the only new element in the ecological picture. Man certainly did not directly destroy all these great extinct forms, but it is possible that his entrance on the scene was sufficient to topple some delicate ecological 'house of cards'. I have suggested that his interference with breeding habits may have had some influence; and Sauer[30] (*cf.* Eiseley reference 10) has pointed out the destructive effect which could have been caused by the habit of various primitive peoples of setting prairie or forest fires as a hunting aid; possibly various other human activities may have been involved.

IX. Conclusions

Above have been outlined certain of the lines of evidence which fossil vertebrates can supply as to the nature of ancient climates. In certain instances, particularly in relatively recent geological times, the known climatic preferences of living vertebrates allow us to draw reasonable interpretations of past climatic conditions. Assemblages of mammals identical with or closely related to existing forms offer strong proof as to temperatures under which Pleistocene deposits were accumulated. The north–south distribution of various mammal types and of reptiles in Tertiary beds yields clues as to Cenozoic climates, and the obvious restriction of east–west migration via the Behring Strait route during the late Tertiary strongly suggests that temperature gradients were becoming increasingly steep at this time.

Back of the Cenozoic, attempts to base climatic arguments on the preferences of modern types become increasingly dangerous, for many of the groups encountered are now extinct, and there is little guarantee that the Mesozoic or Palaeozoic representatives of surviving groups lived under the conditions in which their descendants thrive. However, fairly direct evidence may be derived in many instances from the anatomy of the fossil or the circumstances of the find. For example, the feeble limbs of Pennsylvanian labyrinthodonts, the webbed feet of mummies of duck-billed dinosaurs and the general structure of sauropod dinosaurs indicate that these varied groups all lived amphibious lives in lagoons and swamps under conditions of abundant rainfall. Again, the discovery of Permian lungfish burrows and the mass death of Triassic labyrinthodonts are indicative of seasonal aridity.

Conclusions basically more important may be derived from less direct evidence—from a consideration of the broad picture of vertebrate evolution and the attempt to interpret the environmental factors involved. I have, as an example, attempted to demonstrate above that much of the story of the emergence of vertebrates on to land—evolving from bony fishes through the amphibian to the reptilian stage—is best and most simply explained on the assumption that seasonal aridity was a prominent feature of upper Palaeozoic climates. It is not improbable that increased knowledge of the vertebrate story will correlate other important evolutionary happenings with climatic conditions and climatic changes. However, there are striking instances in which one would expect a correlation between climates and vertebrate historical events—and fails to find it. It is generally assumed that climatic change was influential in reptilian extinction at the end of the Mesozoic, but the connection is tenuous; and the seeming reasonable assumption that the major extinction of Pleistocene mammals was due to climatic fluctuations appears to have little or no basis in fact.

References

1. Bogert, C. M. *Evolution*, **3**, 195 (1949)
2. Brink, A. S. *Palaeont. Africana*, **4**, 77 (1957)
3. Charlesworth, J. K. *The Quaternary Era, with special reference to its Glaciation*, 2 vols. 1957. London: Arnold
4. Colbert, E. H., 'The Record of Climatic Changes as Revealed by Vertebrate Paleoecology' in H. Shapley, ed. *Climatic Change, Evidence, Causes and Effects*. 1953. Cambridge, Mass.: Harvard University Press
5. Colbert, E. H., Cowles, R. B. and Bogert, C. M. *Bull. Amer. Mus. nat. Hist.*, **86**, 331 (1946)
6. Cowles, R. B. *Science*, **90**, 465 (1939)
7. Cowles, R. B. *Amer. Nat.*, **79**, 160 (1945)
8. Darlington, P. J. *Zoogeography: The Geographical Distribution of Animals*. 1957. New York: Wiley
9. Denison, R. H. *J. Paleont.*, **15**, 553 (1941)
10. Eiseley, L. C. *Amer. Anthrop.*, **48**, 54 (1946)
11. Goodrich, E. S. *Palaeobiologica*, **1**, 87 (1928)
12. Goodrich, E. S. *Studies on the Structure and Development of Vertebrates*. 1930. London: Macmillan
13. Haug, E. *Traité de Géologie*, 2 vols. 1911. Paris: Colin
14. Hills, E. S., 'A Brief Review of Australian Vertebrate Fossils' in T. S. Westoll, ed. *Studies on Fossil Vertebrates*. 1958. London: University of London, The Athlone Press
15. Jarvik, E. *Sci. Mon. N.Y.*, **80**, 141 (1955)
16. Lapparent, A. F. and Lavocat, R., 'Dinosauriens' in J. Piveteau, ed. *Traité de Paléontologie, V*. 1955. Paris: Masson
17. Matthew, W. D. *Ann. N.Y. Acad. Sci.*, **24**, 171 (1915)
18. Mook, C. C. *Ann. N.Y. Acad. Sci.*, **27**, 39 (1916)
19. Mook, C. C. *J. Geol.*, **26**, 459 (1918)
20. Ørvig, T. *Ark. Zool.*, **10**, 367 (1957)
21. Osborn, H. F. *The Age of Mammals in Europe, Asia and North America*. 1910. New York: Macmillan
22. Osborn, H. F. *Ann. N.Y. Acad. Sci.*, **26**, 215 (1915)
23. Romer, A. S., 'Pleistocene Vertebrates and their Bearing on the Problem of Human Antiquity in North America', in D. Jenness, ed. *The American Aborigines*. 1933. Toronto: University of Toronto Press

24. Romer, A. S. *Man and the Vertebrates*, 1st edn. 1933. Chicago: University of Chicago Press
25. Romer, A. S. *Sci. Mon. N.Y.*, **49**, 337 (1939)
26. Romer, A. S., 'Relative Growth in Pelycosaurian Reptiles', in R. Broom *Commemorative Volume Spec. Publ. Roy. Soc. S. Africa* (1948)
27. Romer, A. S. *Sci. Mon. N.Y.*, **85**, 57 (1957)
28. Romer, A. S. *Evolution*, **12**, 365 (1958)
29. Romer, A. S. and Olson, E. C. *Breviora, Mus. comp. Zool., no. 30*, 1 (1954)
30. Sauer, C. O. *Geogr. Rev.*, **34**, 529 (1944)
31. Simpson, G. G. *Bull. geol. Soc. Amer.*, **58**, 613 (1947)
32. Stock, C. *Los Angeles County Mus., Sci. Ser., no. 20, Palaeont., no. 11* (1956)
33. Watson, D. M. S. *Geol. Mag.*, **10**, 388 (1913)
34. Watson, D. M. S. *Phil. Trans.*, **214**, 189 (1926)
35. Weigelt, J. *Rezente Wirbeltierleichen und ihre Paläobiologische Bedeutung.* 1927. Leipzig: Weg
36. Woodward, A. S. *British Antarctic ('Terra Nova') Expedition, 1910. Geology*, **1**, 56 (1921)
37. Zeuner, F. E. *The Pleistocene Period. Its Climate, Chronology and Faunal Successions.* 1959. London: Hutchinson

IX

Palaeozoological Evidence of Climate.
(2) Invertebrates

G. Y. Craig

I. Introduction

Fossils have been used as a means of interpreting palaeoclimates ever since Neumayr's pioneer work [24] on the climatic zones of the Jurassic in 1883. Climate, essentially a combination of temperature, pressure, wind and precipitation, is a facet of environment. Its influence is obviously more marked on terrestrial organisms than on marine organisms because of the buffering effect of the water between organism and climate. Unfortunately fossil invertebrates, with which this chapter is mostly concerned, are generally marine and so can tell us little about that part of the environment called climate.

The basis of most geological studies is the theory of Uniformitarianism first formulated by Hutton towards the end of the 18th century—the theory that states that the processes operating at the present day are the same as those which operated in the past. In the present context this statement may be interpreted as signifying that organisms are related to processes operating today in much the same relationship as existed between fossils and processes in the geological past. The use of this comparative method, as it might be termed, is, however, more limited in palaeontology than in other branches of geology because organisms have evolved and are evolving. The mode of life and environment of a living form is not necessarily that of its ancestor; and while it may be relatively accurate to assign the ecology of a living species to its Quaternary counterpart, that accuracy decreases as we penetrate further into the past. The same principles apply to studies of palaeoclimates.

Many invertebrate palaeoclimatic studies are concerned with the geographical distribution of fossils. In this way former latitudinal climatic zones may be inferred. These zones, on occasion, have been found to cut across present latitudes and suggest that continental drift or polar wandering—or both—has occurred and has been responsible in part for climatic changes.

In this chapter the influence of climate on living invertebrates is discussed in an attempt to interpret climate from potentially preservable animal morphology and distribution, and examples are described of palaeoclimatic interpretations based on fossil evidence. Many of these palaeoclimatic studies are limited to interpretations of palaeotemperature zones; occasional studies point to the future use of fossils as indicators of wind directions and precipitation.

The writer is indebted to Drs. D. L. Eicher and T. R. Walker of the Department of Geology, University of Colorado, for their helpful criticisms of the manuscript.

II. The Effect of Climate on the Living Animal

Animal form is an intermittent or continuous record of the action of the external environment on the gene-complex. Thus form may be a means of providing information about the environment or environments encountered by an animal during its existence.

Many marine zoological studies are concerned with the effect of the environment on the animal or community and provide a rich source of material for palaeoecologists. A typical example of shell growth and the external factors influencing it is provided by Mason.[22] Mason considers the development of the pelecypod *Pecten maximus* from temperate inshore waters of the English coast. The shells bear growth rings visibly distinguishable by their lighter colour. These growth rings are laid down annually and are composed of growth laminae more closely spaced than elsewhere on the shell. They represent periods of minimal growth and they are accompanied by changes in the colour of the shell material. Shells of *Pecten maximus*, in this writer's collection, show distinct evidence of wear and tear of some of the laminae within these rings suggesting a prolonged period of mantle retraction and chipping of what was then the margin of the shell. Later growth has repaired these breakages. Mason observes that maximum growth of the shell occurs during the summer and practically ceases during the winter. He finds that there is an approximate correlation between shell growth and temperature changes in the sea, although from his graphs the indicated June temperature of 10°C and breadth increment of 3 mm compares oddly with a similar temperature in December when growth was negligible (Fig. 1). It may well be that there is a hidden third factor such as spring plankton development associated with temperature. Mason suggests that the cessation of shell growth may be due to a combination of cold and feeding, sufficient for slow gonad development but not shell growth.

Gutsell[16] considered a similar problem with *Pecten irradians* from the much warmer waters of North Carolina. Like *P. maximus*, *P. irradians* has an annual growth ring distinguished by its lighter colour; but this ring is formed in the autumn and can be correlated with autumnal spawning. Winter growth follows the formation of these rings. Spawning occurs towards the end of the three-month period of maximum water temperature (about 20°C). The coldest temperature (January) varies between 3° and 15°C.

Both *P. maximus* and *P. irradians* are inhabitants of the northern hemisphere; both lay down annual growth rings on their shells: but *P. maximus* living presumably under minimum-optimum temperature conditions adds to its shell in the summer, whereas *P. irradians* living under optimum-maximum temperature conditions secretes its shell during the winter. Growth rings are therefore related to temperature changes rather than to low temperatures.

Corals also show growth rings in the form of a crowding of the tabulae or dissepiments. Ma[19] discusses and illustrates this phenomenon with regard to the hexacoral *Favia speciosa* living at the present day in Japanese waters. He

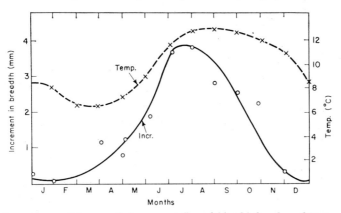

Fig. 1. Average monthly growth increment (breadth) of left valve of *Pecten maximus* in relation to temperature of water. Modified from Mason (reference 22, Fig. 8).

finds that, in the cooler seasons of the year, the vesicular tissue is more closely packed than in the warmer seasons. Two of his text-figures (Figs. 7 and 8, pp. 174 and 175), show that the number of elements in the denser band is much the same as in the less dense band but they are, however, more closely packed. It may well be that the amount of calcium carbonate secretion is similar summer and winter but that the rate of upward growth is greater in the summer. Possibly the differing densities are more directly related to light variations rather than temperature variations. Ma shows that the annual rate of growth (i.e. vertical accretion of the exoskeleton) increases towards the equator where differing growth densities are no longer apparent because of the absence of seasons.

This particular paper of Ma's is not completely convincing because of flaws in the author's technique. Some of the thicknesses appear to be measured obliquely as in Fig. 6, p. 174, and an illustrated coral-section is reversed relative to the marked years. On the basis of differences in the growth rate of *Favia speciosa* from Recent and Holocene coral reefs, Ma considers that the temperature of the sea in Holocene times was greater than now; but of seven other corals which he used for purposes of comparison three would suggest that the reverse was the case. Other factors which may have an effect are possible differences in the development of a species growing on the windward slope, the reef flat, and the leeward slope. The rate of growth is certainly affected by depth, clarity of the water, amount of oxygen, and amount of sediment. Manifestly these conditions vary from the windward to the leeward side of a reef and although there appear to have been no detailed measurements on the variation on coral form (but see Vaughan, reference 41) qualitative descriptions such as those given by Wells,[44] emphasize the great variation in the form of coral colonies on different parts of a reef. In fact for all that is known to the contrary, the morphological variation of one species within one reef might be as great as its morphological variation within its normal range of latitude. These criticisms are necessary since much of Ma's subsequent work on palaeoclimates, discussed later in this chapter, is a development of the ideas and methods propounded in his 1934 paper.

III. The Effect of Climate on the Distribution of Living Animals

The surface waters of the oceans are divisible into temperature zones that correspond roughly with the latitudinal climatic belts of the atmosphere but are by no means always parallel to them, as a map of the surface isotherms of, for instance, the North Atlantic ocean will show.[33] Murray[23] recognized five temperature zones, consisting of a tropical zone bounded by two temperate zones which in turn are flanked by two polar zones. Ekman[12] describes seven shore-and-shallow-water zones, reading from north pole to south pole: Arctic, Boreal, Temperate, Warm-Water, Warm Temperate, Antiboreal and finally Antarctic. Ekman recognizes these zones by means of temperature and faunal differences. Vaughan[41] delimits nine temperature zones of the surface waters, a tropical zone with a temperature range from 25 to 36°C, flanked by two subtropical zones varying from 15 to 33°C, two temperate zones ranging in temperature from 10 to 25°C, two subpolar zones with temperature limits of 5 to 10°C and finally a north and a south polar zone with the temperature varying between 1·9 and 5°C. Vaughan recognizes that on the shore and in shallow water these limits may be exceeded.

Accompanying this geographical zonation is a vertical zonation of temperature expressed by Vaughan (reference 41, p. 445) thus: 'In deep water within the tropics all five of the temperature zones between the tropics and the polar regions of one hemisphere are encountered between the surface and the bottom.'

It is generally agreed that three factors primarily control the distribution of marine organisms—temperature, salinity and the nature of the sea floor (see Jones[17] for discussion). The first two influence the distribution of plankton and nekton, and all three the distribution of benthos. Salinity and the nature of the sea floor are essentially local variants controlled by local conditions as, for example, restricted seas or the discharge of fresh water and sediment at river estuaries. Latitudinal variations in salinity admittedly occur but are slight compared with similar variations in temperature. Thus of these three factors only temperature varies gradually but markedly on a universal scale and as such must be the primary factor influencing the geographical distribution of marine organisms.

Thus we may expect to find duplication in organic conditions occurring in the equivalent temperature zones to the north and south of the equator. Such duplication in organic conditions is known as organic bipolarity and is defined by Ekman (reference 12, p. 250) as the state 'when the higher latitudes in the northern and southern hemispheres resemble one another in positive characteristics and diverge by the same characteristics from the lower latitudes situated between them'. Ekman distinguishes between taxonomic bipolarity and the bipolarity of analogous parallel phenomena. In the former case there is a latitudinal gap in the distribution of related taxonomic units; in the latter, bipolarity is expressed in terms other than that of related species or genera as, for example, in a greater number of individuals or in greater body size.

Among examples of taxonomic bipolarity cited by Ekman may be noted the distribution of the acorn shell *Balanus balanus*, confined to latitudes of 41° or greater in the northern hemisphere but known in the southern hemisphere in New Zealand and Tierra del Fuego; the bipolarity of certain species of Radiolaria; and the occurrence in both the Arctic and Antarctic of the pelagic foraminifer *Globigerina pachyderma*. Bipolarity of analogous phenomena, however, seems to be more common.

Wimpenny[46] points out that calcification appears to increase in warmer waters. Among the more obvious tropical invertebrates with heavily calcified skeletons are *Tridacna, Conus, Triton, Pteroceras* and the reef-building corals. Siliceous diatoms are found to be smaller in the colder waters of their latitudinal range. On the other hand Weymouth and Thompson[45] show that the Pacific cockle grows larger in colder waters. Gunter,[15] in reviewing the evidence of temperature in relation to growth and form, suggests that a general gradient of decreasing size in fossils from pole to equator might indicate something of the climate; but the conflicting state of present opinion indicates that the evidence as yet is unreliable. A more widespread and consistent phenomenon for which Wimpenny[46] gives several examples is that faunas inhabiting warm waters are richer in species than faunas living in cold waters where, however, there is a compensating increase in numbers within species. Thorson[38] shows that prosobranch benthos with planktonic larvae increase in number from cold regions to warm. Prosobranch larvae with a benthonic development tend to have coarse apical shell-whorls whereas those forms with a planktonic development tend to have delicate apical shell-whorls. Thorson suggests that this difference might be of use in distinguishing between the warmer and colder waters of former oceans.

Vertical zonation was first recognized by Forbes[13] in the Aegean Sea where he found eight depth zones, each characterized by its own community of animals. Phleger and Parker[26] recognize six foraminiferal depth facies in the Gulf of Mexico and attribute this zonation primarily to differences in temperature. Ekman[12] refers to the phenomenon as equatorial submergence and considers it to be of common occurrence. Thus littoral Arctic forms which are eurybathyal may be found only in deep water in lower latitudes.

A third kind of zonation, that of a longitudinal distribution (as Ekman terms it) of certain animals, occurs on the west coasts of South America and Africa where the temperature of the sea is lowered and the temperature range narrowed by the upwelling of cold northerly-moving currents. Under these circumstances it has been possible for some eurythermal animals to extend thousands of miles along the coastlines in an approximately North–South trend. Ekman[12] gives as examples of such longitudinal distribution certain crinoids and crabs.

The effects of salinity on the distribution of marine animals are discussed by Pearse and Gunter.[25] Normal marine waters are optimum for most marine forms but as salinity is reduced, as for instance in estuaries and some lagoons, stenohaline animals disappear and there is little replacement by species from fresh waters. This phenomenon is expressed as a reduction in the number of species relative to a reduction in salinity. Size of an animal may also be a function of salinity. For instance the shell of *Mya* is heavier in higher salinities and that of the Gulf Coast oyster is smaller. Pearse and Gunter show also that some invertebrates spend the earlier stages of their lives in areas of low salinities and as they grow they move into areas of higher salinities. Salinity gradients may thus be revealed in terms of increase in the number of species and increase in size (as a function of age) from fresh to salt water. However, estuaries and at the other extreme hypersaline environments can generally be determined more readily from a study of the lithology.

Salinity effects are discussed here not so much for their potential value as indicators of climatic conditions but rather as possible red herrings which may simulate the effects of local temperature changes. A recent study of trace elements in sediments,[9] however, suggests that it may be possible to check the degree of salinity of the water in which fossils lived.

Finally, recent work from the Marine Station at Hull, England, has shown that wind can affect the distribution of animals. Wind-induced currents create a trail of plankton each year in the North Sea. It is difficult to visualize what evidence such a planktonic trail would leave on the sea floor. Possibly as microshells descended from the plankton there would be an increase in their size and numbers in the direction of the wind.

The conclusions to be drawn from the study of the effect of climate on the distribution of living animals can be summarized as follows:

(1) Major zones of related animals or animals with related adaptations occur in the oceans and the distribution of such zones is influenced by the temperature of the water.

(2) Latitudinal zonation is shown by stenothermal organisms and may be duplicated in the northern and southern hemispheres.

(3) Vertical zonation is shown by stenothermal eurybathyal organisms and is most strongly developed in the tropics.

(4) Longitudinal zonation is shown by eurythermal organisms and occurs along the west coasts of major oceans.

(5) Salinity gradients may be expressed locally by diminution in number of species and/or the size of individuals towards fresher water and in the fossil state be mistaken for temperature changes.

(6) Wind may concentrate plankton as a trail.

IV. Palaeoclimatic Interpretation from Invertebrate Fossils

The restricted distribution of geological systems complicates the interpretation of palaeoclimatic zones based on the geographical distribution of fossils. Only part of the widespread life of former seas is preserved and obtainable, and that part is generally to be found in the epicontinental and continental marginal deposits where faunas are notoriously variable. Ancient deep oceanic deposits now part of the land are rare, and boring techniques are not yet sufficiently good to allow long cores to be taken from the sediments accumulating in the deeper parts of the allegedly permanent oceans. The extent and limitations of our present knowledge of palaeobiogeography are well shown by Termier and Termier [36] in their reconstructions of the distribution of the major groups of animals and plants at different times of the geological past. Their book is an exceedingly valuable source of information for anyone interested in the biological aspects of palaeoclimate.

Of the fossils present in sediments, undoubtedly pelagic faunas and shallow-water benthos reflect most accurately the temperature of the upper layers of the former seas. Such faunas, however, are readily susceptible to transport by currents and waves, and eventual deposition far from their normal habitats. Thus interpretations of local palaeoclimates can be unwittingly distorted as a result of such processes. Nevertheless palaeoclimatic zones and changes have been recognized by many workers and in the following discussion a number of their papers are reviewed and their methods and results analysed.

IV.1 World Palaeoclimates of Geological Periods

Undoubtedly one of the most prolific workers in the study of palaeoclimates, based on the evidence of invertebrate fossils, has been Ting Ying Ma. Ma's first essay [19] in the interpretation of Palaeozoic climates is based on a study of the distribution and growth rate of certain species and genera of solitary and compound Devonian tetracorals. He found that in Timan, Russia and Yunnan, China, the growth increment for the same species was greater there than elsewhere: indeed some specimens from these places showed no evidence whatever of seasonality. Ma attempts delicate comparisons of the various Devonian seas as, for instance, that the French seas may have been warmer than the German. His contention that the Devonian seas of New York and Maryland were warmer than those of Germany and that the seas of Iowa, Illinois and Missouri were not much colder, leads the author to the somewhat surprising conclusion from such premises that North America may not have been in contact with Europe during the Devonian period as Wegener believed. Ma attempts a reconstruction of the Devonian equator (Fig. 2) based on the world-wide distribution of these corals. He concludes that the warmest seas, and therefore the equatorial zone, were in the neighbourhood of Timan and Yunnan: but his extrapolation of the equator through South Australia, on the basis of two coral specimens, and its continuation through South America where there are none is, while admittedly stimulating, unwarranted.

Ma subsequently, in a series of papers, discusses the equatorial variations that he considers to have taken place since Cambrian times (e.g. reference 20,

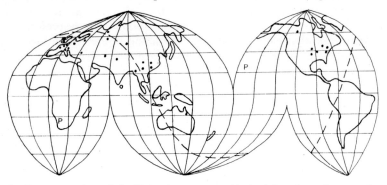

Fig. 2. Reconstruction of the Devonian equator (dashes) based on the growth rate and distribution of Devonian corals (dots). Poles marked P. After Ma.[19]

L. Carboniferous; reference 21, Cretaceous). His work is based mostly on measurements of the annual growth of coral exoskeletons as indicated by growth rings; on the absence of such rings, which may be indicative of continuous tropical growth; and the changes in the geographical distribution of reef-forming corals during geological times. As an example of his more recent work, Ma's 1954 paper[21] may be cited. In this paper, using the above techniques, he interprets the Carboniferous equator as having passed through Western Europe, the Northern Urals, South East Asia, the Japanese Islands, Australia and North America. He recognizes an inner equatorial belt where annual coral growth is greatest or where growth rings are absent, bounded by two exterior zones where annual growth of the corals is less. Similarities in size, shape, structure and growth values between the tabulate coral *Michelinia* and the recent hexacoral *Goniopora*, the tetracoral *Lonsdaleia* and the hexacoral *Favia*, the fasciculate lithostrotions and the hexacoral *Caulastraea* are believed to be the result of similar oceanic environments, and on this basis Ma claims (reference 21, p. 80) that 'the temperature in any belt of the Lower Carboniferous seas was no different from now'. Ma destroys his case by extravagant assumptions unsupportable by the evidence. His basic ideas seem reasonable but as yet we do not know enough about the variations of coral growth and distribution, and the ecological relations between Recent, Mesozoic and Palaeozoic corals to use fossil corals as indicators of palaeoclimate to the extent attempted by Ma.

Teichert's warning [35] is particularly apt in this context. He refers to the assumption that fossil coral reefs are supposedly indicative of tropical regions and observes that there are two groups of corals. Hermatypic corals have symbiotic zooxanthellae and are restricted to warm water above 18·5°C and depths of less than 300 ft: ahermatypic corals, on the other hand, have no zooxanthellae but have a world-wide distribution and are found at all depths down to 20 000 ft. Although the majority of the latter are solitary, some forms are colonial and at times are sufficiently crowded to form coral banks. Teichert draws attention to the occurrence of ahermatypic colonial corals living at the entrance to fjords and along the edge of the continental shelf of the Norwegian coast. The temperature of the water in which these corals grow is generally between 6 and 6·5°C, the depth between 600 and 900 ft. Teichert discusses the problems involved in distinguishing fossil hermatypic and ahermatypic coral banks. Criteria suggested are that ahermatypic corals generally have no associated calcareous algae and that the number of coral species in the community are few. Teichert critically reviews records of some fossil coral reefs, adjudged to indicate warm water environments and concludes that critical reappraisal of fossil coral reefs and their inferred environments is necessary.

The Permian promises to be one of the most fruitful systems for the study of palaeoclimate. It shows great variety of lithology in evaporite deposits, red beds, aeolian sandstones and glacial tillites, in addition to much faunal and floral evidence. At the present time, however, our knowledge of the Permian climate is in a state of flux as a result of the divergent views held by three workers on the subject: Stehli, Bain and Gerth. Stehli[31] determined Permian marine climatic zones by plotting the distribution of fusulinids (Fig. 3) and brachiopods in the Permian outcrops of the world. He finds that certain groups are similarly restricted in distribution in the northern hemisphere, their northernmost boundary occurring between 50 and 60°N. He concludes that this may be the result of temperature differences and that the termination of the faunas indicates the boundary between the subtropical and temperate marine belts. This boundary, as interpreted by Stehli, is parallel to present latitudes. Unfortunately, because of the rarity of Permian strata in the southern hemisphere, he is obliged to confine his deductions to the northern hemisphere. He reasons that if his interpretation is correct then Runcorn[28] is wrong in his conclusion, based on palaeomagnetic data, that the Permian north pole was a considerable distance from its present-day position.

Bain[3] will have none of this. He criticizes Stehli's conclusions and argues that the evidence adduced by Stehli can be interpreted otherwise. Using the same fusulinid groups he finds that their distribution can be contained within an undulating zone with a width of 30–50° of latitude and that this pattern

is displaced northwards relative to the present equator (Fig. 3). He attributes
this displacement to inadequate data in the southern hemisphere, thus having
the effect of shifting the statistical centre northwards, or to the abnormally
low temperature of the southern hemisphere because of glaciation, or both.
To Stehli's invertebrate data he adds information on palaeosols, salt deposits,
desert dunes, glacial striae and Permian ocean-current patterns (how the last
are derived is not explained) and builds up a picture of high and low pressure
zones, precipitation and marine and continental climatic belts, all of which
lead him to the conclusion that the Permian equator passed through Andean
South America, Florida, Hudson's Bay, the Arctic Archipelago, Western
China, Indonesia and Antarctica. The North Pole was thus near Samoa at
$7\frac{1}{2}°$S, 165°W. Bain, naturally, supports polar migration, but his evidence is
less convincing with the incorporation of Stehli's data than without.

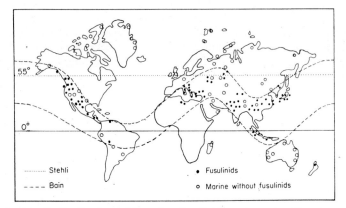

Fig. 3. World distribution of Permian fusulinids and marine Permian outcrops
without fusulinids with the differing interpretations by Stehli [31] and Bain [3] of the zoo-
geographical boundaries. Fusulinid data abridged from Stehli (reference 31, Fig. 4).

Stehli [32] counters Bain's criticisms by showing that Bain had ignored a
fusulinid occurrence in New Zealand and that his argument was possible only
because of the lack of evidence in the Atlantic, Pacific and Indian oceans.
Stehli uses the distribution of Permian reptiles, which he observes are typically
tropical or subtropical forms, as additional plots in his palaeobiogeographical
map. He contends that variations in the width of the tropical–subtropical
zone are due to the absence of controls rather than the displacement of its
margins, as Bain suggests. Stehli reiterates that the present Permian palaeo-
zoogeographic data are most reasonably satisfied in terms of a climatic zone
parallel to the earth's present equator.

    Neither author makes any reference to the earlier paper by Gerth [14] who
takes into account the distribution of faunas, floras, glaciation and coal seams
in his approach to the problem of the climate of the Lower Permian. Gerth
records the occurrence of a fusulinid warm-water assemblage as far north as
Spitzbergen on the 80° latitude but notes that the southern extent of the warm

fauna was only 20°S, in all a zone covering some 100 degrees of latitude. Thus he concludes that the marine warm-water zone of the Lower Permian is displaced to the north of the present day zone. The continental coal seams and plants, however, are distributed in two parallel belts over the continents of the northern and southern hemispheres, in the north the European *Walchia-Callipteris* flora and the Chinese Cathay flora with *Gigantopteris*, intermingling in central Asia, and in the south the *Glossopteris* flora associated with the coals of South Australia, South Africa and South Brazil. These parallel belts, fairly symmetrically disposed relative to the present equator, suggest that the equator of Permian times had much the same position as it has today. Gerth points out that extensive glaciation occurred in the Permian Antarctic but that the North Pole had no ice-cap. He attributes the northerly displaced distribution of the marine climatic zones to warm-water currents which spread further north than they do today because of a different distribution of land and sea, particularly because of the presence of a greater southern land mass. Gerth does not accept the hypothesis of displaced poles during Lower Permian times.

Gerth's additional fusulinid evidence would extend Stehli's northern boundary but would fall within Bain's equatorial zone.

The main difficulty in interpreting the climate of an entire system is that an enormous length of time is generally involved. The Permian spreads over a period of some 45 000 000 years, about equal to that of the Oligocene–Present, during which time exceedingly severe climatic changes took place. It is therefore preferable to work within as narrow a time interval as geological dating will allow. Termier and Termier[36] illustrate the point well, in both senses, by limiting their palaeobiogeographic interpretations wherever possible to one stratigraphic stage. They recognize an Eo- and a Neo-Permian and are able to show considerable biogeographical differences between them.

To consider the Permian as a whole masks many palaeoclimatic differences, and on the other hand raises curious problems such as the apparent association of reptiles with glaciers in South Africa, the former it so happens being Upper Permian, the latter Lower. Such problems are resolved only when the ages are more accurately known.

One of the reasons for the conflicting results of Stehli, Bain and Gerth is due to the use of evidence of different ages being lumped together into one large time interval, the Permian; a second reason lies in the use of different evidence; a third reason is the considerable difficulty of dating worldwide scattered outcrops of marine and continental environments to within the accuracy of one stratigraphic stage.

Perhaps one of the most valuable and cautious reconstructions of past climate is to be found in one of the final chapters of the vast synthesis by Arkell[1] on the Jurassic of the world. Through his researches the nature and distribution of life in Jurassic times are better known than for any other geological system. By means of the ammonite faunas, Arkell is able to correlate the stages of the Jurassic throughout the world and thence to determine

P

and date faunal migrations. From such objective studies he permits himself to speculate on the evolving climate during Jurassic times.

Arkell considers that the occurrence of rich faunas of temperate aspect in both Greenland and Grahamland argues against the development of ice-caps in the Jurassic, at least in the present polar regions. In Lower Jurassic and Bajocian times, temperate and equatorial faunas spread northwards; but at the beginning of Callovian times a distinctive Boreal fauna spread southwards from the Arctic Ocean towards the Mediterranean and California, and during Kimeridgian times coral reefs migrated southwards across Europe, presumably because of the advent of colder waters. That is to say the temperature rose during the early Jurassic and dropped during the later Jurassic.

The criteria on which Arkell relies are: size of shell, location of faunas, occurrence of limestones, geographical position of coral reefs and shell growth-lines. Arkell warns of the dangers of transferring the environmental characteristics of living forms to their fossil ancestors and instances the changes of habitat to be found in three fossil pelecypods, *Trigonia*, *Astarte* and *Pholadomya* which are associated in Jurassic times in a shallow water environment, but which at the present day are found in warm water, boreal and abyssal environments respectively. He observes that the shell gigantism of Portlandian molluscs, if accepted as evidence of subtropical waters, contrasts oddly with the conformably overlying Purbeckian whose fresh-water molluscan fauna is dwarfed, suggesting cooler conditions. Two explanations are possible. Either the temperature cooled between the two stages, or else there were warmer seas and cooler land.

Evidence in favour of the Jurassic boreal seas being cooler than those further south lies mainly in the absence of limestones, yet as Arkell observes, the giant Portlandian ammonites are a typical part of the Boreal fauna. Whether or not limestones are formed depends on two factors; firstly on the temperature which influences precipitation of both organic and inorganic calcium carbonate, and secondly on the amount of inorganic clastics being introduced into the area of potential limestone formation. It is not enough to consider the presence or absence of limestone without also taking into account the possibility that limestone, even given the optimum temperature conditions, might not be formed because of excessive dilution by the influx of non-calcareous sediment.

Arkell concludes that the seas were warmer during the Jurassic than now and that there were apparently no permanent ice-caps, the Arctic ocean of that time being temperate. The evidence, to him, does not preclude polar wandering and he would accept a possible position of the poles in the area of the South Atlantic and the Pacific, where, as he says, there is no evidence! Arkell favours increased solar radiation in Jurassic times as compared with the present day and under such conditions he considers that polar evidence would be lacking and that (reference 1, p. 618) . . . 'geophysicists are at liberty to postulate almost any wanderings of the poles that may be convenient'.

IV.2 *Local Palaeoclimatic Changes*

A somewhat different approach to the problem of palaeoclimates is to study the geological sequence of a limited area and from that interpret the passing climatic scene. Schwarzbach,[30] by this means, reconstructs the climatic history of the Rhineland in Germany. As in most studies of this kind he is handicapped by missing sequences. Most of his evidence is litho-logical and palaeobotanical but he does make use of the fact that reef corals are developed in the Devonian of that area. He likens the climatic changes from Devonian times onwards to a trip at the present time from the equator over dry belts (Permo-Triassic) to the subtropics (Tertiary).

Teichert[34] uses a similar approach in his interpretation of the climatic history of Australia. He bases his argument on the north–south oscillations of coral reefs. Coral reefs first appeared in Australia during Silurian times. They advanced southwards and reached their maximum southerly develop-ment during Middle Devonian times. In the Upper Devonian and Carboni-ferous they retreated northwards. Reef corals next appeared in the Tertiary and moved southwards in West Australia to 32°S latitude, probably during the last Interglacial stage. Since then they have moved northwards to 29°S. Teichert cautions against necessarily accepting this oscillation as evidence of continental drift and points out that comparable differences can be found today among marine faunas of similar latitudes.

Durham[10] interprets the Cenozoic climates of the North American Pacific coast from a comparative study of the Cenozoic fossil assemblages of that area with their living relatives. He defines two principles in the preamble. The first states that within the limits of temperatures normally prevailing in marine waters, stenothermal organisms are in general much more critically limited by minimum temperatures than by maximum temperatures, and in evidence Durham instances the disappearance of such typical shallow-water gastropods as *Conus*, *Cypraea*, *Ficus*, *Oliva* and *Strombus*, which are not found outside tropical waters, and on the other hand the intrusion of the northern pelecypod *Patinopecten* into the region of the Gulf of California Plio-Pleistocene in association with hermatypic corals. The principle is by no means univer-sal, for good cases exist where the opposite holds,[15] and a worker in Arctic faunas might tend to see the problem from the other side. The second and more acceptable principle is that the environments of comparable fossil and living associations are similar.

By a process of compilation and comparison, particularly of fossil and recent molluscs and corals, Durham evaluates the changing temperature of the shallow seas of the Pacific coast from Mesozoic times onwards. Fossil assemblages, representative of different stratigraphic stages, are compared with similar living communities and are assigned a probable minimum temperature. With few exceptions the comparisons are, of necessity, at the generic level, but by these means it is possible to construct a picture of the changing temperatures of the Mesozoic and Cenozoic shallow seas. Durham finds that the 20°C isotherm was probably north of 61°N latitude during

220   G. Y. CRAIG

Jurassic times and that in succeeding periods this isotherm moved south-wards so that by Paleocene times the 20°C isotherm was north of the 49th latitude and in the Pliocene approached the present isotherm distribution of 20°C at 25°N. Minor oscillations, not possible to detect with certainty, probably occurred during the main isotherm drift as, for instance, during the Pleistocene. Fig. 4 is modified from Durham's paper. Durham uses these conclusions and other evidence as arguments against Wegener's hypo-thesis of continental drift.

Durham extends his work on palaeotemperatures by plotting the world

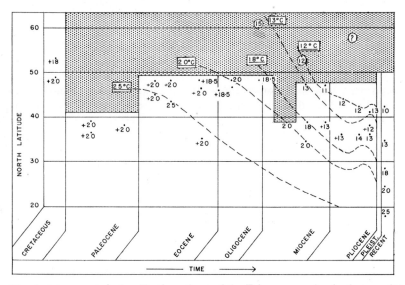

Fig. 4. Movement during Tertiary times of the February marine isotherms of the Pacific coast of North America based on the distribution and inferred lowest environ-mental temperatures of fossil molluscs and corals. The February isotherms represent the coldest temperatures of the year. Shaded area represents latitudes with no known marine deposits (exceptions circled). Simplified from Durham (reference 10, Fig. 2).

distribution of the deduced tropical molluscan faunas of the Paleocene and Eocene periods. He finds that the distribution of the inferred tropical faunas was wider then than now, lying within a broad belt 45°N and 45°S of the equator. From this evidence he concludes that the shallow-water tempera-tures were higher then than they are now. He argues from the distribution of faunas, as for instance, in the lack of similarity between the faunas of the Gulf of Mexico and Tethys, that continental drifting could not have occurred after late Cretaceous times.

Recent work on oceanic sediments [26, 29, 43] has shown that the Foraminifera from corings hold great promise as accurate indicators of temperature changes of the sea during Pleistocene and post-Pleistocene times. Phleger and

Parker[26] have investigated the relationships between living and fossil foraminiferan populations and their temperature and depth environments in the north-western part of the Gulf of Mexico. They believe temperature to be the most important factor controlling the distribution of planktonic and benthonic foraminifers. Analysis of the distribution of the benthonic faunas enables them to delimit six faunal depth facies which, they believe, primarily reflect temperature variations of different depths of the sea-floor. Samples of cores up to about 30 cm in length, taken from the sea-floor, yielded a mixture of planktonic and benthonic fossil foraminifers. The lower parts of the cores yielded planktonic foraminifers which today are characteristic of water temperatures lower than those in the Gulf of Mexico. Phleger and Parker cautiously avoid attributing absolute water environmental temperatures to these fossils but suggest that they probably represent marine water having surface temperature ranges similar to that of present-day continental-slope waters between Cape Hatteras and Cape Cod or even slightly colder. They consider that this cold-water fauna was living and was deposited during the last glacial age. In some cases the cores contained two cold-water faunas and in one case three, each separated by warm-water faunas, and these are taken to represent substages and inter-substages of the last glacial stage. The benthonic foraminifers, associated in the cores with the cold-water planktonic foraminifers, are found at the present day in waters shallower than the depths from which they were taken. From this they conclude that the sea-level was lower during glacial advances.

Thus by analysing living foraminifers and their physical environments Phleger and Parker are able to separate fossil foraminifers into planktonic and benthonic forms. The former they use to deduce the temperature of the surface waters during deposition; the latter, although attributing their distribution to temperature, they use to determine the relative depth of the sea floor. They point out two main limitations to such studies at present. The first is that it is not possible to correlate horizons in widely separated regions of the sea floor because of different faunas and the absence of guide fossils; the second, that the distribution of water surface masses containing different foraminiferal planktonic populations is variable and complicated and should if possible be known for past glacial stages before correlation can be made with confidence.

One of the less frequent uses of fossils is as indicators of land palaeoclimates. Theobald[37] traces the changes in groups of fossil insects in Western Europe from Eocene times onwards. Such groups are composed of a local fauna recognizable by many individuals but few varieties, and foreign elements 'allochtones', which Theobald claims provide information on the climate and which are to be recognized by their comparative scarcity and diversity. That foreign elements can be so used seems odd.

Theobald by a comparison of the fossil forms and their living representatives traces the climatic changes of Western Europe from the subtropical Eocene to the temperate Pliocene. He points out that the latitudinal differences in the Oligocene, as between the insects of the Middle Rhine, Germany and the Baltic, are greater than the changes in the insect fauna of the Middle Rhine throughout the whole of the Oligocene, so indicating a greater climatic zonation in the Oligocene than climatic change at one locality. His views are in general accord with those of Schwarzbach [30] derived from other evidence.

V. Limestones as Indicators of Palaeoclimates

An indirect method of determining past climates is by considering the distribution and abundance of organic and inorganic limestones. Trask [39] has reviewed the factors controlling the distribution and abundance of lime being deposited on the sea floor at the present day. He shows clearly that the $CaCO_3$ content of oceanic sediments is influenced by the temperature and salinity of the sea water, the activity of living organisms, and the amount of terrigenous sediment being introduced. Increase in temperature or salinity in the upper layer of the sea increases the degree of saturation of $CaCO_3$ and increases, to a lesser extent in the case of salinity, the solubility of $CaCO_3$. Marine animals produce CO_2 in their metabolism but in the warm photic zones, phytoplankton, by means of photosynthesis, are capable of removing more CO_2 than the animals can produce. In the aphotic zone the opposite relationship generally holds. Consequently the photic zone is relatively poor in CO_2 and the aphotic zone relatively rich, the former being more highly saturated with $CaCO_3$ than the latter. Precipitation of lime thus takes place mostly in the photic zone and tends to be dissolved in the aphotic zone, aided there by lower temperatures and increased pressures. To this process we may add the fact that the majority of benthonic animals secreting calcium carbonate are confined to the shallow-water neritic zone. Thus both organically and inorganically—the latter being induced in part by organic agencies— precipitated lime is most abundant in warm, saline, shallow areas.

Trask has compiled a map showing the present-day distribution and relative abundance of $CaCO_3$ in the sediments of the ocean floors. Calcium carbonate is absent in the polar areas where salinity and temperature are lower; in deep water where the temperature is lower; and is relatively less abundant in the coastal areas as a result of dilution by the influx of sediments. In spite of this general bipolarity with more lime in the neighbourhood of the tropics, it would be a difficult task to deduce the position of the present equator from this evidence alone. Trask suggests that $CaCO_3$ might be used as an indicator of palaeoclimate in deep-water sediments. There an increase in $CaCO_3$ might indicate an increase in the temperature of the water. He also suggests that alternations of limestone and calcareous shale might indicate climatic variations, especially fluctuations of rainfall.

Phleger and Parker, [26] in the latter part of their study on the foraminifers of the Gulf of Mexico, observe that the cold-water faunas from the lower part of the cores of the sea floor have fewer specimens per unit volume of sediment. This they attribute to increased sedimentation during a glacial substage when rejuvenated streams brought in more sediment, and also to a reduction in phytoplankton and therefore zooplankton, as a result of the limitation of light penetration caused by an increase in sediment carried in suspension. Low temperatures which affect the production of calcium carbonate and slow down the life cycle, are almost certainly a third cause, and dilution by fresh water possibly a fourth.

Wiseman[42] has found a similar phenomenon in the deep-sea cores of the Atlantic, in that the amount of $CaCO_3$ present on the sea-floor is directly related to surface temperatures. If the admixed non-calcareous sediment of land debris, clay and volcanic ash is deposited at a constant rate, then variations in the abundance of $CaCO_3$ should reflect changes in the temperature of the surface waters. Wiseman further observes that the species of foraminifers change with varying amounts of $CaCO_3$ in the sediment.

Revelle and Fairbridge,[27] in discussing the rôle of carbonates and carbon dioxide in the sea, list the most important processes controlling the precipitation of calcium carbonate from sea water as: increase in temperature, evaporation, movement of supersaturated water into an environment where precipitating agents are present, photosynthesis, bacterial production of ammonia or other weak bases tending to raise pH and thus carbonate concentration, organic processes in tissues or fluids of organisms, upwelling of deep water, and mixing of high-carbonate, low-calcium waters with seawater. They quote the work of Arrhenius[2] who found that the calcium carbonate content of the topmost layer of the sediments of the eupelagic zone in the eastern tropical Pacific was lower and contained more warm-water shells of foraminifers than the sediment 20–25 cm below the surface where there was more $CaCO_3$ and more frustules of diatoms, characteristic of lower temperatures. The top layer he correlated with higher temperatures of the sea, the bottom layer with lower temperatures. His conclusions have been confirmed by O-isotope palaeotemperature work on the foraminifers.

Yet a third conclusion is reached by Yalkovsky[47] who finds that carbonate content and temperature are unrelated in samples from a core taken from the Caribbean. He considers this to be explicable on the grounds that the Caribbean during Pleistocene times remained tropical. Thus carbonate in sediments may be related to increased temperatures, to decreased temperatures, or in the case just cited, not at all. Fortunately, as Yalkovsky remarks, most workers in the field find a correlation between increase in calcium carbonate and an increase in the temperature of the sea water.

Bruckner[4,5] suggests that the limestone cyclical sedimentation in the Helvetic series of the Swiss Alps may be the result of variations in climate. He rejects the generally accepted explanation of rhythms—that of oscillations in the level of the sea relative to the land—since shallow-water fossils are found throughout the various sediments of the rhythm. He does not, however, define the limits of shallow water within which vertical movement might have taken place, nor do fossils as yet lend themselves readily to the determination of the finer variations in the depth of the ancient seas. He concludes that the major cycles may represent a latitudinal shift of about 5° and the minor cycles a shift of about 2°. Carozzi[6] will not accept Bruckner's hypothesis on the grounds that the cycles are provedly tectonic, that lateral transition and facies changes are abundant, that the number of cycles varies in different parts of the basin, and that the limestones and shales are of different sedimentary types. His argument, although more appealing, need not exclude climatic influences on sedimentation entirely.

Chave [7, 8] shows by a series of analyses that the magnesium content in the calcite skeleton of numerous invertebrates varies with the temperature of the water in which the animal lived. Fossil invertebrates tend to lose their magnesium but where magnesium remains in solid solution with the original calcite it may be possible, he thinks, to estimate the palaeotemperature.

VI. Conclusions

It has been shown that temperature influences the latitudinal depth and longitudinal distribution of animals and the structure of their skeletons; and that the determination of palaeotemperatures, a facet of ancient climates, can be based on these relationships. The chief methods that have been used are as follows:

(1) By plotting the world geographical distribution of groups of fossil invertebrates, ideally at some instant in geological time, a geographical zonation of fossil groups may be revealed from which temperature zones and possibly the equatorial belt may be deduced.

(2) By examining the successional distribution of fossils and limestones in time, in one geographical area, it is possible to infer temperature changes within that area.

(3) By means of ecological gradients such as shell size, it is possible to infer temperature zones in space or temperature change in time.

(4) The geographical distribution of limestones, which often reflect organic activity, and which today are being deposited *from*—but not necessarily in— warmer waters, may reflect temperature zones.

Two main conclusions may be drawn from this review.

The first is that as yet we have insufficient knowledge of, and therefore control over, the variables that can affect the form and distribution of fossils. Yet on the form and distribution of fossils an important part of palaeo-climatic studies is based.

The second conclusion is that stratigraphic correlation is not yet sufficiently accurate to be certain that we are interpreting palaeoclimates of the same geological age. The Permian is a case in point. Even the Jurassic which, because of its ammonities, has been correlated in greater detail than any other Mesozoic or older system, has only twelve world-wide stages recognized by Arkell, each of them having an average span of some 4 000 000 years. Considerable climatic changes could occur in that time interval.

These conclusions may seem to form a rather pessimistic summary. They are not meant to be. Their intention is to sound a cautionary note, for fossil invertebrate faunas, carefully used, will always be a very necessary tool in the study of ancient climates.

References

1. Arkell, W. J. *Jurassic Geology of the World.* 1956. Edinburgh: Oliver and Boyd
2. Arrhenius, G. *Repts. Swedish Deep-Sea Exp.,* **5**, 1 (1952)
3. Bain, G. W. *Amer. J. Sci.,* **256**, 596 (1958)
4. Bruckner, W. *Geol. Rdsch.,* **39**, 196 (1951)
5. Bruckner, W. *J. sediment. Petrol.,* **23**, 235 (1953)
6. Carozzi, A. *J. sediment. Petrol.,* **25**, 78 (1955)
7. Chave, K. E. *J. Geol.,* **62**, 266 (1954)
8. Chave, K. E. *J. Geol.,* **62**, 587 (1954)
9. Degens, E. T., Williams, E. G. and Keith, M. L. *Bull. Amer. Ass. Petrol. Geol.,* **42**, 981 (1958)
10. Durham, J. W. *Bull. geol. Soc. Amer.,* **61**, 1243 (1950)
11. Durham, J. W. *Amer. J. Sci.,* **250**, 321 (1952)
12. Ekman, S. *Zoogeography of the Sea.* 1953. London: Sidgwick and Jackson
13. Forbes, E. *Rep. Brit. Ass.,* **14**, 130 (1844)
14. Gerth, H. *Geol. Rdsch.,* **40**, 84 (1952)
15. Gunter, G. *Mem. geol. Soc. Amer.,* **67**, 1, 159 (1957)
16. Gutsell, J. S. *Bull. U.S. Bur. Fish.,* **46**, 569 (1930)
17. Jones, N. R. *Biol. Rev.,* **25**, 283 (1950)
18. Ma, T. Y. H. *Sci. Repts. Tohoku Imp. Univ.,* **16**, 165 (1934)
19. Ma, T. Y. H. *Palaeont. sinica,* **2B**, 1 (1937)
20. Ma, T. Y. H. *Research of Past Climate and Continental Drift,* **4**, 1 (1951). Privately published
21. Ma, T. Y. H. *Acta. geol. taiwan.,* **6**, 1 (1954)
22. Mason, J. *J. Mar. biol. Ass. U.K.,* **36**, 473 (1957)
23. Murray, J. *Nat. Sci.,* **2**, 17 (1897)
24. Neumayr, M. *Denkschr. Akad. Wiss. Wien.,* **47**, 277 (1883)
25. Pearse, A. S. and Gunter, G. *Mem. geol. Soc. Amer.,* **67**, 1, 129 (1957)
26. Phleger, F. B. and Parker, F. L. *Mem. geol. Soc. Amer.,* **46** (1951)
27. Revelle, R. and Fairbridge, R. *Mem. geol. Soc. Amer.,* **67**, 239 (1957)
28. Runcorn, S. K. *Bull. geol. Soc. Amer.,* **67**, 301 (1956)
29. Schott, W. *Geol. Rdsch.,* **40**, 20 (1952)
30. Schwarzbach, M. *Geol. Rdsch.,* **40**, 128 (1952)
31. Stehli, F. G. *Amer. J. Sci.,* **255**, 607 (1957)
32. Stehli, F. G. *Amer. J. Sci.,* **256**, 600 (1958)
33. Sverdup, H. U., Johnson, M. W. and Fleming, R. H. *The Oceans: their Physics, Chemistry and general Biology.* 1946. New York: Prentice-Hall
34. Teichert, C. *Geol. Rdsch.,* **40**, 33 (1952)
35. Teichert, G. *Bull. Amer. Ass. Petrol. Geol.,* **42**, 1064 (1958)
36. Termier, H. and Termier, G. *Histoire Geologique de la Biosphere.* 1952. Paris: Masson et Cie
37. Theobald, N. *Geol. Rdsch.,* **40**, 89 (1952)
38. Thorson, G. *Biol. Rev.,* **25**, 1 (1950)
39. Trask, P. D. *Prof. Pap. U.S. geol. Surv.,* **186**N, 273 (1937)
40. Vaughan, T. W. *Rep. Smithson. Instn.,* **189**, 238 (1919)

41. Vaughan, T. W. *Bull. geol. Soc. Amer.*, **51**, 433 (1940)
42. Wiseman, J. D. H. *Proc. roy. Soc.*, **222**A, 296 (1954)
43. Wiseman, J. D. H. and Ovey, C. D. *Proc. Geol. Ass.*, *Lond.*, **61**, 28 (1950)
44. Wells, J. W. *Mem. geol. Soc. Amer.*, **67**, 609 (1957)
45. Weymouth, F. W. and Thompson, S. H. *Bull. U.S. Bur. Fish.*, **41**, 633 (1931)
46. Wimpenny, R. W. *Quart. Rev. Biol.*, **16**, 389 (1941)
47. Yalkovsky, R. *J. Geol.*, **65**, 480 (1957)

X

Palaeobotanical Evidence of Climate

R. KRÄUSEL

I. Introduction

The laws which govern the modern distribution not only of many plant species but also larger taxonomical groups and entire plant communities, are controlled by different factors. Many of these factors, such as mountain uplift, which are effective at the present time have their roots in the past, but more important for consideration here are those which are the result of modern environmental conditions. The plant is affected by a plexus of external influences which collectively have a definite action, and it is thus a basic error to remove one single factor from the whole and consider it separately. On the other hand this is the only possible way of finding out the precise significance of any single factor, for it is the object of this chapter to examine the dependence of plants on the climate in which they grew. That there is such a close connection is a truism, and if plants of unknown origin were to be examined, it would undoubtedly be possible in many cases to draw conclusions about the climatic conditions of their environment. For such a purpose it would often be sufficient to recognize an existing single species and classify it correctly. The greatest restraint, however, must be exercised to avoid making a merely superficial judgement and the larger the group in question the greater the possibility of serious error. The presence

227

of cacti does not necessarily indicate a barren desert any more than palms or Bromeliaceae indicate a tropical jungle. A willow (*Salix*) by itself does not give much information and although most species are found in the temperate zone and Arctic-Alpine species can be recognized, riparian willows are found in the Amazon basin. Obviously it would be better if a whole plant community existed or definite morphological or anatomical features could be recognized.

These few examples may make it clear that the relation of plant to climate is not so simple as it at first appears to be, nor is this the only difficulty. One can perhaps disregard the fact that as a result of recent geological history not every plant takes up all the space climatically suited to it; but the fact that many species are extremely adaptable to a wide range of conditions cannot be disregarded. Thus for example, the bracken fern (*Pteridium aquilinum*) has an almost world-wide distribution. If because of an historical accident such a plant now only occupied a small 'relict' region, the question would arise as to whether it did in fact reflect the climate of that locality. If its survival in a place, in no way fully suited to it climatically speaking, was only because this place was still more unsuitable for its rivals the relation 'plant = definite climate' would certainly not result. Even when this is not the case, the fact remains that the propagation of a plant is in no way bound to rigid climatic limits although there is an optimum climate in which it thrives best. It is rather a question of maximum and minimum values of temperature, humidity and so on. These 'threshold values' determine the area in which a plant will exist and they must be very carefully taken into account when making climatic inferences. Since they vary considerably from species to species, the certainty of any climatic inference becomes all the stronger, the greater the number of different species on which it is based. The plants need not necessarily belong to the same systematic group, but, on the contrary, it is most important that they form an ecological unity. When speaking of climate, it must not be forgotten that this is no uniform concept. The temperature, its maxima and minima, just as their distribution over the course of the year, the amount, pattern and distribution of rainfall, light and wind conditions interact in a variable manner. These factors not only determine the propagation of the single species, but they also give rise to quite distinct communities. Thus both the Puna and Paramo are mountain formations of the Andes, but how different they are from each other.[124, 144] The one contains a barren steppe flora poor in species while in the other the flora indicates a humid jungle with grasses, ferns and trees.

Plants are not only suited physiologically to their environment but also develop special morphological or anatomical features characteristic of their habitat. The example of the Arctic dwarf willow has already been mentioned. In similar manner the dwarf birch (*Betula nana*) is quite distinct from its dendriform relatives, while the leaves of xerophytic Bromeliaceae are quite different from the forest forms. Water plants such as the water lilies (*Nymphaeaceae*) possess air spaces in their tissue, and floating leaves have stomata only on the upper surface while these are lacking completely in submerged leaves. The wood of the tropical mangrove and the swamp cypress (*Taxodium distichum*) in the Dismal swamps of Louisiana develops thick pneumatophores, a construction quite different from the normal trunk. (For present purposes it is immaterial whether it is really a question of 'respiratory roots'.) Many tropophytic woods on the other hand react to the alternation of damp and dry periods (the summer and winter of temperate climates constitute such periods for plants) externally by the shedding of foliage and internally through the acquisition of tree rings. Finally, xerophytes manifest a whole series of characteristics which are commonly interpreted as adaptation to their environment, but here again caution is commendable; for moorland plants, too, are in many ways similarly constructed.

These examples can be augmented at will, but are enough to show how such plants depend on the climate. It controls, if not exclusively, at least in some measure, which species and even which classes of plants will be present in a given area; it determines the essential features of whole communities and formations, and sets its mark on the structure of many plants.

Nor was it otherwise in the geological past, and the attempts to make use of fossil floras as a 'palaeoclimatic key' are almost as old as the scientific study of fossils in general; even in recent work such attempts still play an important rôle. The reception of such climatic conclusions has ranged from unreserved acceptance, to the extent of using the information as the centre point of many studies, through unfavourable, to complete rejection, at least where the pre-Quaternary eras are in question. Thus the object of this chapter must be to consider critically the possibilities and limitations of palaeobotany as a palaeoclimatic method. It must be recalled that every plant fossil is not only a member of a definite taxonomic and ecological unity, but also belongs to a definite period. The plant world has changed very considerably in the course of the earth's history. Many genera which could not alter in accordance with, or adapt themselves to, changed living conditions have become extinct and new forms have taken their place. Only a fraction of these floras is preserved in fossil form and even these few make it clear that the older the plant community, the more it diverges from that of the present. Thus one would commonly expect that the possibilities of interpretation, based solely on the comparison with present-day conditions, decrease with increasing geological age. Thus the necessity arises of viewing every era in the earth's history separately, thereby raising the following questions:

(1) Can one separate form serve as a palaeoclimatic 'key fossil' on the grounds of its systematic position?

(2) How strong is the evidence afforded by a fossil flora consisting of several or many species?

(3) Do the fossils possess structural characteristics which can be brought to bear on the problem of climate?

II. The Quaternary

II.1 *Macrofloral Evidence*

Plant remains from the Quaternary belong, with comparatively few exceptions, to living species, and certainly to genera whose present-day habitat is known. Thus false conclusions can to a large extent be avoided by evaluating critically the possible sources of error which do exist. Furthermore fossil floras are not the only evidence; zoological, lithological and other observations also fit in. Thus the floral evidence can be matched against other lines of evidence, just as the distribution of plants can be gauged by their modern region of distribution.

The Quaternary, although covering only the last very short section of the earth's history, approximately 1 000 000 years, was a period of marked climatic variations in many parts of the earth. Repeatedly the northern continental ice sheet advanced far towards the south, with simultaneous strong glaciation of the high mountains and even many of the lower mountains (altitudes up to 1500 m), the ice retreating northwards again during the considerably warmer Interglacials which lasted several thousands of years. The distribution of land and sea results in these events appearing primarily in the northern hemisphere, yet traces of them are also found in the Antarctic and particularly in South America. Glacial sediments, like interglacial sediments, are frequently plant bearing. They include peat bogs which are generally formed in a humid, cool or cold climate.* The climatic variations become clear on detailed consideration of the macroflora. In the '*Dryas* Flora', so called after the small *Dryas octopetala*, dwarf birches and dwarf willows, *Ericaceae*, *Ranunculaceae* and many other plants combine to indicate the climatic environment; *Dryas* itself, the dwarf willow (*Salix herbacea*) *Polygonum viviparum*, and cotton grass (*Eriophorum scheuchzeri*) are Arctic-Alpine, the stunted willow (*Salix retusa*) is purely Alpine, but the polar willow (*Salix polaris*) and the Arctic Ranunculus (*Ranunculus hyperboreus*) are purely Arctic. This is the assemblage of the Arctic tundra, which spread out in front of the continental ice sheet even if not found everywhere. Based on the climatic requirements of this community it has been estimated that at that time the yearly mean temperature must have been at least 6–10° lower than that of today. The amount of rainfall is also critical for the plant and as today it decreases in quantity towards the east. More recent maps, for example Büdel[2] (see also Mägdefrau, reference 96, Fig. 337; and Ebers, reference 48, Fig. 37) or Zeuner (reference 153, Fig. 40) also indicate great extents of dry loess steppes where conditions were against plant preservation. Nevertheless, the umbelliferous *Crambe tatarica* is a cold continental steppe plant, as is *Ephedra strobilacea*[145] which today is limited to the Turan–Iranian desert regions. *Helianthemum*,[108] and *Artemisia* and other Chenopodiaceae

---

* There are also peat bogs or similar sediments in warm regions (South America, Central and East Africa, Ceylon, Sumatra, Hawaii), but these contain a completely different floral assemblage.

point in the same direction. The latter are particularly abundant in Eastern Europe especially in Russia,[106,107,152] and preliminary studies are in progress for a more exact classification of genera which cannot as yet be distinguished with certainty by pollen analysis. On the other hand, an interglacial flora consisting primarily of pine and deciduous trees is proof of a considerably warmer climate. The objection to the use of *Dryas* as a climatic indice is that it occurs today on the slopes of the Alpine valleys. It has also been pointed out that fruit trees bloom at the foot of the Norwegian glaciers. A picture from New Zealand might be still better known (Seward, reference 138, frontispiece) where, only a mile from the end of a valley glacier, tree ferns (*Hemitelia smithi*) grow,[40] just as the glaciers of the northern Rocky mountains stretch down deeply into the pinewood zone. The explanation of how far a valley glacier descends, however, is that it depends entirely on the amount of rainfall at its point of origin, so that a glacier edge may well lie in an environment which climatically is inappropriate to it. Hence the occurrence of tree ferns and a glacier appearing on the same picture which may seem particularly impressive to the observer is not significant climatologically. The *Dryas* flora of the Alps is a 'relict' flora in every case related to local conditions. The conditions in the periglacial zone in front of the great continental ice sheet were completely different. Thus these plants, like those from the interglacial beds, are important pointers to the climate.[54]

In the Tegelen clays of Holland and the roughly equivalent Villafrancian of Southern Europe (considered as Quaternary on account of recognizable preceding cooler periods), plants like the conifer *Tsuga*, beeches, *Carya* and *Phellodendron*, and particularly *Magnolia* and the wing nut (*Pterocarya*) which occur today only in South East Europe, all indicate a climate that was warmer than it is now. Probably the water fern *Azolla tegeliensis* also points in the same direction.[53] In later interglacials *Magnolia* is absent although *Sambucus pulchella*,[125] presumably an extinct form of elder, *Pterocarya* and *Tsuga* were present; [81] and in the tufa of Weimar (Riss-Würm Interglacial) a cypress flourished (*Thuja thuringiaca*) (references 143; 96, Fig. 332). The Alpine rose of the Hötting Interglacial in the Tyrol is well known,[146,111] and although its age is disputed, it is generally placed in the Mindel-Riss Interglacial. The leaves at least are very similar to the Pontic Alpine rose which today lives in the region of the Black Sea, and from this it has been concluded that in the Tyrol at that period it was on average 2–3° warmer than today with the snow line considerably higher. Many water plants such as the water lilies *Brasenia*, *Nymphaea* and *Nuphar*, also *Najas*,[9-13] provide valuable evidence both for the Riss-Würm Interglacial in which the common beech (*Fagus silvatica*) was replaced by the hornbeam (*Carpinus betulus*),[86] and for other periods. Very important too are the Diatoms (cold and warm water species) which were so abundant in the Quaternary, and as an example the Inter-glacial of *Pianico Sellere* on Lake Iseo (North Italy) may be mentioned.[126] Woldstedt[151] has briefly summarized the floras of the different Interglacials.

II.2 *Microfloral Evidence*

Pollen analysis provides another means of investigating a fossil flora. First used qualitatively by Weber in Germany and a little later by Lagerheim in Sweden, it was then developed by von Post in Stockholm as a quantitative method. Starting from post-glacial times, the study has been extended to the whole of the Quaternary. It augments the macrofloral history primarily in that it reflects not only the conditions of a local flora, but also the course of forest history over a greater area and therefore the fluctuations of climate at that time. An almost overwhelming flood of separate studies has appeared, mainly from North, West, East and Central Europe.[51, 52] Impressive summaries have been published, especially since the statistical examination included grasses and shrubs, as well as forest trees, from other sediments in addition to peat. Not only have graphs been produced, but also forest maps for the different periods have been drawn (reference 19, Figs. 89–94; reference 57, Figs. 18, 19; reference 159, Figs. 22, 23), in which the proportions of the various tree species in the forests of the time are set out. Until recently there were fewer pollen analysis studies in North America,[2, 121–123] but they did show an alternation of warmer and colder phases similar to that in Europe. This even applies to the south, for in old lake deposits near Mexico City seven stages of forest development can be detected by pollen analysis.[135]

Eastern Asia, the tropics and countries in the southern hemisphere still present a wide field for future studies. In these regions, research is made difficult by the fact that the number of the pollen forms is not only greater, often considerably greater, but also because the identification and classification even of the still existing forms is not yet well enough known. A beginning has, however, already been made, for instance in Hawaii,[136] South America,[1–3] South Africa,[154] East and West Africa,[154] Australia[41, 118] and in New Zealand[66, 104, 105] and the islands lying to the south.

II.3 *Survey of Quaternary Climates*

Returning to Europe, a climatically uniform picture for the separate Interglacials in different areas can be sifted out, when the evidence is viewed as a whole. In the earliest strata trees are absent, the flora representing more or less treeless tundra with at most only scattered dwarf pines and birches; then gradually the number of trees increased, the hardiest types appearing first and being later replaced by species of a rich mixed-oak forest. The interglacial profile is completed by reversing the sequence. This series is especially well-known in the final phase of the last, the Würm, Glaciation, where less important shorter climatic fluctuations can also be recognized (Interstadials), and in post-glacial times (Table I). The study of peat bogs (fens, muskegs in North America) show that the climate was much the same in post-glacial times. During the optimum of the post-glacial warm period a series of warmth-loving species extended farther northwards. However, it is true that not every facies change need necessarily have a climatic cause, for example the change of moss, grass and woody peat into blanket or raised bog type could equally be a function of the rate of peat accumulation, so that a careful, critical evaluation is not out of place here. However, when 'recurrence surfaces' are found in the peats of Northern and Central Europe,

Table I. Palaeobotanical and Climatic Division of Late and Post-Glacial Times in Central Europe (after Firbas and others)

Forest type	Period	Phases after Blytt–Sernander	Approximate date
Beech		Post-warm period (Subatlantic)	Present
		Climatic deterioration	800–500 B.C.
Transition from mixed-oak forest to beech	Post-glacial period	Late warm period (Subboreal)	
Mixed-oak forest		Central warm period (Atlantic)	2500 B.C.
Hazel and early mixed-oak forest (last glaciers melting)		Early warm period (Boreal)	5000 B.C.
Birch and fir		Pre-warm period	
Period of sparse vegetation (ice margin in Central Sweden)		Late Tundry (Dryas) period	8000 B.C.
Birch and fir	Late Ice Age	Alleröd period	9000 B.C.
Trees absent		Middle Tundry (Dryas) period	10 000 B.C.
Birch and fir		Bölling period	11 000 B.C.
Trees absent		Early Tundry (Dryas) period	
Ice margin in Northern Germany	Ice Age		18 000 B.C.

or boundary horizons (Grenzhorizont) in many north German peats, the latter explanation is not tenable. These surfaces correspond to dry, warm periods, during which peat growth was not only halted, but the earlier peat was even extensively eroded, and only after renewed climatic deterioration did the formation of *Sphagnum* peat re-establish itself. This interpretation remains correct, even if the original correlation of all or many local boundary horizons has to be rejected.[4,115] In any case the stratigraphy of the post-glacial period, first developed by Blytt[20] and Sernender,[137] can with some modifications still claim to be valid today. Similar correlation tables for Denmark,[72] Southern Sweden[113] and England[58] agree, with minor exceptions, with the results set out here. In North America too, a similar sequence emerges (Table II) which Deevey[42] believes can be correlated with the European succession.

Yet the post-glacial climatic fluctuations are not distinguished floristically as clearly everywhere. In Iceland the only tree is the birch. In spite of various attempts, including the use of statistical methods, it has not yet proved possible to distinguish beyond doubt between the pollen of the woodland birch and the ecologically distinct dwarf birch (*Betula nana*). Hence, in this case it is scarcely possible to count on floristically well defined periods and at the most only insignificant fluctuations in a generally uniform graph appear.[139] The climatic development in East Asia too has gone its own way since the end of the Pliocene. However, numerous Pleistocene floras from

Q

Japan are known which indicate climatic fluctuations.[100-102] Thus today the Korea pine (*Pinus koraiensis*) is limited to heights of 1000–2600 m and its appearance with associated species in considerably lower altitudes in early Pleistocene is a proof that it was considerably colder in Japan at that time

Table II. Correlation of the Post-glacial in North America (after Deevey)

European phases	Vegetation eastern North America	Connecticut zones	Climate
Subatlantic	Oak–Chestnut–Spruce (Oak–Beech)	C–3	Cool, wet
Subboreal	Oak–Hickory	C–2	Warm, dry
Atlantic	Oak–Hemlock (Oak–Beech)	C–1	Warm, moist
Boreal	Pine	B	Warm, dry
Preboreal	Spruce–Fir	A	Cool
Arctic ⎫ Subarctic ⎬ Missing in North American pollen diagrams Arctic ⎭			

than it is today. Conversely, the flora of the Uegahara[103] beds contains evergreen species and Miki is certainly right in considering this an inter-glacial flora, and other coeval floras lead to the same conclusion. As a result of these data a good picture of the development of the Japanese flora since the end of the Tertiary has emerged, and from it an understanding of the climate of that time.

II.4 *Dendrochronology*

In North America, tree ring chronology, studied particularly by Douglass[47] and his school, and later by Schulman[130-132] has become widespread and there is even a special periodical ('Tree Ring Bulletin') and laboratory. By counting and comparing the tree rings in prehistoric trunks and living trees—for example, those of the Californian giant redwoods (*Sequoia, Sequoiadendron*) and the yellow pine (*Pinus ponderosa*)—exact data have been obtained cover-ing a period of 3000 years. The method is based on the assumption that every tree ring corresponds to a vegetative period, in this case, one year, which is generally true in the temperate zone. The discovery in the White Mountains of California by Schulman[132] of living trees over 4000 years old (foxtail pines—*Pinus aristata*) may be of special value.

Similar, albeit shorter, chronologies have also been worked out for numerous regions in Europe, although conditions are not so favourable as in North America (see the detailed synopsis of Zeuner[153]). Climatically, the variation in width rather than the number of tree rings is important. The width variations represent microclimatic changes from one year to the next, and depend primarily on rainfall variations. Any succession of relatively dry or relatively wet years will show up in the width of the rings, particularly the latter, giving rise to the possibility of comprehending even short-term fluctua-tions. It is true that not all trees react to these fluctuations in the same manner and this must be taken into consideration when comparing the graphs obtained from various species, particularly when they come from widely separated areas (such as North America and Northern Europe). After the investigations of Douglass the eleven-year sun-spot cycle can be recognized in the tree-ring graphs.

II.5 *Non-Glaciated Regions*

Before leaving the Quaternary it is worth considering briefly some areas which were not glaciated and which were only influenced either indirectly or not at all by the glaciations. As the continental ice advanced far to the south, entire climatic zones were pushed in the same direction. In the Mediterranean area, rainy and dry periods were established corresponding to the glacials and interglacials. The fossil floras from Southern Europe and particularly North Africa [21, 39] are not well known, but tree leaves are evidence of forestation in areas now barren. The same is true of western North America. In the tropical zone conditions must have been little different, leaf and wood remains from Indo-China and the islands situated to the south belong to the *Leguminosae* and other families which still live in the same area today. Here climatic conditions can have scarcely altered and the Dipterocarpaceae give important additional information in this respect. [22, 25, 134]

III. The Tertiary

The Tertiary period covers about 60 million years [84] and according to radio-activity age determinations may even cover 70 million years. [153] In any case it represents a period of time many times greater than the duration of the Quaternary. It is the custom to subdivide this period into the Upper Tertiary or Neogene (Pliocene and Miocene, roughly 30 million years) and the Lower Tertiary or Palaeogene (Oligocene, Eocene and Paleocene). Just as at the present day, the Angiosperms were at that time floristically predominant and, although fewer in number and species, yews (*Taxales*) and pine trees (*Coniferales*) were also important forest forms. In general the later Tertiary species are very close to those of the present day when not actually identical with them. The flora of the Early Tertiary however contains many distinctive forms, reminiscent of the Cretaceous, and which have since become extinct. As observed on p. 246 the Upper Cretaceous belongs to the 'Neophytikum', the age of the Angiosperms. Thus when it is stated there is a close link between the Tertiary floras and the modern plant world, this is true principally for the Upper Tertiary or Neogene, and applies in some degree to the Oligocene, but only to a much more limited extent to the Eocene.

III.1 *General Problems of the Tertiary Macroflora*

Tertiary floras in great number are known in almost all the regions of the earth. If the study of the Northern Hemisphere has a very big lead, this is due only to the historical development of palaeobotany. It is the absence of workers rather than of fossils which hindered and still hinders the development of palaeobotany in many countries. It is no exaggeration to claim that the number of the Tertiary fossils amassed in collections is greater than the floras of all other ages put together. This is true as much for the actual number of fossils as for the number of described species. Both their frequency of occurrence and their presumed close ties to flora of today make them valuable raw material for palaeoclimatology. On the other hand the strong criticism mentioned in the introduction applies in the first instance directly to the Tertiary flora. It is startling to note that in a recent textbook of Tertiary stratigraphy[118] the Tertiary flora (pollen excluded) is dealt with on barely one page. Certainly the study of stratigraphy and palaeoclimatology are on quite different levels, but Papp's view is important since for the most part it rests on the assumption that many, if not the majority, of the Tertiary plants are incorrectly classified or at most very doubtful. If that were the case, then this section on the Tertiary flora could be concluded. That such a point of view is unjustified must be proved although it is only possible for reasons of space to touch upon the arguments here.

The literature on Tertiary flora is prodigious, and can be divided into two groups. In the 19th century the material amassed was reviewed in the form of extensive treatises on local floras as in the works of Unger and von Ettingshausen in Austria, Heer in Switzerland, Göppert and Engelhardt followed by many others in Germany, and Hollick and Berry in North America. These workers were concerned primarily with the Tertiary leaves (for these were found most abundantly) whose systematic position they sought to recognize by comparison with the leaves of living species. These painstaking comparisons were often not sufficiently thorough, a fossil leaf found to be only partially similar to a living genus was often regarded as 'classified'. The possibility was not admitted that similar leaf forms could occur within quite different groups; nor was the variability of the leaf form in the same genera or even species taken into account. Thus 'species' were created which only represent leaf individuals, and serious mistakes were made, partly out of preconceived opinions. Thus Ettingshausen, on the basis of his concept of a world-wide uniform Tertiary flora, compared Australian fossils with European genera, just as he thought he recognized numerous *Proteaceae* in the European Tertiary. Today both conclusions are known to be incorrect. Material suitable only for the waste-paper basket was 'classified' and studies of this kind extended right into very recent times. In the second category are many other workers, especially in North America, who took the trouble to found leaf comparisons as thoroughly as possible, or to consider characteristics previously disregarded, such as 'cuticular analysis'[74,90,147] which successfully makes use of the structure of the leaf epidermis as a basis for classification.

Other fossils in addition to leaves have been examined, for example wood has been studied, and here too the story revealed by leaves is repeated. Earlier research was hampered by inadequate knowledge of wood anatomy and even today many specimens defy every attempt at classification. On the other hand successful revisions of older material[109,110] or redescriptions [24-27] have been made which show how valuable the study of the wood can be. In more recent times seeds and fruits have been given special attention, as in Reid and Chandler's[125] description of the Eocene flora of the London Clay and other strata, Barghoorn's work on the brown coal of Vermont[14,16] and Kirchheimer's study of the brown coal of Central Europe.[75,76]

The families of the living plants are based primarily on the structure of flowers, fruits and seeds, which is why the corresponding fossil remains are particularly informative, although it would be a mistake to underestimate the value of fossils of other kinds. Errors of identification are as much in evidence here as they are in studies of Tertiary leaves and wood. Chaney[33] describes an *Eopuntia* from the Eocene of Utah which according to Brown[26] is in fact the rhizome of a sedge (*Cyperaceae*). Fruits of the Pliocene *Stuartia*, a relative of the tea shrub, were originally thought to be cones of conifer; with them were found the fruits of *Eucommia*, a modern monotypical genus of Eastern Asia, which were actually thought to be the cocoon of an insect, while the large winged fruits of a *Malpighiaceae* were interpreted as maple fruits.[85,75] In the Miocene flora of Öningen, made famous by Heer,[68] impressions are found which Hantke[65] takes as elm fruits, but which according to Nötzold[114] are the husks of a Leguminosa. This list could easily be extended but it would be wrong to conclude that the Tertiary floras described are completely worthless on this account. It simply means that older identifications must be examined critically, and not necessarily rejected, although in some particular cases this may prove to be necessary, e.g. *Eopuntia*.

The climatic implications of forms which from their present-day area are to be regarded as 'conservative endemic' is restricted. In this latter category belong Ginkgoales, and the group of conifers containing, for example, *Sequoia*, *Sequoiadendron* and *Metasequoia*, *Taxodium* or *Glyptostrobus*, also *Taiwania* and *Amentotaxus*. In the Tertiary they all occupied a very large area and in places they were predominant members of many Tertiary floras until the Pliocene. Their present extremely limited distribution does not give a true indication of the range of climatic variations of that earlier time. If the regions in which many of these tree species are *cultivated* today are taken into consideration, they can become a guide to climate. Certainly it raises the question whether in the course of many generations species may have become adapted to a different range of climatic variations since the Tertiary, whether wider or narrower, or have adapted themselves directly to adverse conditions. This cannot be answered and it is very much a matter of personal choice whether it is considered likely or unlikely.

The basis for climatic comparisons obviously improves as the number of contemporary species found in the same place and indicating the same conditions increases, especially if this number becomes so great that we may speak of a fossil 'flora' or if the leaves of such a flora display uniform morphological characteristics. The rôle which ferns and palms can play has been examined by Mahabelé.[97] Tertiary palm remains are abundant, although their connection with living species is problematical.[141] *Nipa* seems to be of special importance in this connection, indicating as a member of the tropical Mangrove formation a quite definite climate.

III.2 *General Problems of the Tertiary Microflora*

Pollen analysis has not only been extended to the Tertiary, but judging by the number of papers, is actually one of the outstanding methods of floral investigation. Yet there are several reasons why the Tertiary pollen flora can offer little help to the palaeoclimatologist. Since the richness of tree species was much greater than in the Quaternary, botanical classification of the many pollen forms is faced at the outset with considerable difficulties, and until recently has been virtually neglected in a literature overwhelmingly concerned with stratigraphic studies. The chaotic nomenclature of pollen forms also contributes to making matters considerably more difficult.

Botanically it is generally only possible to determine the family and at best the genus[120] of a pollen form and as a result little can be said as regards palaeoclimatology. Only a few authors are of the opinion that Tertiary pollen, or spores, can be related to living species. There are of course exceptions and Macko[94] describes a pollen flora from the Miocene of Upper Silesia which contained a variety of species, including twelve kinds of pine, *Araucaria*,[9] and *Podocarpus*,[7] which are today limited to the Southern Hemisphere, in addition to *Microcachris* (today a single species only found in Tasmania) and three *Dacrydia* (found today in Tasmania, New Zealand and New Caledonia). Also represented in the flora are numerous tree ferns, including *Thyrsopteris* (found today in the Juan Fernandez Islands), the Cycads, *Stangeria* (South Africa) and *Zamia*, which with *Ephedra*, *Welwitschia* and *Gnetum*, palms, bamboos and so on, formed a community of which 79 genera appear today in Florida, while 27·6 per cent are tropical. Macko believes that two floras are involved, one lowland and the other highland, which have lived in a subtropical climate (warmer than Florida today). If this were correct (which is open to doubt) microfossils would then afford one of the forms of evidence of former climates. Nagy[112] is far more cautious as regards their value in his work on the Hungarian Pannonian floras.

What is the bearing of macrofossils on this point? There is such an abundance of forms from Silesia that in this respect the province is one of the most thoroughly investigated in Germany. Neither here, nor in Central Europe viewed as a whole, do the two floristic results agree. This is probably a case similar to that of Ettingshausen's European Tertiary *Proteaceae*, in that it is not enough to show that a fossil pollen form is similar to a certain modern form; one must also know that it is identifiable with one *only*. This position is still a long way off but it is already known that 'pollen convergences' occur and many features are common to different families, just as in the case of the leaf shape. Provisionally, observations on the macrofloras remain of first importance for Tertiary climates. Van Hammen[64] draws a quite different conclusion from his studies of the Columbian floras. The botanical origin of the majority of the pollen grains from the Maestrichtean and the Tertiary of Columbia is not yet known, so that the interpretation of the significance of the quantitative shifts in proportions of one pollen form from one profile to another—i.e. floristic changes which can be recognized— is fraught with difficulties. He believes that the fluctuations in the pollen spectra have a primary periodicity of 6 000 000 years and a secondary period of 2 000 000 years. At the base of the Tertiary the change is particularly strong and is believed to indicate a major period of 60 million years. He considered the cause of this change, with which the origin of new forms is bound up, to be a periodic decrease in temperature connected with concurrent increase of the cosmic radiation, together with the effects of tectonic events. This synthesis of terrestrial and cosmic causes is certainly far-reaching, but needs much more proof from the study of the pollen flora of other Tertiary regions.

III.3 *Floral Evidence of Climatic Change during the Tertiary*

A. *Europe and Asia*

It is true that for macrofossils, matters are not so simple as in the Quaternary. For example the Pliocene flora of Frankfurt a.M. contains about 150 species, amongst which are many trees and shrubs and, without going into details, it can be established that this Pliocene forest was a mixed coniferdeciduous forest, distinguished by a great number of species. Many of these still exist today or else are very close to existing forms,[95, 83] but nowhere on the earth is there a forest of the same composition today. Elements of it, found in modern Central European forests, were mixed with some forms from Southern Europe, and also with forms now found in North America and many from Eastern Asia. The same is true of other Tertiary floras irrespective of whether they were found in Europe, North America or Asia. Thus it is more correct to speak of a uniform Arcto-Tertiary floral province. This uniform province was destroyed with the passing of the Tertiary, when many of its members became extinct while others were scattered to the four winds and only here and there found a limited refuge. At this time very extensive plant migrations must have taken place and it seems reasonable to look for the reasons for these in a climatic deterioration. This reached its climax in the Quaternary cold periods, particularly in Central Europe where the flora was hemmed in between the E–W mountain chains lying to the south, and the ice to the north, and only a few species were able to find a refuge farther to the south by migrating 'sideways'. During the earlier interglacials many Tertiary forms returned once more but the number of these 'Tertiary relicts' steadily diminished in the course of the Quaternary.

The process was, however, established long before the end of the Tertiary. This can be illustrated from the floral history of the Frankfurt area, where a series of floras cover the earlier Tertiary forest history. The oil shale of Messel is early Tertiary, probably Upper Eocene[50] in age; in it a few conifer branches and conifer seeds and thousands of leaves have been deposited.

Although, as has been shown by the anatomical examination of leaf cuticles, many of the leaves (provisionally) identified by Engelhardt are incorrect, it is certain that this leaf flora is quite different from that of the later Tertiary. Many of these leaves are remarkably large, often sharply pointed, with very thin cuticles and many stomata. These are characteristics of a community of a warm, humid climate, which is also indicated by the large number of species. Engelhardt supposes this flora to have close connections with the forests of Southern Asia, a conclusion which would agree well with other results.[125] The leaves from the floras of the Oligocene and Miocene are shaped quite differently. In many other parts of Central Europe palms still occur, but the tropical species become increasingly rarer and are replaced partly by conifers and partly by deciduous or evergreen trees during the course of the Tertiary. Thus one can observe a succession of floras which have been called the Palm, *Lauraceae*, *Myricaceae* and *Magnolia* floras.[84] The change can only have had climatic cause for a similar, if not identical, course of events is met with in other parts of Europe.[6]

Nearly related floras need not necessarily have been contemporaneous, for example it is known that many Pliocene floras of south-east Europe still contains numerous elements which at that time no longer lived farther to the North. Hence Pliocene floras from Bulgaria and Rumania[55,56] or Yugoslavia[116,117] are closer to the Miocene or even Oligocene floras of Central Europe than to the Pliocene flora of Frankfurt a.M. Thus climatic belts can be detected during the later Tertiary at least, and within these climatically distinct areas with ecologically different floras which disappeared in the course of the Tertiary. The varied floras of the Eocene London Clay is interpreted as tropical rain forest[125] which in its composition comes closest to the modern forests of the Indo-Malayan area. Mangrove plants are also represented in it[30] including the highly significant palm Nipa whose fruit, and especially seeds, were spread by sea currents. This palm has been found elsewhere in Europe and in the southern United States (maps in Berry[18]); it has also recently been found in the Eocene of Sumatra[78] and Egypt.[31,82] At the same period temperate mixed forests of conifers and deciduous trees were flourishing in the Arctic, in Greenland and Spitzbergen,[128] forms which in the later Tertiary are found in Central and Southern Europe. The Vienna Basin, which has been dealt with in a number of papers by Berger,[17] affords an example of an ecologically different flora. The local floras extend from the lower Middle Miocene to the Lower Pliocene, and by the use of morphological and taxonomical considerations, Berger[17] traced climatic changes during this time interval. In the earliest strata (Table III period 1), fairly large, entire, often tough and leathery evergreen leaves (*Cinnamomophyllum*) are predominant. This 'Poltawa' element, so-called by Kryshtofovich,[91] then declined (in period 2) while small serrated, thin-skinned deciduous leaf forms became more numerous ('Turgaya' elements). During the transition to the Sarmatian (period 3) a remarkable change occurred, the 'Poltawa' forms with the exception of *Cinnamomophyllum* disappeared while the Turgaya elements also became more rare and pines became abundant. The principal

Table III. Late Tertiary Floras in the Vienna Basin (from Berger,[17] modified)

Period	Cinnamomophyllum	Poltawa-elements	Small leaved xerophytic forms	Turgaya-elements, smaller forms	Turgaya-elements, larger forms	Climate and Vegetation
4 Lower Pliocene (Pannonian)	Absent (very rare?)	Very rare	Very rare	Very common	Predominant	Warm to moderate, fairly humid—deciduous forest
3 Upper Miocene (Sarmatian)	Rare	Absent	Predominant	Rare	Absent	Warm to moderate or subtropical, dry—Savanna, with woods only along watercourses
2 Upper Middle Miocene (Tortonian)	Very common	Rare	Rare	Common	Rare	Subtropical, moderately damp (somewhat cooler and drier than 1)—mixed evergreen—deciduous forest
1 Lower Middle Miocene (Helvetian)	Very common	Common	Rare	Rare	Absent	Subtropical—damp evergreen forest (laurels)

change was the appearance of tough, mostly smooth-edged, rounded leaflets which for the most part are clearly pinnules of woody *Leguminosae*. They cannot be more exactly classified but must certainly represent the remains of a warm, dry savanna vegetation. Willows, poplars and water elms which occur occasionally must have grown along the water courses. A new cycle then follows in the lower Pliocene,[4] when the xerophytic forms, like the 'Poltawa' elements, completely disappeared and were replaced by predominantly large leaved 'Turgaya' elements, pointing to extensive deciduous forests in a moderately warm, fairly damp climate (period 4).

The process described in this particular example is repeated in many regions, especially over a large area in Siberia, where Kryshtofovich[91, 92] has recognized great floristic provinces (see also reference 140), the variations in which can be traced back to changing climatic factors. On the other hand, small local differences are evident in East Asia, as the numerous later Tertiary floras of Japan show.[102] Here the number of 'Tertiary' species still extant in the same area is considerably greater than in Europe, although their areal extent may have changed; or become more restricted. The gymnosperm, *Metasequoia*, has become famous. First described by Miki from the Japanese Pliocene[99] the living tree was then discovered in Central China. Subsequently Chaney[35, 37] and Schloemer-Jäger[128] were able to show that it could be identified amongst the many fossil remains previously described from the North American and Arctic Tertiary, but it has not yet been found in Central Europe.[129] Today *Metasequoia* is planted in parks both in Europe and North America and it is an excellent example of how, through cultivation, the value to palaeoclimatology of such a relict can be considerably augmented.

The Tertiary coal beds have at all times played an important rôle in palaeoclimatology. Indubitably they can only have originated in a climate favouring swamp and peat formation. They are at least in part the result of forest swamps, as can be seen from abundant autochthonous wood (horizons of tree stumps) found not only in the floor of the coal seams but also in the coal itself. At first it was thought that the swamp cypress (*Taxodium*) might be particularly common among them, and their modern counterpart was regarded as being the 'Dismal Swamps' of Louisiana. Then it became apparent that the supposed swamp cypresses were mostly Sequoias and the opinion arose that the brown coal peats must have been considerably dryer. Today it is known that the *Sequoia* forests were only one phase in the course of coal formation, during which the plant community changed in a way resembling the growth of Quaternary or recent peats. The leaves, twigs and other remains which were incorporated into the peat in the course of coal formation were generally broken up into small fragments, whose substance is still retained and is anatomically classifiable in the coal. In many beds, grasses and other monocotyledons are particularly common while wood plants are more or less absent. This is the flora of a blanket bog (muskeg). In the flora of other coal seams shrubs or trees such as *Myricaceae* or *Magnoliaceae* predominate with a few palms. All this points to a warm and humid climate at the time of coal formation. Whether the successive vegetation types indicate climatic fluctuations on a smaller scale needs careful consideration. This is not necessarily so, although there are exceptions such as the extreme cases of the change from a grass peat to a *Sequoia* forest. Perhaps application of tree-ring studies to lignitic wood may lead to new results.

Tree-ring chronology methods can also be applied to silicified wood which, in places, is common. The 'Petrified Forest' at Mount Mokattam near Cairo has long been famous, although the name is misleading, for it consists primarily of drift-wood often of giant proportions which floated down rivers and was deposited.[82] Similar occurrences are to be found in Somaliland [39] and French Africa.[23] This kind of deposit suggests large rivers and strong currents, while the structure of the timber indicates an alternation of wet and dry periods.

Enough examples have already been given to show that during the Tertiary in the Northern Hemisphere there were botanically comprehensible climatic belts which were progressively displaced. Within these zones there were larger and smaller areas with their own changing climate, and all these climatic conditions are indicated by the Tertiary flora. It cannot have been much different in the Southern Hemisphere; although this cannot be gone into in detail. Clearly it was quite different in the modern tropical zone. Whether in the West Indies,[70, 71] South-east Asia [77-79] or Central Africa [38, 98] the pattern is the same as in the Quaternary, the Tertiary flora of each area agreeing substantially with that of the present day. The assumption is justified that in these areas the climate has hardly changed, at any rate since the later Tertiary. This is not the place to try to account for this different behaviour. Let it suffice to say that the fact itself can be gleaned from the fossilized flora.

B. *North America*

The Tertiary floras of North America require a special survey for several reasons, even if the survey has to be short. There are a large number of local floras known, the number already exceeding 200,[7] and many of them have been described by Chaney,[34, 36] Dorf,[44, 46] Axelrod [6, 7] and other Californian workers. The floras range from Eocene to the latest Tertiary in age and occur on both sides of the Rockies extending from the northern frontier of Mexico to Alaska and Northern Canada. As in modern times, so too in the Tertiary, climatic and thus floristic zones existed which ran from east to west. These zones have since been displaced in a southerly direction. The folding and uplifting of the Rockies, confined to the west, created new climatic contrasts between the Pacific, Central and Atlantic areas, while the arrangement of the mountain chains unlike Europe favoured the North–South migration of the flora. This also applies to the Quaternary and explains why in North America many more Tertiary forms survived than was the case in Europe. Thus the conditions are particularly suitable for palaeoclimatic investigation; the 'prerequisites' of Dorf[44] are the same as those mentioned in the introduction (p. 227).

It appears [6] that two large floral groups can be distinguished in the early Tertiary. From California to Washington on the Pacific Coast, and inland from New Mexico to Colorado, a 'neotropical Tertiary flora' existed, primarily comprising large leaved evergreen plants without, or almost without, conifers but with some *Cycads* and Palms. To the north lay the region of the 'Arctotertiary' flora, in which deciduous trees and conifers predominated.

Table IV. Cliseral Relations in Western California (from D. I. Axelrod, abbreviated)

Flora	Vegetation	Climate
Modern (lowland)	Oak woodland and savanna; chaparral; border-redwood forest	Sub-humid to semi-arid; rainfall from 17 in. in savanna to 25 in. at edge of forest; mild summers, cool winters
Mulholland & Petaluma (Middle Pliocene)	Madro-Tertiary woodland and chaparral dominant; Arcto-Tertiary forest on the bordering slopes	Semi-arid, with sub-humid aspect to forest; 18–23 in. rain in summer and winter. Summers warm, winters milder than in area today
Black Hawk (Early Pliocene)	Arcto-Tertiary plants dominant, Madro-Tertiary plants rare	Temperate, with 25 in. rain in summer and winter. Mild summers and winters
Alamo (Basal Pliocene)	Arcto-Tertiary plants characteristic, Madro-Tertiary plants rare	Temperate, 30 in. rain, bi-seasonal occurrence with dry season less well marked than later in epoch. Mild winters and summers
Loma Ranch (Late Miocene)	Arcto-Tertiary forest dominant, Madro-Tertiary plants very rare	Temperate, with 30–35 in. rain well distributed through the seasons. Mild winters and summers

As today (for example, in East Asia) the transition between the two was gradual and both great floras were separated by a mixed flora (ecotone of Chaney). During the Early Tertiary, all three lay about 20° to the north of the regions in which a community of similar composition lives today. With

Table V. Cliseral Relations on the West Sierran Piedmont (from D. I. Axelrod, abbreviated)

Flora	Vegetation	Climate
Modern (lowland)	Live-oak–digger pine woodland and savanna; grassland; scattered chaparral	Semi-arid, rainfall from 15–20 in. increasing up slope; hot dry summers, cool wet winters
Oakdale (Middle Pliocene)	Madro-Tertiary plants dominant, Arcto-Tertiary plants (only riparian species of *Salix Populus*)	Semi-arid, with 15–18 in. rain, in summer and winter. Summers and winters more mild than in area today
Table Mountain (Late Miocene)	Arcto-Tertiary forest characteristic, Madro-Tertiary plants common	Temperate, with sub-humid facies. Rainfall near 30 in., as summer showers, winter rains. Mild summers and winters
Valley Springs (Late Miocene)	Arcto-Tertiary plants prominent, Madro-Tertiary plants in small numbers	Temperate, with sub-humid aspect. Rainfall from 30–35 in., in summer and winter. Mild winters and summers

Table VI. Cliseral Relations on the East Sierran Piedmont (from D. I. Axelrod, abbreviated)

Flora	Vegetation	Climate
Modern (lowland)	Steppe (sage), piñon-juniper woodland, scattered yellow pine forest	Semi-arid, 10–13 in. precipitation as winter rain and snow chiefly. Cold winters, hot summers
Red Rock (Middle Pliocene)	Riparian woodland, interspersed with grassland in the interfluvial areas	Semi-arid, 12–17 in. rain, in summer and winter. Cool winters, warm to hot summers
Verdi (Middle Pliocene)	Dominant riparian woodland with scattered Madro-Tertiary oak-woodland and chaparral on nearby flats; Arcto-Tertiary forest on bordering slopes	Rainfall 18–20 in. in lowlands, increasing to 25 in. at edge of forest, chiefly in winter but some in summer; warm summers, mild winters
Mansfield Ranch (Early Pliocene)	Arcto-Tertiary forest, Madro-Tertiary plants in small numbers	Rainfall near 25 in. in lowlands, bi-seasonal. Warm summers, mild winters
Chalk Hills (Early Pliocene)	Arcto-Tertiary forest dominant, Madro-Tertiary plants rare	Rainfall near 35 in., distributed in winter and summer. Winter mild, summers warm
Mohawk, Denton Creek (Late Miocene interpolated)	Arcto-Tertiary forest predominant, Madro-Tertiary plants unknown	Rainfall from 40–45 in., in summer and winter. Mild warm summers and winters

the Tertiary decrease in temperature these zones shifted towards the south, a movement that has been represented by Dorf[45, 46] in a series of maps ranging from the late Eocene period right up to the present day. East of the rising Rocky Mountains the rainfall diminished and the 'Madro-flora'

Table VII. Cliseral Relations in Western Nevada (from D. I. Axelrod, abbreviated)

Flora	Vegetation	Climate
Modern (lowland)	Great Basin desert, with sage on middle slopes	Desert to marginal steppe, 4–7 in. precipitation, as winter rain and snow. Summers hot, winters cold
Truckee-Hazen (Middle Pliocene)	Small flora, chiefly of Madro-Tertiary origin	Semi-arid, with 15 in. rain in summer and winter. Warm to hot summers, mild winters
Parran Junction (Early Pliocene)	Madro-Tertiary oak woodland dominant; Arcto - Tertiary plants rare, represented chiefly by *Picea* seeds	Semi-arid. 20 in. yearly rain in winter and summer. Warm summers, mild winters
Fallon Chloropagus (Late Miocene)	Madro-Tertiary woodland dominant in lowlands, Arcto-Tertiary forest on cooler slopes	Sub-humid, with 25 in. yearly rain, increasing on bordering slopes, bi-seasonal distribution. Mild winters, warm summers
Old Gregory (Late Miocene)	Arcto-Tertiary plants dominant, Madro-Tertiary plants in small numbers	Temperate. Approximately 30 in. rain, bi-seasonal occurrence. Mild winters and summers

developed,[7] the species of which are characterized by small, often tough, leathery leaves. As early as in the Eocene, this plant community was rich in species, and taxonomically specialized as well as climatically adjusted. According to Chaney numerous species may have originated from it, and given rise to the flora of the modern semi-arid oak–pine woods of the plains, and even the subtropical dry bush of the Chaparral, the semi-deserts and the deserts.

Shortage of space precludes a closer study here of the many individual floras and their changing ecology, yet at least two examples may be given. Axelrod,[5, 8] not content with describing four varied flora from Nevada, makes comparison with contemporary flora from the western U.S.A., and contrasts them with modern flora. This forms the basis for ascertaining the rainfall, temperature, ecological and environmental conditions, the final result being a palaeogeographical map, which illustrates the spread of Arcto-Tertiary, Madro-Tertiary and neotropical Tertiary flora of that era, as well as the climatic differences over a large area. This area stretches from California far northwards and westwards to Nevada. It is a particularly pleasing synthesis of diverse results, and far superior to the usual scheme for a similar floristic study.

Axelrod has also studied other local flora lying on both sides of the Rockies. His summary in table form [6] is reproduced in brief on p. 244. Unfortunately the detailed data on the genera in question has had to be omitted although it is precisely these details that are important for the understanding of the finer climatic differences. Some readers may regret the omission of more precise numerical data in column 3 on the separate climatic factors but there are enough papers covering this topic. In the last resort, with the exception of a few particular cases, no more is gained than is in Axelrod's table. The value of the Tertiary flora must not be underestimated by requiring too much from it. In this sense Dorf's 'Thermometers of the Ages' (from the latest Cretaceous to the Pliocene) can clearly only be regarded as giving averages (reference 44, Fig. 3).

IV. Mesozoic–Palaeozoic

IV.1 General Problems of Mesozoic Flora

The 'Neophytikum', the age of the Angiosperms, embraces the Upper and indeed, according to some recent publications, almost the whole of the Cretaceous, reaching back in its beginnings into the Jurassic.[44] Even if it can be established that the Angiosperms of the later Tertiary were closely related to those of the present day, it does not follow that this also applies to the Early Tertiary, and particularly Upper Cretaceous, forms. It can be said that the main groups of Angiosperms were in existence even at that time. Apparently numerous species appeared quite suddenly, which leads to the supposition that they must have had older forebears; in fact the number of Jurassic and still older floras in which the presence of one of those oldest Angiosperms has been conjectured is considerable. Kräusel [88] has recently tried to show that none of these fossils has been identified as an Angiosperm with complete certainty, and since then the position has not changed. The edict of Edwards [49] still holds good: 'All palaeobotanists would agree that Angiosperms must have been in existence before the end of the Jurassic, but let us be certain before we indulge in flag-waving. The time is not yet ripe and even if it were otherwise, it would scarcely help us in palaeoclimatology'. In the introduction it was emphasized that even species of the same genera which are taxonomically very alike can have quite different climatic requirements. What can be said about forms whose connections with modern flora are still more tenuous? Of what use is it to know that the *Dryophyllae* of the early Tertiary and the Upper Cretaceous are probably *Lauraceae*? The same is true of the Gymnosperms of the Earlier Mesozoic. The *Ginkgo* of today has a certain palaeoclimatological implication; but the extinct genera of the *Ginkgoales* have none. Similarly the spore bearing plants, the ferns *Dipteris* and *Matonia*, still exist in Malaya and only in direct sunlight, but how their extinct Mesozoic relatives behaved in this respect we do not know. The most useful groups from the climatic stand-point are those groups still rich in species today and at the same time occupying a climatically more or less uniform area. This applies, for instance, to the Dipterocarpoids (*cf.* p. 235) which today are confined to the forests of South-east Asia but which appear in North Africa during the Tertiary. *Woburnia porosa* found in the Lower Greensand of England is also a Dipterocarp, but it is an exception.

It does not need to be emphasized that pollen analysis cannot be of assistance, although it is very important stratigraphically, in both the Mesozoic and the Palaeozoic for making possible extensive floristic comparisons. Countless individual forms have already been described pointing to far more plant species than are covered by macro remains. Palaeoclimatically this is no help. Even if pollen or spores can be successfully allocated to a particular parent plant, the plant itself remains, as a rule, 'anonymous', at least palaeoclimatically. Abel's hypothesis, that the Alpine, Upper Cretaceous Flysch originated in a mangrove region bordering the coast, is well known and Hofmann[69] has tried to adduce confirmatory evidence by relating some pollen forms and epidermal remains to living mangrove plants. The same pollen forms, however, are also present in strata whose formation has nothing to do with mangrove swamps, and moreover their taxonomical position is extremely doubtful. Therefore this interpretation must be rejected.

Another pollen from Permian strata has been compared with *Welwitschia* and *Ephedra*.[142, 93] The only living species of *Welwitschia* is limited to a narrow strip of the South-west African coastal desert and is adapted to extreme dryness, and in general the majority of *Ephedra* species prefer dry locations. Even Leschik,[93] however, must concede that the comparison is by no means certain.

The main point emerging from the discussion is that with the earliest Tertiary the study of palaeoclimatology based on plant taxonomy ends, with but a few exceptions. So even in the Cretaceous, leaves of the *Nymphaeaceae* indicate the existence of shallow water. Perhaps one should mention here the occurrence of reef-forming chalk algae like the *Dasycladaceae*, which, extending back into the Palaeozoic, experienced repeated outbursts in favourable conditions both in the Triassic and in the Permian, but even in this case the validity of drawing an analogy from modern to former times can be queried.

If one pursues the development of the higher plants from their oldest representatives in the Lower Devonian (and Upper Silurian), two things become clear. First, repeated and taxonomically very decisive changes in the floras can be established, and secondly, there were periods in which the flora of the whole earth appears to have been quite uniform, in contrast with other periods, in which there was a splitting up into areas floristically sharply defined. In both cases one is inclined to relate such changes to climatic variations. Edwards[49] and Dorf[44] have treated these subjects admirably and their work is very instructive, but on the whole speculation outweighs the facts.

It remains to ask, then, whether, in view of the fact that the taxonomy of the older plants is of no help, their structure and appearance might still be of use. Some examples of this kind have already been indicated. If for example *Credneria* of the Cretaceous possess very tough leaves with thick, sharply prominent veins, a dry locality might be predicted. In accordance with this is the fact that they are often found in dune sandstone. The fern *Weichselia* which appears with them shows similar features. In the Cretaceous sandstone of the Harz Mountains *Weichselia reticulata* was found *in situ* still upright, and everything indicates that these were xerophytes which had been entombed together in sand dunes. Perhaps such a conclusion might be extended to the fossils associated with them, but when *Weichselia* also appears in marine strata together with conifers and other remains, such a community is of little climatic value. The short, thick stems of *Pleuromeia* in the Bunt-sandstein also suggest a dry locality, but on the other hand the horsetails (*Equisetales*) which were so common in the Triassic, suggest a region that was generally sandy and damp, as in the Triassic of Neuewelt near Basel (Switzer-land), where a complete root bed, with rhizomes of horsetails, has been dis-covered. Many Mesozoic conifers, and the *Cycadales* and *Bennettitales*, which are like them as regards vegetative structure, possess tough leathery leaves like the contemporary *Cycadales* with sunken stomata, the outer stomatal cavity often being closed by pappillae. They were certainly not members of a warm, humid, primeval forest! In many Mesozoic floras these hard-leafed plants appear together with large-leafed ferns. As these fossils have com-monly been deposited in lacustrina or even marine sediments it is not certain whether they present a single community. Nevertheless, they suggest a relatively humid source, and this applies particularly where coal beds have been formed. Although there are Mesozoic coals, attention must be confined to most important features of the Carboniferous.

IV.2 *The Coal Formations of the Carboniferous and Permian*

A. *Northern Hemisphere*

The autochthonous coal beds of the Northern hemisphere which belong mainly to the Upper Carboniferous will first be considered. The fossils found in the intervening beds also occur in the coal and in 'coal balls' even their tissues are preserved so that the structure of many Carboniferous plants is very well known. They comprise ferns and the closely related seed ferns

(Pteridosperms): *Calamites* and *Sphenophyllae* which are related to the horsetails (*Equisetales*), dendriform *Lepidophytae* related to the club mosses (*Lycopodiales*) and *Cordaites* which belong to the seed plants. They all formed part of a forest swamp community, the composition of which, viewed as a whole, was more or less similar everywhere. Like modern bog plants, many species possess layered roots ('*etagen*' structures), or their subterranean rhizomes extend a long way horizontally, while some *Sigillaria* are thickened at the base. The *Sphenophyllae* were originally mostly regarded as water plants but the view based on Halle's observations, that some of them at least were lianae (climbing plants) is more probably correct. On the other hand many Pteridosperm seeds possess an inner structure which can only be explained as an adaptation for floating in water. The stems of the *Lepidophytae* have an extremely narrow stele compared with the thick cortex characteristic of the group. This may have phylogenetic causes, but the broad meshed parichnos tissue of the stem leading up to the leaf bases is a climatic adaptation.

Certainly this was no forest of a temperate climate. There were hardly any herbaceous plants and the ferns and Pteridosperms are mostly trees or lianae with giant leaf-fans; other trees have a smooth cortex without any notable development of bark. These are all characteristics of a tropical and subtropical rain forest. It is particularly important in this connection that the stems of the *Cordaitales* have no growth rings. It proves that there was no significant seasonal change and there was therefore an even, warm, damp climate. In the Carboniferous forest there are features of yet another kind. The narrow leaves of many *Lepidophytae* are thick, leathery or fleshy and carry the stomata in two deep grooves on the underside, while many Calamites have thick, needle-like leaves. These are structures found in many xerophytic plants. Thus 'hygromorphic' and 'xerophytic' features exist side by side. The same is found in modern bog plants. How warm was it then? H. Potonié thought it was a tropical forest and, as is well known, Wegener on the same assumption has made use of the coal beds in the construction of the Carboniferous tropical zone. It must, however, be mentioned here that there are rain forests outside the tropics; the rain forests of Chile or New Zealand range from subtropical to temperate. In these forests undergrowth is hygrophilous, while the trees show xerophytic characteristics, and it is in such forests that conditions of the Carboniferous may be most closely approached.

The Arcto-Carboniferous coal formations do not extend far into the Permian. With the reduction in the number of Carboniferous species, which were gradually supplanted by such forms as conifers and *Ginkgoales* with tough leathery foliage, come signs of a climatic revolution. In the later Permian, in particular, clearly marked growth rings in some trees suggest an alternation of dry and humid seasons.

B. *Southern Hemisphere*

Perhaps these events have some connection with the development in the southern hemisphere. The floras of South America, South Africa, India,

R

Australia and the Antarctic have developed differently from those in the northern hemisphere since the Carboniferous, when these Gondwana lands underwent recurrent glaciations. In the lower Carboniferous of Sumatra a flora of Arcto-Carboniferous type is found. Later quite different species were established, so that the genuine 'Gondwana flora' has a quite different character. It is true that here, too, the great taxonomic groups are the same, but not their genera. Instead of *Calamites* other *Articulatae* are present. True Lepidophytes are probably absent, and it is significant that there is no parichnos tissue (see p. 249) in their southern related forms (*Lycopodiopsis*), while large leafed ferns and Pteridosperms are rare. *Glossopteris*, which is present in all Gondwana strata, may belong to the latter, and like *Gangamopteris*, which is closely allied to it, has tongue-shaped, smooth-edged leaves, the epidermal cells often bearing papillae, especially around the stomata. This '*Glossopteris* flora' extends right into the Mesozoic and certainly did not form in warm humid conditions. It is true that coal beds were formed, but their petrography, as is common with dull coal, indicates other conditions for their development. Analytical study of their spore content is still in its early stages.[93]

The peculiarities of this flora were early connected with the Permo-Carboniferous glaciations. It cannot however be a glacial flora; nor does the fact that some species have been found in strata which are interpreted as moraine deposits prove it. It is more probable that the flora lived in the warmer interglacial periods. The fossilized gymnospermous wood once more seems very important in this connection, for it is widespread, being found in the Karroo beds of South and South-west Africa, as well as in Brazil[89] and India, and it has even been found in the Antarctic. The 'Petrified Forest' in the Kaokoveld of South-west Africa deserves especial mention in this respect. The first accounts of it were by Rodin[126] and Kräusel.[79] The stems of the Kaokoveld plants do not all belong, as Rodin assumed, to the same species[87] although this is not the decisive point; what is important is that they were deposited in the sandstones at the edge of a wide valley in Karroo times. The size of the transported trunks prove that the currents must have been very powerful for one trunk measured almost 2 m in diameter and more than 30 m in length without an obvious tapering being in evidence at the upper end. As a rule the branches are no longer attached to the trunks, but were probably broken off during transport. All the trunks show clearly defined tree rings, which are of astonishing width in the larger trunks with the cells of the early wood growth very wide and thin walled. This indicates sharply marked seasons in which really favourable conditions must have predominated during the periods of growth. Rainy seasons and dry seasons must have existed, but even during the former it was certainly cooler than in the Carboniferous forests of the Northern Hemisphere. It must be remarked that simultaneously in North and East Asia other floras developed (Angara and Cathaysia (*Gigantopteris*) flora), the members of which again indicate differing climatic conditions.[49, 73]

Thus a climatic differentiation followed the uniformity of the Lower

Carboniferous, a difference which can well be connected with the simultaneous mountain uplift and the related oceanic transgressions. It leads into the several ice ages in the Gondwana region. It would be surprising if on the borders of the great floral regions mentioned above no mixing had occurred. The presence of *Glossopteris* in Russia has been reported and *Lepidodendron* and *Sigillaria* have been described in Gondwana strata. In both cases these occurrences may be due to misidentification, however the Wankie flora in Rhodesia seems also to be mixed. As there are still problems associated with these floras no climatic conclusions should be drawn from them as yet.

IV.3 *The Earliest Flora*

The Upper, Middle and Lower Devonian are characterized by typical flora[44] and the *Psilophyton* flora of the Lower Devonian also occurs in the Gotlandian. All statements on still older remains of land plants are dubious. These oldest land plants are of greatest significance in plant history. They obviously grew in shallow water or in swamps, but apart from that they tell little about their environmental conditions. The uniformly simple organization of the Psilophytales (this in the broadest sense!), like their wide distribution in the Lower Devonian, does not need to have been due to climate. The same applies to the subsequent *Hyenia* and *Archaeopteris* flora.

The conclusion reached from palaeobotany is that the question formulated at the end of the introduction (p. 229)—namely, whether the problem of climate can be elucidated through the study of fossil plants—can, within certain limits, be answered in the affirmative, but one cannot guard too carefully against misplaced optimism leading to a transgression of these limits.

References

1. Auer, V. *Acta geogr., Helsingf.*, **5** (1933)
2. Auer, V. *Mem. geol. Surv. Can.*, **162** (1930)
3. Auer, V. *Handbuch der Moorkunde*, **VII**, pp. 224–243. 1933. Berlin: Gebr. Bornträger
4. Averdieck, F.-R. *Nova Acta Leop. Carol.*, (n.F.) **19**, 75 (1957)
5. Axelrod, D. I. *Bull. geol. Soc. Amer.*, **68**, 19 (1957)
6. Axelrod, D. I. *Amer. J. Sci.*, **255**, 690 (1957)
7. Axelrod, D. I. *Bot. Rev.*, **24**, 433 (1958)
8. Axelrod, D. I. *Bull. Dep. Geol. Univ. Calif.*, **34**, 91 (1958)
9. Backman, A. L. *Acta bot. fenn.*, **30**, 3 (1941)
10. Backman, A. L. *Acta bot. fenn.*, **31**, 3 (1943)
11. Backman, A. L. *Acta bot. fenn.*, **43**, 3 (1948)
12. Backman, A. L. *Comment. biol., Helsingf.*, **10**, No. 19 (1950)
13. Backman, A. L. *Act. bot. fenn.*, **48**, 3 (1951)
14. Barghoorn, E. S. *Bull. Vt. bot. Cl.*, **18**, 21 (1950)
15. Barghoorn, E. S., in Shapley, H., ed., *Climatic Change*. 1953. Cambridge, U.S.A.
16. Barghoorn, E. S. and Spackman, W. *Econ. Geol.*, **45**, 344 (1950)

17. Berger, W. *Berg-u. hüttenm. Mh.*, **97**, 125 (1952)
18. Berry, E. W. *Amer. J. Sci.*, **37**, 57 (1914)
19. Bertsch, K. *Geschichte des deutschen Waldes*, 4th edn. 1953. Jena: Fischer
20. Blytt, A. *Engl. bot. Jb.*, **2**, 1, 177 (1881) Leipzig
21. Boureau, F. *Bull. Mus. Hist. nat.*, *Paris*, (2) **23**, 462 (1951)
22. Boureau, F., *Mém. Mus. Hist. nat.*, *Paris*, **IIC**, 1 (1952)
23. Boureau, F. *Bull. Mus. Hist. nat.*, *Paris*, (2) **27**, 247 (1955)
24. Boureau, F. *Anatomie végétale*, **III**, p. 525. 1957. Paris: Press. Universit
25. Boureau, F. and Tardie-Blott, M.-L. *C.R. Soc. Biogéogr.*, **282**, 107 (1955)
26. Brown, R. W. *J. Paleont.*, **33**, 120 (1959)
27. Büdel, J. *Naturwissenschaften*, **36**, 105 (1949)
28. Campo, M. van. *Bull. Inst. franc. Afr. noire* **19**, 659 (1957) Dakar
29. Campo, M. van. *Bull. Inst. franc. Afr. noire*, **20**, 753 (1958)
30. Chandler, M. E. J. *Proc. Geol. Ass., Lond.*, **62**, 271 (1951)
31. Chandler, M. E. J. *Bull. Brit. Mus. (nat. Hist.)*, **2**, 150 (1954)
32. Chandler, M. E. J. *Bull. Brit. Mus. (nat. Hist.)*, **3**, 73 (1957)
33. Chaney, R. W. *Amer. J. Bot.*, **31**, 507 (1944)
34. Chaney, R. W. *Bot. Rev.*, **4**, 371 (1938)
35. Chaney, R. W. *Proc. nat. Acad. Sci., Wash.*, **34**, 503 (1948)
36. Chaney, R. W. *Proc. nat. Acad. Sci. Wash.*, **35**, 356 (1949)
37. Chaney, R. W. *Trans. Amer. phil. Soc.*, **40**, 172 (1951)
38. Chesters, K. M. I. *Palaeontographica*, **101**B, 1 (1957)
39. Chiarugi, A. *Palaeontogr. ital. 32* suppl. **1**, VI, **4**, 97 (1933)
40. Christ, H. *Die Geographie der Farne*. 1910. Jena: Fischer
41. Cookson, I. C. and Pike, K. M. *Aust. J. Bot.*, **2**, 197 (1954)
42. Deevey, E. S. *Amer. J. Sci.*, **241**, 717 (1943)
43. Deevey, E. S. *Amer. Scient.*, **32**, 39 (1944)
44. Dorf, E., in 'The Crust of the Earth'. *Spec. Pap. geol. Soc. Amer.*, **62**, 575 (1955)
45. Dorf, E. *Weatherwise*, **10**, 53 (1957)
46. Dorf, E. *Contr. Palaeont. Univ. Mich.*, **13**, 181 (1959)
47. Douglass, A. E. *Publ. Carneg. Instn*, **289**, I–III (1919, 1928, 1936)
48. Ebers, E. *Vom großen Eiszeitalter*, Verständl. Wissensch. **66**. Springer, Berlin, 1957
49. Edwards, W. N. *Adress. Brit. Ass. Bristol Meet.* (1955); Adv. Sci. No. **46** (1955)
50. Engelhardt, H. *Abh. hess. Landesanst. Bodenforsch.*, **7**, 17 (1922)
51. Firbas, F. *Spät- und nacheiszeitliche Waldgeschichte Mitteleuropas*, **I**. 1949. Jena: Fischer
52. Firbas, F. *Spät- und nacheiszeitliche Waldgeschichte Mitteleuropas*, **II**. 1952. Jena: Fischer
53. Florschütz, F. *Rec. Trav. bot. néer.*, **35**, 932 (1938)
54. Gams, H. *Experientia*, **10**, 357 (1954)
55. Givulescu, R. *Monogr. Geol. Palaeont., Bukarest*, **3** (1956)
56. Givulescu, R. *Neues. Jb. Geol.*, **78**, 216 (1957)
57. Godwin, H. *New Phytol.*, **33**, 278 (1934)
58. Godwin, H. *New Phytol.*, **39**, 370 (1940)
59. Godwin, H. *The History of the British Flora*. 1956. Cambridge: University Press
60. Grangeon, P. *Mém. Soc. Hist. nat., Auvergne*, **6**, 10 (1958)
61. Groß, H. *Eiszeitalter u. Gegenw.*, **7**, 87 (1956)
62. Groß, H. *Abh. naturw. Ver. Bremeá*, **35**, 259 (1958)
63. Hammen, Th. van der. *Leid. geol. Meded.*, **17**, 71 (1951)
64. Hammen, Th. van der. *Boll. geol., Bogotá*, **5**, 53 (1957)
65. Hantke, R. *Denkschr. schweiz. naturf. Ges.*, **80**, 31 (1954)

66. Harris, F. W. *Compt. rend. 8me Congr. internat. Botan.*, Sect. **6**, 268 (1954) Paris
67. Hedberg, O. *Oikos*, **5**, 137 (1954)
68. Heer, O. *Die tertiäre Flora der Schweiz*, I–III. 1855–1859. Winterthur: Wurster
69. Hofmann, E. *Phyton*, **1**, 80 (1948)
70. Hollick, A. *Bull. N.Y. bot. Gdn.*, **12**, 261 (1924)
71. Hollick, A. *Sci. Surv. P.R.*, **7**, 177 (1928)
72. Jessen, K. *Act. archaeol. Copenhagen*, **5**, 185 (1935)
73. Jongmans, W. J. *Compt. rend. 8me Congr. internat. Botan.* 1954. Sect. 6, 135 (1957) Paris
74. Jurasky, K. A. *Biol. gen.*, **10**, 384; **11**, 227; Tl. 2, 1 (1934/35)
75. Kirchheimer, F. *Grundzüge einer Pflanzenkunde der deutschen Braunkohle.* 1937. Halle a.d.S.: Knapp
76. Kirchheimer, F. *Die Laubgewächse der Braunkohlenzeit.* 1957. Halle a.d.S.: Knapp
77. Kräusel, R. *Verh. geol.-mijnb. Genoot. Ned. Kolon.*, **5** (1922)
78. Kräusel, R. *Senckenbergiana*, **5**, 77 (1923)
79. Kräusel, R. and Range, P. *Beitr. geol. Erforsch. dtsch. SchGeb.*, **20**, 1 (1928)
80. Kräusel, R. *Verh. geol.-mijnb. Genoot. Ned. Kolon.*, **9**, 335 (1929)
81. Kräusel, R. *Decheniana*, **95**A, 207 (1937)
82. Kräusel, R. *Abh. bayer. Akad. Wiss.*, n.F. **47**, 3 (1939)
83. Kräusel, R. *Natur u. Volk*, **70**, 446 (1940)
84. Kräusel, R. *Versunkene Floren.* 1950. Frankfurt a.M.: Kramer
85. Kräusel, R. *Abh. senckenb. naturrf. Ges* , **485**, 75 (1951)
86. Kräusel, R. *Palaeontographica*, **97**B, 47 (1955)
87. Kräusel, R. *Senckenbergiana*, **37**, 411 (1956)
88. Kräusel, R. *Bot. Mag., Tokyo*, **69**, 537 (1956)
89. Kräusel, R. *Palaeontographica*, **104**B, 115 (1958)
90. Kräusel, R. and Weyland, H. *Palaeontographica*, **91**B, 7 (1950); **96**B, 106 (1954); **105**B, 101 (1959)
91. Kryshtofovich, A. N. *New Phytol.*, **28**, 303 (1929)
92. Kryshtofovich, A. N. *Palaeobotanica*, **1**, 1 (1956)
93. Leschik, G. *Senckenbergiana*, **40**, 51 (1959)
94. Macko, St. *Trav. Soc. Sci. Wrocław*, **88**B (1957)
95. Mädler, K. *Abh. Senckenb. naturf. Ges.*, **446**, 1 (1939)
96. Mägdefrau, K. *Paläobiologie der Pflanzen*, 3rd edn. 1956. Jena: Fischer
97. Mahabelé, T. S. *Palaeobotanist*, **3**, 33 (1954)
98. Menzel, P. *Beitr. geol. Erforsch. dtsch. SchGeb.*, **18**, 17 (1920)
99. Miki, S. *Jap. J. Bot.*, **11**, 261 (1941)
100. Miki, S. *Bot. Mag., Tokyo*, **89**, 447 (1956)
101. Miki, S. *J. Inst. Polyt., Osaka*, **7**D, 247 (1956)
102. Miki, S. *J. Inst. Polyt., Osaka*, **8**D, 221 (1957)
103. Miki, S., Huziota, K. and Kokawa, Sh. *Proc. imp. Acad. Japan*, **33**, 41 (1957)
104. Moar, N. T. *N.Z. J. Sci.*, **1**, 449, 480 (1958)
105. Moar, N. T. *N.Z. J. Sci.*, **2**, 35 (1959)
106. Monoszon, M. K. *Trans. geogr. Inst. Acad. U.S.S.R.*, **52**, 127 (1952)
107. Monoszon, M. K. *C.R. Acad. Sci. U.R.S.S.*, **114**, 646 (1957)
108. Müller, H. *Nova Acta Leop. Carol.*, **16**, No. 110, 1 (1953)
109. Müller-Stoll, W. R. and Mädel, E. *Senckenbergiana*, **38**, 121 (1957)
110. Müller-Stoll, W. R. and Mädel, E. *Senckenbergiana*, **39** (1959)
111. Murr, J. *Jb. geol. Bundesanst., Wien*, **76**, 153 (1926)
112. Nagy, E. *Jb. ung. geol. Reichsanst.*, **47**, 1 (1958)
113. Nilsson, T. *Geol. Fören. Stockh. Förh.*, **57**, 385 (1935)

114. Nötzold, Th. *Mitt. bad. Landesv. Naturk.*, **6**, 327 (1956)
115. Overbeck, F. K. O., Münning, K. O., Aletes, L. and Averdieck, F. R. *Flora*, **145**, 37 (1957)
116. Pantić, N. *Prvi jugosl. geol. Kongr.* 1954, 123 (1956)
117. Pantić, N. *Ann. géol. Pén. balkan.*, **24**, 209 (1956)
118. Papp, A. *Grundzüge regionaler Stratigraphie, Handbuch der stratigraphischen Geologie*, **III**, *Tertiär* 1. 1957. Stuttgart: Enke
119. Pike, K. M. *Aust. J. Bot.*, **4**, 13 (1956)
120. Potonié, R. *Beih. geol. Jb.*, **31** (1958)
121. Potzger, J. E. and Courtemanche, A. *Rev. canad. geogr.*, **9**, 109 (1955)
122. Potzger, J. E. and Courtemanche, A. *Butler Univ. bot. Stud.*, **13**, 12 (1956)
123. Potzger, J. E. and Courtemanche, A. *Canad. J. Bot.*, **34**, 437 (1956)
124. Rauh, W. *S.B. Heidelberg. Akad. Wiss.*, 1958, **1** (1958)
125. Reid, E. M. and Chandler, M. E. J. *The London clay flora*. 1933. London: British Museum
126. Rodin, R. J. *J. Paleont.*, **25**, 18 (1951)
127. Rytz, W. *Veröff. geobot. Inst. Rübel*, **33**, 189 (1958)
128. Schloemer-Jäger, A. *Palaeontographica*, **104**B, 39 (1958)
129. Schloemer-Jäger, A. *Palaeontographica*, **105**B, 158 (1959)
130. Schulman, E. *Tree-Ring Bull.*, **13**, (2) (1947)
131. Schulman, E. *Bull. Univ. Ariz.*, **18**, (3) (1947)
132. Schulman, E. *Bull. Univ. Ariz.*, **27** (1956)
133. Schwarzbach, M. *Das Klima der Vorzeit*. 1950. Stuttgart: Enke
134. Schweitzer, H.-J. *Palaeontographica*, **104**B, 1 (1958)
135. Sears, P. B., Foreman, F. and Clisby, K. H. *Bull. geol. Soc. Amer.*, **66**, 471 (1955)
136. Selling, O. H. *Spec. Publ. P. Bishop Mus.*, **37–39** (1946–1948)
137. Sernander, R., 'Postglaziale Klimaverschlechterung' in *Ebert, Reallexikon der Vorgeschichte*. 1926. Berlin
138. Seward, A. C. *Plant life through the ages*. 1931. Cambridge: University Press
139. Straka, H. *Neues Jb. Geol.*, **7**, 262 (1956)
140. Takhtajan, A. L. *Bot. Zh. S.S.S.R.*, **42**, 1635 (1957)
141. Takhtajan, A. L. *Bot. Zh. S.S.S.R.*, **43**, 1661 (1958)
142. Tchiguriaeva, A. A. *Grana palyn.*, **1**, 95 (1954)
143. Vent, W. *Wiss. Z. Univ. Jena*, **4**, 467 (1955)
144. Weber, H. *Abhandl. Akad. Wiss. u. Lit. Math-naturw. Kl. Mainz* No. 3 (1958)
145. Welten, M. *Ber. schweiz. bot. Ges.*, **67**, 33 (1957)
146. Wettstein, R. *Denkschr. Akad. Wiss. Wien*, **59**, 479 (1892)
147. Weyland, H. *Palaeontographica*, **103**B, 34 (1957)
148. Weyland, H. *Fortschr. Geol. Rheinl-Westf.*, **I** and **II**, 527 (1958)
149. Woldstedt, P. *Norddeutschland und angrenzende Gebiete im Eiszeitalter*, 2nd edn. 1955. Stuttgart: Koehler
150. Woldstedt, P. *Das Eiszeitalter—I. Die allgemeinen Erscheinungen*, 2nd edn. 1954. Stuttgart: Enke
151. Woldstedt, P. *Das Eiszeitalter—II. Europa, Vorderasien und Nordafrika*, 2nd edn. 1958. Stuttgart: Enke
152. Zaklinskaya, E. D. *Trans. geogr. Inst. Acad. U.S.S.R.*, **59**, 3 (1953)
153. Zeuner, F. E. *Dating the Past*. 4th edn. 1958. London: Methuen
154. Zinderen-Bakker, E. M. van. *Proc. 3rd Pan-Afr. Congr. Prehist.*, **56**, (1955)

XI

The Climatic History of Europe and North America

M. Schwarzbach

I. Introduction

The climatic histories of Europe and North America have many features in common. This is due to a similar latitudinal position, at least for the later history of the earth, which perhaps shows itself best in the fact that the great Pleistocene glaciations follow a similar course in both continents. During the Palaeozoic Era the climatic history of both continents is in marked contrast to that of Gondwanaland. On the other hand there are naturally plenty of differences between them; for even the different spatial dimensions or a difference in strike of mountain chains must lead to radical climatic differentiation.

The climatic history of the earth is above all characterized by the contrast of 'ice ages' with warm ages, when polar ice-caps were absent. This, however, is not so important in Europe and North America because the great Permo-Carboniferous Ice Age had little effect in this region, and thus a really warm climate prevailed right into high latitudes from the Cambrian to the end of the Tertiary period—over 500 million years.

There are not many comprehensive descriptions of regional climatic history, with the exception of the Quaternary period. The textbooks of palaeoclimatology mostly focus on other problems, although Ruedeman[145] has given a short but lucid account of North America, while a detailed account is given by Schwarzbach.[161]

II. The Pre-Cambrian Era

II.1 *General*

The farther we go back in the earth's history, the more uncertain becomes the reconstruction of the climatic picture. In Pre-Cambrian times not only do we lack most of the organic climatic evidence, but in the absence of fossils it is also difficult to correlate correctly the few remaining indications of climate. Thus chronological uncertainties of some 100 million years often arise, yet, as it is known from the Quaternary period, even some 10 000 years can bring a complete reversal of climatic conditions, so that the most exact time comparisons are essential.

II.2 *Glacial Evidence*

It is of prime significance that there are moraine-like deposits even in the Pre-Cambrian era. While it is true that in Europe only a few uncertain discoveries have been made in Finland, traces of the *'Huronian Ice Age'* have been discerned in North America, which Coleman[42] considers to be one of the earth's greatest ice ages. It is characterized by the Cobalt 'tillite' (Gowganda Formation, late Huronian) which can be traced from Lake Huron via Cobalt and Noranda to Lake Chibougama; in this distance of at least 800 km, striated boulders and glaciated pavements have occasionally been found.

Likewise, Coleman placed 'tillites' of the Medicine Bow Range in South Wyoming (west from Laramie; Snowy Range Series) and of the Wasatch Mountains into the Huronian.

The Snowy Range Series in Wyoming have been comprehensively described by Blackwelder.[23] Their precise age is not known but an early Huronian is suggested by Fenton.[61] The 8000-m thick succession contains three tillite horizons 40 m, 8 m, and 30 m thick, and also some banded phyllites ('varves'). In the upper part of the succession, however, dolomites appear (algal reefs?) so that a progression from cooler to warmer conditions may be accepted. The Fern Creek tillites in Michigan might well be earliest Huronian[89] but it is possible that they might belong to the next stage.

A still older occurrence which might be mentioned is the tillite-like boulders in the Keewatin of the Upper Lake (Doré conglomerates) and in the Timiskaming Series (Timiskaming Lake, S. Canada), the Seine Series (West of Lake Superior) and the Sudbury Series (Wanipigow conglomerates). The significance of all these occurrences is very uncertain and even Coleman, who was strongly inclined to glacial interpretations of them, has not ruled out other possibilities of origin in some particular instances. Quite recently, moreover, the glacial origin even of the Gowganda tillite has been questioned (E. L. Winterer, personal communication to J. C. Crowell[45]).

A recent survey of the relationships of these tillites is shown in Table I (absolute age after Farquhar and Russell[60]).

Table I. The Relationship of the Pre-Cambrian Tillites of North America

Cobalt series (Gowganda) Snowy Range series; Fern Creek	} Huronian	1300 million years
Timiskaming, Seine, Sudbury Series	Later Archean	} Older than Huronian
Doré conglomerate	Earlier Archean (Keewatin)	

II.3 *Other Climatic Evidence*

Apart from these 'moraines' there is little other climatic evidence. Considerable warmth can be inferred during late Algonkian times on the evidence of the bioherms up to 50 m thick[61] in the Belt Series in the Belt Mountains and the Glacier-Waterton Lakes Parks areas in Montana and south-west Alberta. The same investigators[61] also conclude that fairly arid conditions existed, since among other things the red colour of the sediments is combined with desiccation fissures. A similar argument holds for the red sediments in the late Pre-Cambrian of Northern Europe, the Dalasandstone and Jotnian sandstone in Sweden, and Torridonian sandstone in Scotland. It is remarkable that no Pre-Cambrian salt deposits are known here or in other parts of the earth,[107] but salt crystals from the Belt formation have been mentioned.[61]

III. The Eo-Cambrian Era

III.1 *General Notes on Eo-Cambrian Glacial Traces*

The turn of the Pre-Cambrian–Cambrian era presents an important palaeoclimatological datum—actually the first known in the earth's history. In order to distinguish the exceptional position of this period of time, it has been described as the Eo-Cambrian or Infra-Cambrian. In this period, which dates from something over 520 million years, tillites and tillite-like formations were so widely spread on the earth that one is justified in speaking of a world-wide ice age (Varanger Ice Age of Kulling[102-103]).

Admittedly two things must be borne in mind: (1) that only one part of the occurrences can be considered with any certainty as genuine tillites and (2) that in by no means all of them is an absolutely similar age established.

III.2 *Europe*

In Europe the occurrences are limited entirely to the northern part of the continent. The most certain discoveries are those made in Norway and Sweden, of which detailed accounts have been published.[69,103] Striated pavements (Varanger Fjord) have been found, in addition to striated boulders. The tillites, which are directly overlain by fossiliferous lower Cambrian rocks, occur in a series in which arkose occurs and which is known in Norway as the 'Sparagmite series'.

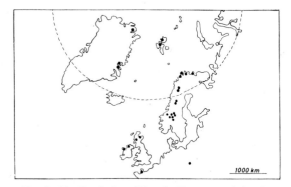

Fig. 1. Eo-Cambrian tillites in Europe and Arctis.

Eo-Cambrian tillites or similar rocks are said to appear in the British Isles, and to include the boulder-bearing graywacke and similar rocks in the Dalradian of Scotland and Northern Ireland.[3,174] The characteristic horizon (with granite blocks up to 1 m in diameter) can be traced for over 430 km; the boulders are thought to have been deposited from icebergs. Further occurrences are instanced in Normandy, where the tillites form the steep cliffs near Granville,[46] and finally (still very uncertain) they are also cited in the Eisengebirge in the north-eastern Bohemian Massif.[62]

III.3 *Arctis*

Glacial traces play an important rôle in the Arctic region, namely at Spitzbergen (Hekla Hook formation of Nordostland) and in Greenland.

In the Hekla Hook formation of Nordostland (Spitzbergen) Kulling[102] has identified *ca.* 100-m thick tillites (Sveanor tillites) with striated boulders (mostly dolomites). The overlying Cape Sparre formation has yielded fossils which unfortunately have no stratigraphic value but nevertheless could belong to the Cambrian era.

In east Greenland (latitude 73°) two tillite horizons occur in the Cape Oswald formation (up to 540 m thick), separated by a sandstone–shale–limestone series.[139] The lower tillite mainly contains limestone boulders, while the upper contains gneiss, granite and quartzporphyry, suggesting two separate ice ages. In the succeeding tillite-bearing Canyon Formation there are fine varves. A Lower Cambrian fauna appears about 400 m above the tillites.

In north-west Greenland there appear to be no tillites but in southern Peary Land (latitude 82°) they are again identified.[182] Here there is a single horizon up to 100 m thick; the base is horizontal for at least 100 km and the boulders (mostly quartzite), which are up to 3 m in size, are striated, so that the interpretation of these as moraines appears fairly certain. Fossiliferous lower Cambrian follows 750–800 m higher in the succession.

III.4 *North America*

In North America the conditions are less clear. Traces of Eo-Cambrian glaciation have been found in Utah.[25]

Murray[123] described a polished and striated surface of Michigamme slate (Upper Huronian) at L'Anse, Michigan, which is overlain by Jacobsville sandstone (Cambrian or late Keweenawan?) and could thus belong to either a late Eo-Cambrian or late Keweenawan period of glaciation.

III.5 *Summary*

The general problem of the Eo-Cambrian glaciations in Europe and North America can only be partly resolved. Almost all occurrences in these two continents lie in regions which were also glaciated in the Quaternary period; so that they should actually present no more problems than the Quaternary ice ages do. Only the occurrences in other continents and the climatic development in the following Palaeozoic era make the Eo-Cambrian age appear puzzling in climatological respects.

IV. The Early Palaeozoic Era

IV.1 *Reef Belts*

The Cambrian, Ordovician, Silurian and Devonian periods may be considered collectively. There is still little climatic evidence available for these periods, yet what there is forms a relatively consistent picture. A characteristic of this picture is the fact that both continents show indications of a warm and very dry climate right up into high latitudes. The reef belt, which in the Cambrian was characterized by archaeocyathinae and later by coral limestones, lies farther north; see the maps published by Schwarzbach[160] or, for example, the spread of the middle Silurian Niagaran reefs as in Lowen-

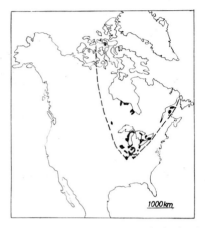

Fig. 2. Niagaran reef areas in North America (Silurian); simplified after Lowenstam.[109]

stam[108,109] (Fig. 2). In this period the spread of reefs in North America is particularly great; it begins in the South of Illinois and Indiana 4° farther north than the present-day coral reef limit and extends to latitude 75° (Cornwallis Island). 'This depicts the most extensive areal spread of reefs in North America during geological time' (Lowenstam[109]).

In Europe the Silurian reefs of Gotland and the Devonian of the Ardennes[106] and of the Rhineland[91] constitute exceptionally well investigated examples.

IV.2 *Evidence of Arid Climatic Conditions*

Evaporites constitute the most significant evidence of an arid climate.[107] In the Cambrian period in our region they are comparatively rare (gypsum in the middle Cambrian of Devon Island, arctic North America; reference 104; and in the Macdougal Beds of the Mackenzie Range); rock salt, however, is economically important in the Upper Gotlandian of northern U.S.A. and of Ontario and in the Devonian of South Canada, just as on the Russian platform. There are also the Silurian sand dunes (Sylvania sandstone in Ohio and Michigan), and desiccation fissures have been found in Maryland. The sandstone facies of the Old Red Sandstone in Northern Europe,[64] Spitzbergen and Greenland, is further evidence of a periodically arid climate.

IV.3 *Glacial Traces*

In Europe there are no definite early Palaeozoic glacial traces at all, and in North America they are at the most very sporadic. Most of what has been described as glacial is now disproved or quite uncertain; for example, the widely distributed Ordovician breccias of the lower St. Lawrence River, are now identified as submarine landslide masses.[12,129] Whether in fact specific occurrences, especially in Alaska, really represent tillites requires rescrutiny involving modern techniques (Silurian of Heceta Island, latitude 55–60°N,[94] and other places in Alaska according to Blackwelder;[24] also south-east Columbia after Shepherd[170] and Maine after Smith[172]). The Devonian 'glacial traces' of the northern hemisphere have been repeatedly represented as doubtful, especially the 'tillites' of the Mediterranean island Minorca, for these are far more likely to be submarine slip masses.[165]

IV.4 *General Climatic Picture*

The way in which the climatic conditions of Europe and North America fit into the whole picture of the earth at that time can be particularly well illustrated by the example of the Devonian period:[165] both these northern continents belong to a warm climatic zone, in contrast to South America and Central and South Africa. The position of the geomagnetic pole, which is determined palaeomagnetically, falls in the south Atlantic region;[43] if one

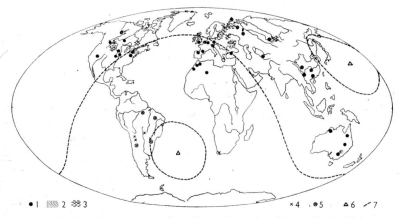

Fig. 3. Climatic map of the Devonian, after Schwarzbach.[165]

1: reef limestones.
2: Old Red Sandstone facies.
3: evaporites (after Lotze[107]).
4. Iapo Formation and Table Mountain tillite.
5: upper Devonian tillite.
6: palaeomagnetic south pole (after Runcorn) from which the north pole, equator (7) and polar circle have been constructed.
B = bauxite.

assumes that the geographical pole is also in the same position at that time the peculiar climatic conditions can be explained, for the equator would then pass through North America and Europe.

V. The Late Palaeozoic Era

V.1 Glacial Traces

In the main, similar conditions appear to obtain in the late Palaeozoic as in the early Palaeozoic, for the evidence of glaciation lies still more clearly in the Southern Hemisphere, whilst the Northern Hemisphere exhibits abundant evidence of a warm and to some extent arid climate (see map in reference 84). Of the reported occurrences of glacial deposits in the Northern Hemisphere the only one which is regarded by many investigators as being glacial is the Squantum 'tillite' (upper Roxbury conglomerate) near Boston.[105,152,153] These 'tillites' reach a maximum thickness of 200 m and contain striated boulders. Their exact age is not known; some consider them of Permian origin, others rank them as earlier (Devonian of Bell[18]). It must further be mentioned that very recently doubts were expressed[45] even about the glacial origin of the Squantum tillite; similarly, the glacial interpretation of the boulders found in the Carboniferous Caney shale and Johns Valley slate (Ouachita Mountain, Oklahoma) and in the Haymond formation (Pennsylvanian of West Texas) has given way to the interpretation of them as slip masses or similar phenomena.[79,93,99,119] The same applies to the Permian 'moraines' in North Mexico.[85,126]

In fact the North American tillites do not fit well into the climatic picture of early times. They could at most have originated from mountain glaciers,[52] but certainly not from continental sheets.

V.2 Coral Reefs and Other Limestones

Among the evidence for a warm climate are coral reefs, although these are not so widespread as in the earlier Palaeozoic. Carboniferous limestone facies are nevertheless intensively developed in Western Europe (Carboniferous limestone in England, Belgium and elsewhere), in Eastern Europe, in North America (60-m thick cryptozoon reefs in New Mexico[134]), and in the polar regions (Bear Island, Spitzbergen). The limestones of the Upper Carboniferous extend into the Permian epoch in some places (South Ural, Alaska, Arctic), and Permian foraminiferal limestones are found particularly in the European Tethys (Carnic Alps, Balkan region). The (upper) Permian coral reef which has been most thoroughly investigated is the 70-km long Capitan reef in the Guadeloupe mountains.[127]

Stehli[173] made use of the various species in the Permian fauna to infer a cool climate in what are now polar regions, but in doing so he has grossly underrated the element of chance involved in finding fossils (see also reference 14). The limestone facies richly developed even in the far north (Permian limestones in Alaska, coral limestones up to more than 100 m thick in the upper Permian of East Greenland) is rather evidence of a really warm climate there too, although that is not to say that under the influence of the great Gondwana glaciations it was not on the whole cooler during the Permian than in the preceding periods.

V.3 Coal Flora and some Other Climatic Evidence

One particular characteristic of the Carboniferous, above all of the Upper Carboniferous, is the extensive coal beds both in Europe and in North America. Their palaeoclimatological significance has been much discussed. For comparison one can quote the modern spread of peat in the predominantly cool, mid-latitudes just as easily as the 'tropical' habitat of coal flora, and accordingly infer either a cool or a warm climate. Yet one thing must not be overlooked; peat accumulates if the decomposition of the vegetable material is slow. This happens today, predominantly in cool climates, but it is very probable that the same effect would be obtained in a warm climate if rapid sedimentation occurred. The latter has certainly been the case in the tectonically labile troughs in the Variscan mountains. Accordingly cool and warm climates alike in the Carboniferous could lead to peat accumulation, hence the presence of the thick coal formation alone is not valid climatic evidence for the determination of temperatures, although it does indicate high humidity. The vast extent of the European and North American coal regions shows that one must not think of 'oases' with locally high water levels, but instead a really humid climate (particularly in the Upper Carboniferous) must be presumed.

Besides the limestones previously mentioned, certain peculiarities of the Carboniferous flora may perhaps be quoted as evidence of a simultaneously warm and humid climate (tree ferns—kauliflorie). The monstrous size of some of the insects and the frequency of Lingula, fire-clays, which are derived from laterites,[82,100] are further evidence of this.

V.4 The Problem of Periodic Climatic Fluctuations

In the Carboniferous period many workers assume a seasonally uniform climate because the Carboniferous woods of the Northern Hemisphere rarely show annual rings. This argument is not very positive, for today some tropical trees show rhythmical growth phenomena, and one must concede as much seasonal climatic change to the forests in the Carboniferous as in the present tropics. Thus it seems rather to be a matter of the primitive state of development of the Carboniferous plants, which could not react to seasonal fluctuations as modern plants do.[4]

How far the rhythmic sedimentation of the North American and European Upper Carboniferous period (cyclothems) reflect a manifold climatic change of a greater magnitude, is disputed. Many workers assign tectonic, that is, non-climatic causes for the origin of the cyclothems. Furthermore, with a non-climatic interpretation of this kind, it would be credible that a less marked climatic rhythm parallels the sedimentary rhythms, because the changing tectonic–orographical conditions would also influence the climate.[192]

On the other hand, many workers think the cause of the cyclothems was climatologically-induced fluctuations in the sea level, although this hardly seems likely. The comparison with the Quaternary ice age and its eustatic fluctuations is not admissible, for then we would have to accept hundreds of glacials and interglacials in the Upper Carboniferous, for which there is no supporting evidence. For the time being, connections between Carboniferous and Permian fine stratification (varve stratification) and large climatic fluctuations[98,144] appear to be similarly problematical.[107,161] In any case the proof of the 'sun-spot cycle' in these sediments has not as yet been convincingly demonstrated.

V.5 *Aridity in the Carboniferous and Permian*

There is no lack of gypsum in the Carboniferous (occurrences in the U.S.A., the Mississippian of Nova Scotia and New Brunswick; Spitzbergen and East Greenland and elsewhere) but rock salt is completely lacking. This accords well with the humid climate which we have already assumed for the wide-

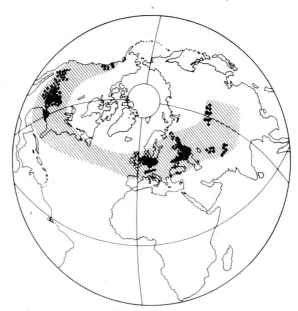

Fig. 4. Northern hemisphere evaporite zone during the Permian (after Lotze).

spread coal fields. In the Lower Carboniferous, North America might have been affected by monsoon winds, caused by a land mass in the north-east, with a sea to the south, as suggested by Bucher and others[34,131] interpreting the NW–SE ripples found in the Bedford formation in Ohio.

The conditions in the Permian are quite different, and rocks of this formation constitute the main source of salt both in Europe and in the U.S.A. There are extensive potash salt deposits in the lower Permian of western Ural foreland and in the Upper Permian of Germany and south-eastern U.S.A. If we take the equally extensive facies of the European Rotliegendes and the American Coconino sandstone, together with red fanglomeratic sediments, silicification and aeolian deposits, then everything combines to form the picture of a warm and at times (especially in the Zechstein) extremely dry climate in vast areas of North America and Europe. The high aridity is proved above all by the salt deposits; while the red products of weathering, on the other hand, were washed into the sedimentary basins from marginal areas having seasonal precipitation.

V.6 *Wind Direction*

Particulars of the wind directions in the Permian are interesting, even if they provide partly random values, and not necessarily average values.

Europe. Rotliegendes of the Nahe basin; wind from SW;[142] Zechstein of Central Germany: SSW to ESE;[112,143] Permian of England: E.[128,158,171]

North America. Late Palaeozoic and Upper Mesozoic of the Colorado Plateau: wind from N;[136] Upper Pennsylvanian to Lower Permian of Wyoming and Utah: NE.[128]

Shotton[171] considers that England at that time lay in a lower latitude and Poole[136] that the Trade Wind belt reached farther to the North. Thus both theories would fit in with the possibility, already reviewed in the section on the Devonian, of an equator running through North America–Europe. A similar view has been expressed by Opdyke and Runcorn[128,149] and Schove *et al.*[158] Clearly, however, many more observations of wind direction are required.

V.7 *Summary*

The arid conditions of the Permian persist in the Triassic, and in this respect the European and North American Permian belongs climatologically much more to the Mesozoic. Yet if one considers the earth as a whole, the mainly damp Carboniferous and the arid Permian of the northern regions have an important feature in common; evidence of positive glaciation—as already mentioned at the beginning of this chapter—is lacking, whereas in the Southern Hemisphere such evidence does exist. Thus in the North conditions are the opposite of those in Gondwanaland.

Certainly the great tectonic events of the late Palaeozoic—the young folded mountains of Variscan (Hercynian) orogeny—must have exerted a considerable influence on the climate. In particular the aridity of the Permian (as that of the Triassic) seems to be conditioned partly by the increased spread in the land area.

S

VI. The Mesozoic Era

VI.1 *Triassic*

The Triassic, which likewise is mostly geokratic, is climatologically so closely linked with the Permian that even the sediments are very similar and often cannot be separated stratigraphically ('Permo-Triassic'). In the Triassic, too, evidence of a warm and arid climate is found extensively. Typical of such evidence is the German Buntsandstein, with red sandstones and shales almost devoid of fossils, and closely connected with them are the evaporite deposits (rock salt occurs particularly in the Middle Muschelkalk but is also found in other horizons in the Triassic). This 'Germanic facies' of the Triassic can be found elsewhere in Europe (in England with its rich Keuper salt deposits, Spain, Sardinia; and the potash salts in the Keuper of Southern France). Somewhat damper periods are occasionally indicated by beds such as the 'Lettenkohle' of the Lower Keuper, while the red-coloured fanglomerates evince Savannah-like, i.e. semi-arid–marginal, regions.

North American equivalents of the variegated sandstone are the Newark Group in the Appalachian area and the extensive red beds of the West (Moenkopi and Chinle,[114] 'Painted Desert' of Arizona, 'Great Red Valley' of the Black Hills). Gypsum deposits are widespread in the Triassic of the U.S.A.

Striking climatic evidence of the European Triassic is afforded by the massive reefs, particularly well developed in the South Tyrolean Dolomites and the Northern Calcareous Alps. Coral reefs have been instanced in Nevada.[122] The Upper Triassic limestones hundreds of metres in thickness in the Alaska range[117] and the *Stegocephalus* found in Spitzbergen and East Greenland show that even the extreme north had a mild climate.

The statement that middle Triassic moraines are present on the Russian platform (at Gorki, east of Moscow[180]) cannot be reconciled with these climatic features. The claim rests mainly on unbedded breccias, some of which contain gypsum cement, which till now were classed as Quaternary moraines, but which were covered by the Jurassic deposits. This evidence must be examined more closely to see whether it is not, in fact, a fanglomerate.

VI.2 *General Climatic Conditions in the Jurassic and Cretaceous Periods*

Although the climate of the Jurassic and Cretaceous periods was in no way uniform throughout that time, for example the Liassic period counts as relatively cool and damp, it can be said in general that, during these periods, North America and Europe were still much warmer than they are today although a marked division into a very warm zone in the south and a 'boreal' zone nearer the pole can be established. The main evidence for this is as follows.

(*a*) The northern limit of reef limestones during the Jurassic passes through England, that is, it lies 30° farther north than today. In North America the limestone facies is less distinctly marked, and it is significant that Heim,[83] coming as he does from the Alps with their well-developed limestones, thought of cool sea currents (similar to the present day Californian current) to account for the dearth of limestone in the Rockies.

(b) The great saurians (cold-blooded animals needing warmth) live in the later Mesozoic period as far north as latitudes of Alberta (Canada) and England.

(c) Rich tree floras still flourish in Greenland during the Cretaceous (bread-fruit tree, *Artocarpus*, among others).

(d) Bauxites are widely spread in the lower Cretaceous period of Europe (Southern France, Hungary;[16] Harz foreland;[186] Urals[101]).

VI.3 *Determinations of Temperature by the* ^{18}O *Method*

Supplementary climatic data are offered by 'exact' temperature determinations based on the ^{18}O method.[110,124,185] These yielded the values listed in Table II.

The result of comparing these figures with present-day values is the same as the comparison of other climatic features: namely, considerably higher

Table II. ^{18}O-Temperatures for the Mesozoic Era

Locality	Age	Mesozoic temp. in °C	Modern sea temp. in °C
Skye (Scotland)	Jurassic	17–23	7–13
England	Belemnites of the Upper Cretaceous	16–23	5–15
Krim	Campanian	17·6	
Volga and Emba region	Campanian	15–21	
Tennessee	Maestrichtian	20–27	

temperatures in the Mesozoic era than today. According to Lowenstam and Epstein[110] a temperature maximum occurs in the Upper Cretaceous in the Coniacian-Santonian. According to the ^{18}O determinations, the difference from today seems to be rather less than one would expect from the other climatic evidence. The uncertainty of the method may possibly play some part in this.

VI.4 *Cretaceous 'Gulf Stream'*

As early as 1847, Roemer while engaged on investigations in Texas, had recognized that the Cretaceous 'Reef' facies with rudistids stretched farther north in Europe than in North America, and he had compared this with the analogous modern conditions brought about by the Gulf Stream.

VI.5 *Rainfall Conditions in the Jurassic and Cretaceous Periods*

The arid climatic conditions and evaporites which prevailed in the Permian and Triassic periods were beginning to recede in the Jurassic and were later replaced by coal seams. Bauxites should also be mentioned here. The gypsum and salt belt in the Upper Jurassic lay in Western U.S.A., where aeolian Navajo sandstone with its dunes also occurs (Zion National Park, Utah; Rainbow Natural Bridge); in Europe, gypsum is occasionally found in Sussex, North Germany and the Jurassic of the Swiss Jura. During the Cretaceous there are only sporadic, insignificant occurrences of gypsum in both continents. Thus the rainfall in the later Mesozoic era is on the whole more akin to the present day than to that of the Permian and Triassic periods.

VII. The Tertiary Period

VII.1 *General*

Although up until the end of the Mesozoic era the climatic picture can only be reconstructed in its broader aspects, more and more details can be recognized for the Tertiary period (and still more for the Quaternary). This is chiefly because faunal and floral evidence from the more recent epochs can be compared directly with present-day forms.

General characteristics of the Tertiary period are as follows: the early Tertiary was considerably warmer everywhere than today, the limit of the warm to temperate zone lay on average 10–15° north of its present position; and the polar regions still belong to the temperate zone. (Compare the climatic maps for the early Tertiary by Chaney[38] and Schwarzbach.[159])

In the course of the Tertiary period a gradual cooling-off process set in, leading to the establishment of conditions approximating to those of the present day.

VII.2 *Temperate Conditions in Europe and North America*

Numerous plant finds bear witness to the warm climate of the early Tertiary—plants which are found today in the temperate climatic zone are of subtropical character. Characteristic of these are, for example, palm trees, whose northern limit during the Early Tertiary lay in Alaska (62°N) and England (50°N).

In addition to specific identification, general characteristics of flora can be used, as for example the high percentage of smooth-rimmed leaves or leaves with serrated edges, though such characteristics indicating a hotter climate (Table III) must be used with caution. The work of several investigators has been of guidance in this field.[13, 37, 151]

The plant evidence is supported by other climatic evidence. Coral reefs still exist in the European area, albeit to limited extent; thus around the edges of the Miocene (Vindobonian) sea from Morocco via Catalonia to Southern France and thence to the Near East, coral reefs occur.[41] The Sarmatian sea of Southern Russia was similarly fringed.[191] Crocodiles which today are not found farther north than North Africa and Florida were prolific in the Eocene epoch in the Geisel valley near Halle, in England, and in the Early Tertiary of New Jersey. Lateritic weathering was predominant in the Early Tertiary of Southern Central Europe, Northern Ireland[58] and Arkansas.[75]

The differences of present-day conditions are on the whole greater in Europe than in North America although it is true that the 20°C yearly

Table III. The Frequency of Occurrence of Smooth-Edged Leaves in Dicotyledon Flora

Flora	Frequency, %
Eocene ⎰ Wilcox flora (Gulf coastal plain[20])	87
Goshen flora (Oregon[39])	61
Geiseltal near Halle (Central Germany[159])	75
Recent tropical wood, Panama[13]	88
Recent wood in temperature climate (North-east Germany)	24

marine isotherm on the west coast of North America in the Paleocene epoch lay north of 49°N (the present position being 27°N), as has been shown by means of molluscs.[54] It has thus shifted by about 20° of latitude. The flora of Alaska also indicates considerable differences from modern times; but at least on the east coast the coral reefs lay only a little further north than now [68] and the surface temperature of 28·3°C of Middle Oligocene north of the

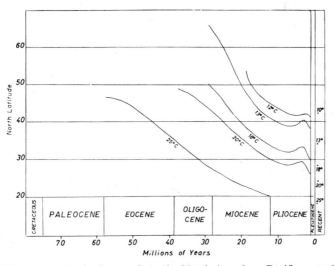

Fig. 5. February marine isotherms along the North American Pacific coast from the Palaeocene to recent times, simplified after Durham.[54]

Bahama Islands as determined by Emiliani[57] with the [18]O method corresponds to the present August temperature there (28°C), if this determination can be accepted. The temperature of the Miocene epoch was found to be only 24·1°.

The favourable climate that predominated in Europe, particularly in the Early Tertiary period, might have been influenced to a considerable degree by the broad sea connection that still existed between the Mediterranean Sea and the warm Indian ocean.

As evidence for marked seasonal climatic fluctuation, the very finely banded oil shale of the Eocene Green River formation in Colorado, Utah and Wyoming[29] deserves especial mention. European examples are afforded by the Oligocene molasse sandstone of Lausanne[22] and the Oligocene lignite of Rott near Cologne.[161]

VII.3 *Climatic Deterioration in the Tertiary Period*

The gradual falling-off of temperatures during the Tertiary period is well illustrated by the flora: at first, warmth-loving species which today are found in more southerly regions preponderate; but later more and more indigenous species come to the fore. An example for north-west Europe is given in Table IV.

Table IV. Occurrence of Modern Genera in Fossilized Flora of North-west Europe[140, 141]

Flora	Frequency, %
Lower Pleistocene epoch (Cromer)	97
Lower Pleistocene epoch (Tegelen)	78
Upper Pliocene epoch (Reuver)	53
Lower Oligocene epoch	34
Upper Eocene epoch (Hordle Beds)	23
Lower Eocene epoch (London Clay)	2

The yearly average temperatures (for north-west and central Europe) have been calculated and are given in Table V.

Table V. Yearly Averages of Temperatures in the Tertiary Period of Europe

Epoch	Locality	Author	Yearly average in °C Tertiary	Modern
Eocene	London Clay	Reid and Chandler[141]	21	ca. 10
Upper Oligocene	Rott near Cologne	Weyland and Schwarzbach[162]	18 ⎤	
Miocene	Oeningen (Lake Constance)	Hantke[80]	16 ⎬	ca. 9
Pliocene	Frankfurt a.M.	Estimated after Madler[113]	14 ⎦	

For the more central latitudes of western U.S.A. an instructive climatic graph has been given by Dorf.[51]

It appears then that climatic variations similar to those of the Quaternary are indicated, at least in the Pliocene epoch. This is shown not only by glaciations which are followed by warmer times (as in Iceland[166]), but also by the fauna of the marine Pliocene epoch of Tjornes in Iceland,[15] or by the pollen flora of the Pliocene brown coal of Wallensen (Harz foreland[2]). In the latter case, other factors too (e.g. rainfall) could be decisive.

VII.4 *Rainfall in Europe*

The extensive brown coal beds in Germany—with stocks of 13 milliards (thousand millions) tons in the Eocene and 45 milliard tons in the Oligocene–Miocene—are proof of considerable humidity for long stretches of the Tertiary; but at different times and in different places the dryness was still more extreme than today. In Europe certain places must be particularly mentioned in this connection:

(1) *The Upper Eocene to Lower Oligocene* of the Paris basin and northern Pyrenees foreland (thick beds of gypsum), and of the Ebro basin and Upper Rhine Valley (potash salt).

(2) *The Lower Miocene* in Rheinhessen (rock salt), and in the northern Carpathian foreland (rock salt and in part potash salt).

(3) *The Upper Miocene* (Sarmatian) in the Spanish and Italian Tertiary basins (rock salt, with potash salt in Sicily); in the Vienna Basin (desert flora and fauna [19,177,178]); and in Bessarabia, between Dnjstr and Pruth. Although in Bessarabia the Lower Sarmatian is still fairly humid (1 000–1 100 mm),[88] the Middle Sarmatian is drier (600–700 mm).

(4) *The Pliocene* of the Aquitanian basin, which according to Crouzel[44] is drier than the Miocene (*cf.* the 'Aegeis' dunes[116]).

It seems, therefore, that we are concerned, at times, with a fairly general widespread tendency towards aridity, as in the Upper Eocene and Sarmatian. A slight northward shift of the modern north African dry belt would explain the conditions during these periods, which may also have been influenced in part by marine regression. In any case a combination with the brown coal periods of Germany gives the following results:

Upper Miocene	Marked aridity
Lower Miocene	High humidity (brown coals)
Lower Oligocene/Upper Eocene	Generally arid
Middle Eocene	High humidity (brown coals)

Local orographic factors must be added to the spatial shifting of a dry belt, with the rising mountains holding off the rain-bearing winds. In the upper Rhine valley (Vosges), the Carpathian and Pyrenean forelands and the Vienna Basin (Alps), such an influence could easily be credited.

Russia develops somewhat differently from the rest of Europe, for during the Tertiary period it was generally much more moist than today and the Ukraine was not the predominantly unwooded steppes it is now. This is shown clearly by the vegetation maps of Pokrowskaja[135] (compare with Klotz[97]). In the Eocene of the Ukraine, evergreen 'tropical' and subtropical woodlands predominated; in the Oligocene mixed coniferous–deciduous woods contained many evergreen subtropical species and *Taxodium*; and then in the Miocene deciduous trees were succeeded by coniferous–deciduous

woods. Not until the Upper Miocene do the desert floras establish themselves. This change is undoubtedly closely connected with the palaeo-
graphical development of eastern Europe; during the Eocene an east-Uralian
sea-way joined the extensive Tethys with the North Sea, but marine
regression followed in the course of the Tertiary period until the present
continental state was reached. The temperatures of the Pliocene epoch in
eastern Europe were clearly higher than at the present day. This is shown
by the flora (for example, in the middle Pliocene Kinelj-beds of the Volga
estuary, *Juglans*, *Carya*, *Taxodium*, *Sequoia* occur [78]) as well as by the severe
red earth weathering in the Pliocene of Batum on the Black Sea.[17]

VII.5 *Rainfall in North America*

The influence of the mountains in western North America is shown in a
classical manner.[9, 10, 38] The present-day intermontane desert regions, particularly the Great Basin and Mohave desert, have yielded numerous
Cretaceous and Neozoic flora, which prove rich forest vegetation in the
Upper Cretaceous period and in most of the Tertiary period. The climate

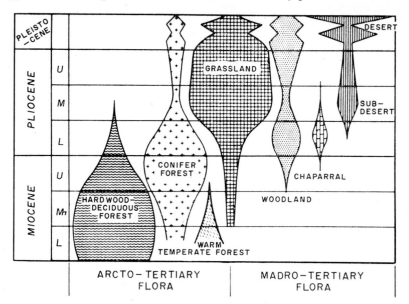

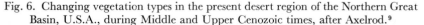

Fig. 6. Changing vegetation types in the present desert region of the Northern Great
Basin, U.S.A., during Middle and Upper Cenozoic times, after Axelrod.[9]

was at first warm and damp. The first indications of subhumid climate are
found in the Middle Eocene, Green River flora of the central Rocky Mountain region, then in the somewhat later (Lower Miocene) Florissant flora of
central Colorado. In the Miocene, the Great Basin contained an arcto-
Tertiary hardwood deciduous and conifer forest flora, with 900–1300 mm

rainfall uniformly spread over the whole year; the Mohave Basin contained a madro-Tertiary 'live oak woodland, chaparral and thorn forest vegetation' with a semi-arid climate and winter rainfall of 400–650 mm. A low mountain uplift occurred at this time in the west, and the coastal slopes carried a flora of a more markedly humid climate. In the Middle Pliocene a semi-arid climate developed with a preponderance of grass and shrubland; the rainfall is estimated at *ca.* 400 mm in the north, 250–300 mm in the south. The main uplift of the Sierra Nevada and coastal mountains followed still later; leading finally to the present-day state with 100–200 mm rainfall in the Great Basin. Certainly this condition was reached prior to the events of the Pleistocene.

How precise man's knowledge already is about the rainfall conditions, particularly of the late Tertiary period, is shown by the rainfall maps of the larger regions (Late Tertiary of south-western U.S.A.[10]), even if the maps cannot be taken quite literally. A weather forecast has been jokingly given[10] for a 'summer's day at Middlegate' (Lower Pliocene of Nevada): 'Continued clear with afternoon showers'.

VII.6 *Arctis in the Tertiary period*

Especially impressive are the rich tree floras of Arctis which were partly described 200 years ago and which are found in regions north of the present-day polar tree limit. The pioneer in this work was O. Heer, whose findings reported in his 'Flora fossilis artica' (1868–1883) have been revised many times (Berry[20]). Important floras are known from Iceland, Greenland, Spitzbergen, Grinnell-land (81° 45′N—the nearest to the pole of the Tertiary fossil floras!). Unfortunately the more exact stratigraphic reconstruction is uncertain, although the floras everywhere are of a cool-moderate climate. Since it is apparent from other observations that no substantial shifting of the pole is acceptable for the Tertiary, the additional problem arises here in the North of the unusual light conditions (polar night, photo periodism[1]), although the results of the Icelandic hot-house gardener show directly that they are not a decisive factor, at least with many plants.

The best known floras are from Iceland, which is quite distant from the Pole, and modern pollen analysis investigations have been carried out both on these and Spitzbergen flora, where the majority of finds are of Early Tertiary age. The Pliocene is much cooler and perhaps in the Icelandic region there may have been a pre-Pliocene glaciation.[92,166] Late Tertiary glaciers are also suspected in Alaska.[115] However, on the whole, inland ice glaciation in the North Polar region in the Tertiary period must have been absent.

VII.7 *Glaciation in the Tertiary period*

Except for the above-mentioned local glaciation in Iceland and Alaska, few positive Tertiary moraines are known, although they would be expected in other arctic regions. The tillites described by W. W. and W. R. Atwood[7,8] in the San Juan mountains in Colorado (Ridgway and Gunnison tillite) can also be interpreted as volcanic sludge streams.[188] Likewise in the Big Horn Mountains (Wyoming), the glacial evidence (as Hares[81] interpreted certain conglomerates of the Rocky Mountains) is probably Early Tertiary fanglomerates.[169] However, Scott[167] has also claimed to have found tillites in Montana (with striated boulders) and equated them with the 'Eocene glaciation'. Their exact age cannot, however, be established with direct methods.

VIII. The Quaternary Period

VIII.1 General Definition

The Quaternary period, lasting about 1 million years, is by far the shortest 'formation' or 'period', but it is climatologically characterized by its ice ages in a unique way. Discovery of these first occurred about 1800 in the Swiss Alps and since then their investigation has developed into a separate branch of geology, particularly in Europe and North America. Hence only little can be mentioned here, and the excellent texts which have recently been published should be consulted.[40, 66, 95, 196]

(a) The Quaternary in the Northern Hemisphere is especially characterized by considerable periodic lowering of temperature, so that vast areas of North America and Northern Europe were covered by inland ice sheets. The Fennoscandian glaciers in Europe stretched to 49° latitude, and in North America to 37° 30′ latitude; that is, to south of St. Louis—the latitude of Seville (Spain), Catania (Sicily) and Athens!

The Scandinavian ice sheet covered at its maximum 5 500 000 km², and the North American (Laurentian) 13 135 000 km², while the Greenland ice cap today covers 1 726 000 km² (all figures from Flint[66]).

(b) Numerous mountains were glaciated which today are free of ice. The lowering of the snow line amounted to 800–1200 m in Europe, and 1200 (Washington)–1700 m (Colorado) in the North American Cordillers.

(c) There were several ice ages alternating with interglacial periods.

It was decided by the International Geological Congress of 1948 in London that the distinctive peculiarity of the 'glacial climate' should serve as the top limit of the Tertiary period. Obviously this is not unambiguous in such well-known regions as Europe and North America, where Tertiary glaciations are acceptable in the arctic region. In standard profiles of Italy the limit is set where cold-loving marine animals (Cyprina islandica amongst others) appear for the first time. This results in zones which earlier were ascribed to the Pliocene epoch (Villafrancian, Calabrian) now being interpreted as Quaternary. Today the Quaternary is divided into the Pleistocene epoch (Ice Age s.s; diluvium of older writers) and the Holocene epoch (= 'Post-glacial', = 'Alluvium' in earlier German usage). In time the Holocene epoch embraces only about the last 15 000 years.

VIII.2 *Climatic Conditions of the Actual Glacial Regions*

The extraordinary spread of the Scandinavian and Canadian ice sheets presupposes a radical change in climatic conditions. Today it is generally accepted that a lowering of the temperature (and not an increase in rainfall) was the decisive factor. The climatic conditions changed in detail during one single ice age, and also varied markedly according to latitude. In general, one can suppose that the advance of the glaciers was linked with a cool and damp climate, and that then a colder and drier climate was established in the region of the ice sheet.

As evidence of former glaciation, moraines, both boulder clay and also corresponding relief features (terminal moraines and so on), erratic blocks and striated pavements, roches moutonnees, drumlins and glacial drainage channels have the greatest significance. These features form the typical glacial landscapes in northern Europe, Canada and northern U.S.A. However, it should be remembered that these landscapes mostly originated from the last glaciation; even the regions affected by the penultimate glaciation show only fragmentary terminal moraines, and scarcely any glacial lakes and drainage channels. (Examples in Germany[76] and in Iowa.[146])

In the foreland of the glaciers, the 'Peri-glacial regions', various phenomena appear: ground frost (permafrost) with ice wedges, kryoturbations, wind-blown loess deposits and asymmetrical valleys. In Europe, for example, France belonged to the peri-glacial region.[36,181]

To the inorganic climatic features must be added the organic ones: cold loving floras (*Dryas* etc.), which are very suitable for investigation by means of pollen analysis, and faunas (musk ox, reindeer, mammoth, woolly rhinoceros, etc.). Furthermore, quantitative determinations of temperature lowering have been given, some examples of which are compiled in Table VI.

Table VI. Lowering of Temperature during the Ice Age

Climatic evidence	Pleistocene lowering of temperature	Author
Dryas octopcetala in Central Europe	6–10°	Gagel
		Range
		Werth (see reference 161)
Picea glauca and *P. mariana* in Texas	8° in July	Potzger and Tharp[138]
Picea and *Abies* in Florida	7–8° in July	Davis[47]
Frost fissures in Central Germany	11°	Soergel (see reference 161)
Frost fissures in Montana	8°	Schafer[155]
Depression of the snow line in the Alps	6°	Penck (see reference 161)
Depression of the snow line in Colorado	5·5°	Antevs[4]

Accordingly a maximum temperature drop of 8–12°C must be reckoned with in the northern temperate latitudes. In the first instance, this applies most of all to the last (Würm) ice age; but since the extension of ice in the preceding glacials was still greater, the temperature fall can scarcely have

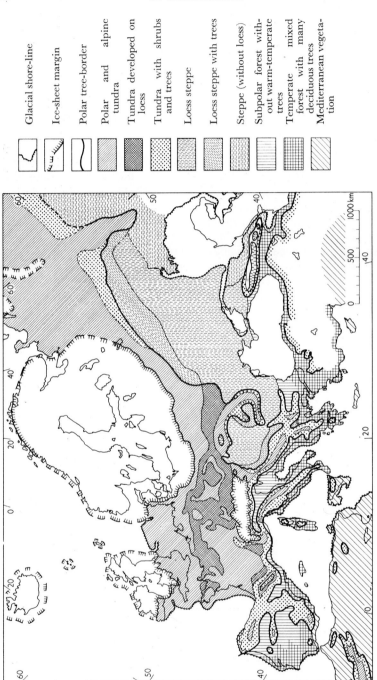

Fig. 7. Climatic zones of Europe during the Würm glaciation, after Büdel[35] and Woldstedt.[194]

Legend:

- Glacial shore-line
- Ice-sheet margin
- Polar tree-border
- Polar and alpine tundra
- Tundra developed on loess
- Tundra with shrubs and trees
- Loess steppe
- Loess steppe with trees
- Steppe (without loess)
- Subpolar forest without warm-temperate trees
- Temperate mixed forest with many deciduous trees
- Mediterranean vegetation

been less than in the Würm glaciation. Moreover, it is possible that, as Mortensen supposed,[120] the lower temperature in lower levels was more significant than at higher levels.

VIII.3 *The 'Glacial Ages' in Lower Latitudes and in Dry Areas*

Since the snow line was lower in mountains lying farther south, and even in equatorial mountains, we must suppose a marked ice-age lowering of temperature even for the warm zones. It might not have reached the same degree there as in higher latitudes and, in any case, it has not exercised any influence worth mentioning on sedimentation and organic life in the tropical lowlands.

The westerly wind belt in the Northern Hemisphere was pressed southwards by the great glaciations. This led to a higher rainfall in the present-day desert belts, at least on their northern edge, and thus 'pluvials' in the south correspond to the glaciations in the north; this is all the more important because the temperatures were lowered. Well-known examples are found in North America; the Great Basin was filled with great lakes during the last ice age, and the old lake terraces show the high levels of that time. The classical description is that of Gilbert, but the Franciscan monk Silvestre Velez de Escalante had recognized them correctly as early as 1776 (see reference 87). The semi-arid regions like the Great Plains of the U.S.A. perhaps reveal the increased humidity during the glacial ages, in the variations and profusion of water snails.[71] In Mexico the pollen diagrams show a manifold sequence of humid and dry periods,[168] but the correlation with the more northerly areas is still uncertain.

In Europe with its relatively poorly developed semi-arid areas fewer observations are available. In the Spanish Mediterranean area the Pluvials (i.e. warm wet ages) are characterized by red coloration, and the warm dry ages (the present time and the interpluvials) by the formation of lime crust.[150]

VIII.4 *Climate of the Interglacial Periods*

Numerous observations show that the climate of the interglacial periods was similar to today's, and at times was even somewhat warmer.

Examples in Europe. The much discussed Mindel-Riss interglacial of Hotting near Innsbruck (a scree breccia) contains amongst other plants the Pontic alpine rose (*Rhododendron ponticum*) and vine (*Vitis silvestris*) which no longer grow there today.

In the last interglacial period the marsh-turtle (*Emys orbicularis*), which requires a warmest month of 19° and a dry summer,[184] still lived near Weimar (Central Germany), where the July temperature today is 17°. Marls of the last interglacial near Lehringen (Lower Saxony) contain the snail *Belgrandia marginata*[28] which today is found only in South-east Europe; while *Helicigona banatica*[111] today is found only in the South Carpathians. Marine beds of the last interglacial (Eem) in the North Sea region are characterized by southern ('lusitanic') species such as *Tapes aureus*.

The English interglacial periods yielded the water weed *Najas minor*,[74] which needs higher summer temperatures than those of England today.

Examples in North America. The Sangamon Interglacial of Toronto (Don beds) shows a 2–3° higher temperature than today. The marine shellfish *Rangia cuneata* (today found in the Gulf of Mexico) occurs frequently in an Interglacial period (Aftonian?) of Maryland.[26]

Examples in the Arctis. The Icelandic Interglacial of Stod contains the alder *Alnus viridis*, which no longer flourishes in Iceland.[6,164] The earlier interglacial periods were probably even somewhat warmer than the later ones. In the Tegelen beds of Holland an ape, *Macaca florentina*, has been identified whose last modern representative of the family in Europe lived in Gibraltar.

VIII.5 *Course of the Ice Age in Europe*

During the Quaternary in Europe there were three great glaciation centres: Scandinavia (Scandinavian ice sheet), the British Isles and the Alps. There were also countless small glaciers in other mountain ranges. The Scandinavian and British ice sheets formed at periods one more or less continuous continental ice-cap. The Scandinavian ice penetrated more than 2000 km beyond the Baltic Sea basin far into Central and Eastern Europe, while the British ice was confined to the British Isles, and indeed, southern England remained ice free. The centre of the ice-cap in Scandinavia lay somewhat to the east of the watershed of the present-day high mountains, but nonetheless was quite asymmetric with respect to the whole ice-cap, which in the centre reached about 3000 m in thickness. In the Alps the valleys and some of the passes were covered by a network of glaciers, over which the higher peaks towered. Several great glaciers penetrated out of the mountain range as Piedmont glaciers of the Malaspina type, especially in the North (southern Germany) where they reached a considerable size (Rhone glacier 360 km, Inn glacier 340 km, Rhine glacier 200 km;[95] compared with the longest modern Alpine glacier, the Aletsch glacier 26 km).

The maximum southern extent of the Scandinavian ice, marked by the most southerly occurrence of characteristic erratic blocks, often clearly follows the pre-existing relief, i.e. bulging in the river valley far towards the south (also found in North America). It runs through Holland, Central Germany and the northern edge of the Carpathian to the Dnieper and the Don basin. The first workers to give detailed proof of the existence of several Quaternary ice ages were Penck and Bruckner,[130] working in the Alpine glacier region. They distinguished and named after Alpine rivers four glacial periods from the earliest Gunz, to Mindel, Riss, and finally Würm, the last glacial.

It became apparent later that a partial splitting up of glaciations into phases separated by shorter warm periods (interstadials) was possible. In particular, the river gravels of Central Germany and the Alpine region led to very detailed divisions, whereby deposition of gravel could be equated with glaciation and erosion with interglacial or interstadial. In the same way the widely spread loess, a fine wind-blown sediment of the cold period, with intercalated loam horizons (corresponding to weathering products of a warmer climate) could be interpreted stratigraphically. The meaning of the combination of the different profiles is still uncertain, and so is the

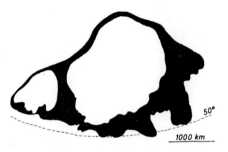

Fig. 8. The spread of the Scandinavian and British ice-caps during the Würm glaciation. Older glaciations shown in black.

meaning of almost all the more subtle divisions of the Quaternary period. Even the divisions of the otherwise well-known Last Ice Age are passionately disputed about in Europe; and Woldstedt,[194] who is best informed about the conditions in Central Europe, ranges them today in two chief stages with a distinct Interstadial (Gottweiger horizon). In addition to this the stratigraphy of the Alps and Northern Europe cannot be directly correlated, so that local characteristics independent of each other have to be chosen. On the other hand, it seems certain that before Penck's earliest ice age still a further, if less marked, cold period can be accepted (Danube Ice Age). Thus we get the plan set out in Table VII.

Only the last ice age is at all well-known, and only with respect to the three last ice ages can one estimate the extent of the continental ice sheet which spread out from Scandinavia. The maximum spread previously delineated belongs partly to the Elster ice age, and partly (in Russia) to the Saale ice age. The retreat of the ice of the last glaciation was completed in stages, with pauses in between. These are well marked morphologically by terminal moraines with sands extending in front and ancient drainage channels.

In the Alps, too, the Würm glaciers did not extend as far as in the earlier ice ages. No moraines of the Danube ice age are known; yet an important climatic change in the Early Quaternary period at the southern edge of the Alps has been detected by pollen analyses and according to Venzo[189] this climatic variation belongs partly to the Danube ice age. In the remaining mountain ranges, which today still carry small glaciers in a few places (Pyrenees, Abruzzi), during the Ice Age only valley glaciers and corries are known, with the degree of glaciation falling away towards the east, corresponding to the increasing continentality of the climate. This is clearly revealed in Central Europe where the maximum length of the Pleistocene

Table VII. Division of the Quaternary Period in Europe

	Alps	Northern Germany and Holland
Last glacial	Würm	Weichsel
Last interglacial	Riss–Würm	Eem
Glacial	Riss	Saale { Warthe / Drenthe
Interglacial	Mindel–Riss ('Great interglacial')	Holstein
Glacial	Mindel	Elster
Interglacial	Gunz–Mindel	Cromer
Glacial	Gunz	Weybourne
Interglacial	Danube–Gunz	Tegelen
Glacial	Danube	Pretegelen

glaciers reached 40 km in the Vosges, but only 5 km in the Riesengebirge. Similarly the snow line rises towards the east (Table VIII).

Table VIII. Pleistocene Snowlines of Some European Mountain Ranges

Locality	Snowline, height in metres
British Isles	600
Vosges–Black Forest	900
Riesengebirge	1200
Tatra	1500–1600
Transsylvanian Alps	1900

A stratigraphic reconstruction of these mountain glaciations is only possible in some exceptional cases. All forms which stand out morphologically, especially corries, U-shaped valleys and terminal moraines, have their origin in the last ice age.

VIII.6 Course of the Ice Age in North America

In North America, too, there were several glaciation centres, but the following differences from Europe exist:

(a) The centre of the main ice mass (the 'Laurentian ice') lay over a relatively low-lying region.

(b) The Cordilleran ice complex, which was similarly fairly large, was directly connected with the Laurentian ice sheet.

(c) The ice covered plain was much larger than that in Europe.

The origin of the Laurentian ice sheet can be pictured thus (according to Flint[66]) : in the high regions of north-eastern North America (North Quebec and Labrador, on the St. Lawrence River, Newfoundland, Baffin, Bylot, Devon, Ellesmere Islands) valley glaciers and small ice-caps were formed, then Piedmont glaciers extended towards the west and south. This was caused by a relatively small drop in temperature, for Arctic North America even today is heavily glaciated and the remaining regions do not lie far below the snow line. The Piedmont glaciers trapped the main part of the rainfall and therefore grew more quickly than the mountain glaciers, so that eventually in the lowlands greater thicknesses of ice were formed than in the mountains; and the mountains disappeared under a homogeneous continental ice-cap.

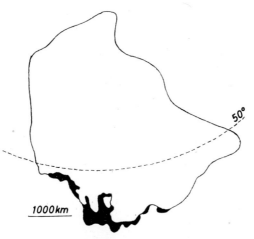

Fig. 9. The spread of the north American ice-caps during the Würm glaciation, with older glaciations shown in black. Eastern and northern boundaries uncertain, most probably similar to those shown in Fig. 8.

As in Europe, the last glaciation did not extend as far as the two previous glaciations, which penetrated from the Laurentian ice centre almost to St. Louis. The southern boundary jumps according to the relief and south-western Wisconsin was in fact never covered with ice ('driftless area') and is today surrounded on all sides by moraine covered regions. Yet during the last glaciation, the Catskill and Adirondack Mountains, New York State, were covered with ice, so that its thickness there must have amounted to at least 1000–1300 m.

The Laurentian ice joined up in the west with the considerably smaller Cordilleran ice. The ice sheet stretched continuously from the Columbia River to the Aleutian Islands, i.e. over more than 3500 km. It embraced not only the network of valley glaciers and Piedmont glaciers, as in the Alps, but also an inland ice-cap at least 2500 m thick, the centre of which lay in British Columbia.

T

The glacier formation began in the high rainfall areas of the Coast Range and shifted gradually more and more eastwards, where more favourable topographical conditions for ice accumulation prevailed. Apart from the actual Cordilleran ice, numerous independent glaciers existed (the largest in the Sierra Nevada in East California).

As in the south, high temperatures put an end to the spread of ice in North America, so in the extreme north the low rainfall did the same. The northern and central regions of Alaska were never glaciated (with the exception of the Brooks Range), and obviously correspond to the ice-free cold wastes in northern Greenland today.

Four main ice ages have long been known in North America (Table IX): the Nebraskan, Kansan, Illinoian and Wisconsin, with interglacial periods Aftonian (after Afton Junction, Iowa), Yarmouth (after Yarmouth, Iowa) and Sangamon (after Sangamon County, Illinois); and here too the Last Ice Age (Wisconsin) has the most important rôle in the formation of the present landscape (including the history of the formation of the Great Lakes). The loams (gumbotils) produced by the weathering of the ground moraines are

Table IX. Correlation of the Quaternary in Europe and North America (after Flint)

Europe		North America
Würm	W	Wisconsin
	R/W	Sangamon
Riss	R	Illinoian
	M/R	Yarmouth
Mindel	M	Kansan
	G/M	Aftonian
Gunz	G	Nebraskan
	D/G	
Danube	D	

important products of the interglacial periods. Florules are rarer than in Europe, and much less is known in North America even about the pre-Nebraskan section of the Quaternary Period.

The comparison with Europe can be set out (after Flint [66]) as in Table IX.

VIII.7 Course of the Ice Age in Arctis

Several interglacial horizons have been proved beyond doubt, in particular in Alaska (survey in Flint [65]) and Iceland. [164] Interglacials are also instanced in Greenland and in the Southern Kola peninsular. [190] According to this evidence the ice age has obviously run a course in the high latitudes similar to that farther south, i.e. the glaciers have at times been much more extensive. An exact stratigraphy is clearly impossible at present.

VIII.8 Variations of Sea-Level and Sea Temperature

The eustatic variations of sea-level were marked, during the glacial periods, by the lowering of the sea-level, and, during the interglacial periods by higher sea-levels. This regular rhythm is superimposed on a gradual lowering of the sea-level since the beginning of the Quaternary period, so that the early Quaternary wave cut platforms lie much higher than the later ones.

In Europe they have been particularly closely studied in the Mediterranean area.[27,132] Unfortunately, in this tectonically labile region schematic comparison of the absolute altitudes can easily lead to correlation errors. Particularly easily recognized are the Tyrrhenian terrace (32 m above MSL: Mindel–Riss–Interglacial period), Monastir II (7–8 m above MSL: last Interglacial period), and Tapes Terrace (3–6 m above MSL: post-glacial warm optimum). The gradation of the Tapes Terrace into the post-glacial warm optimum has been doubted.[66]

As a North American example the Bermudas might be mentioned.[154] There, the low (glacial) sea-level led to the exposure of calcareous sands, which were blown up dunes; followed by weathering or marine sedimentation in the interglacial periods. Five dune phases thus indicate five cold phases which can be equated, though only tentatively,[147] with those of the mainland.

The post-glacial isostatic uplift of Scandinavia and North America, and elsewhere to a smaller extent, which were produced by the ice melting and are thus climatological in cause can only be mentioned here.

Deep-sea sediments are of great significance. As a result of the slow rate of sedimentation, very long periods of time are actually covered in bores of a few metres' depth (even going back into the Tertiary). Whether in fact sedimentation has really always gone on without interruption is, however, doubtful.

The examination of the bores in the Atlantic and the Caribbean Sea has yielded evidence of multiple alternations of normal (i.e. modern) and cooler periods. This variation is proved by (among other things) a variation of the foraminifera fauna; according to Schott[157] the relatively warmth-loving *Globorotalia menardii* only occurs at certain horizons, which can be equated with 'Interglacial' or 'Interstadial' periods.[30,31,133,193] Similarly Emiliani[56] found directly with ^{18}O determinations that the individual horizons were clearly formed at different temperatures; the surface temperature of the ocean fluctuating with an amplitude of 6°. Up to seven cycles have been identified.

The 'glacial' temperature of the eastern equatorial Atlantic was according to the ^{18}O experiments about 2° lower than today.

The problem consists of correlating the temperature curves of cooler and warmer periods, which have been ascertained in this way, with the divisions of the ice age of the neighbouring continents. Up to now this has not been possible beyond all doubt, for certain key horizons are not yet known in deep-sea cores, and an absolute chronology is non-existent. The extrapolated time evaluations of Emiliani[56] with the aid of sedimentation rates are possible, but still have too little foundation, while other workers[31] have arrived at substantially differing evaluations.

VIII.9 *Absolute Chronology of the Quaternary Ice Age*

The varved clay studies of de Geer in Sweden as early as the beginning of this century showed that the ice of the last glaciation had begun to retreat from Schonen (southern Sweden) about 15 000 B.C. About 8150 B.C. the ice withdrew from the terminal moraine of Salpausselkä in Finland towards Sauramo. Similar investigations made in North America led to less positive values, since the sequence of varved clay there is not continuous.

The ^{14}C method has corroborated de Geer's results and enabled an age to be given to further fixed points. Unfortunately the ^{14}C dating only reaches back a little more than 50000 years and thus does not extend as far back as the Last Interglacial period.

All attempts to date absolutely the remaining and much greater period of the Quaternary have till now only yielded uncertain or dubious values.

VIII.10 *Post-Glacial Period in Europe*

The fluctuation of climate since the last great ice age, i.e. in the last 15 000 years, follows a parallel course in Europe and North America; it is well founded on pollen analysis and absolute time determinations. In Europe the following series has been recognized, which is dated partly by ^{14}C determinations and partly by varved clay examinations:

(*a*) Gradual retreat of the Scandinavian ice.

(*b*) First climatic climax of the late ice age; Allerød fluctuation *ca.* 10 000–9000 B.C. July 4° cooler in Central Europe than today.

(*c*) Renewed climatic deterioration ('Later Dryas' period, *ca.* 9000–8000 B.C.). Scandinavian ice at Salpausselkä in Finland.

(*d*) Final ice retreat into the Scandinavian high mountains. Rise in temperature with mid-year 2–3° higher than today; 'Post-glacial warm optimum,' (*ca.* 5000–3000 B.C.). *Corylus, Trapa natans* and other similar species more widespread than today: in northern Eurasia treeless tundra almost disappeared.[70,125]

(*e*) Gradual return of temperature to modern conditions, and relatively dry conditions 2300, 1200 and 600 B.C. (weathering of the peat deposits, recurrence surfaces).

(*f*) The following periods stand out in historic times:

500–700 A.D.	Particularly dry
1000–1250 A.D.	Heavier rainfall than today
Before 1600	Glacier retreat
1st half of 17th century	⎫ Glacier advance
1810–1820	⎬ ('Little Ice Age' of roughly 1540–1890 with 'Interglacial'
1850–1860	⎭ 1680–1740)
Since end of 19th century	Glacier retreat

VIII.11 *Post-Glacial Period in North America*

In North America the general ice retreat is also characterized by terminal moraines which owe their origin to halt phases or even to occasional readvance phases. Such a small readvance penetrated *ca*. 10 500 B.C. once more to Port Huron (southern end of Lake Huron); and was followed by a retreat to the Straits of Mackinac (between Lake Michigan and Lake Huron) with peat formation at Two Creeks (Wisconsin), in 9500 B.C. After this came the powerful Valders readvance to the northern edge of Lake Erie 8700–8800 B.C. and not until then did the final ice retreat come.

The events in Europe and North America can be correlated as follows:

Europe	North America
Later Dryas period	Valders
Allerød period	Two Creeks
Earlier Dryas period	Port Huron–Mankato

The post-glacial climatic optimum ('Hypsithermal' of Deevey and Flint[49]) is less marked in North America than in Europe; nevertheless it is shown in the pollen diagrams—in Maine with oak maximum; hemlock and birch minimum.[48]

The increase of temperature of 8°, suggested for the post-glacial warm period in western U.S.A. by Moore[118] does not seem probable. He reasoned that calcite is formed in many caves today, but that some time ago aragonite was deposited, and today aragonite is characteristic of caves which have yearly temperatures of over 15·6°C. This interesting method needs more exact verification; also the dating of the earlier aragonite formation is still uncertain.

The ^{14}C datings have shown that single characteristic events of post ice-age times are contemporary in both continents, especially the Allerød and Two Creek stage. This is a point of great significance to the question of the cause of the climatic fluctuations, indicating especially the unimportance of local events.

VIII.12 *Post-Glacial Period in Arctis*

The post-glacial climatic optimum in the Arctis is easily recognizable in many places; this is so in Spitzbergen and Greenland, where there are beach deposits containing the edible mussel (*Mytilus edulis*) which no longer exists there today.

In Iceland glacial advances occurred in 1750–60 and 1840–50 but since 1890 the glaciers have become very much reduced.[179] This partly corresponds to the European conditions. The latest glacial retreat is coupled with elevated yearly and winter temperatures, but with a summer temperature remaining the same.[59, 111]

IX. Summary

Taking Europe and North America together, it is apparent that during the last 500 million years a climate mostly warmer and much drier than today's prevailed. Only at the beginning and end of this long period of time do ice age conditions with extensive glaciers obtain; those of the Eo-Cambrian and the Quaternary ice ages. Very little can be said as regards climate in Pre-Cambrian times; but it seems clear that glaciations were already known.

It is difficult to say how much warmer it has been in the past, but until now no actual proof existed that the temperatures since the Cambrian age had ever exceeded to any great extent those of the modern warm regions of the earth. The greatest differences between the mean annual temperatures of present and earlier times are found in the present cold regions; differences of up to 40°C and more may be accepted for the Arctic, to which lowering of temperature during the Quaternary ice age can be added. In Central Europe and northern U.S.A. the figure is perhaps 20°C rising to nearly 30°C when comparison is made with the lower temperatures of the Quaternary ice ages.

It can be accepted with some certainty that in the Palaeozoic Era the present north polar regions had a warmer climate than in the Mesozoic Era

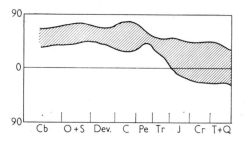

Fig. 10. The spread of reefs about 40°E longitude from the Cambrian (Cb) to the Quaternary (Q). 0 = equator, 90 = north and south poles, abcissa time after Schwarzbach[160]

and the Tertiary period. This can be seen from the shift of the 'reef belt' which gradually moved from the polar region to its present equatorial position (Fig. 10). The movement of the belt of evaporites tells the same story. It is true that the relationship between land and sea distribution and climatic development on a small scale can be recognized in many ways, but a close connection between climatic history and tectonic history in Europe and North America can best be seen in the temporal succession of the 'Alpine' mountain formations and the Quaternary ice period, although naturally such problems cannot be fully understood from a study of two continents only.

The Quaternary ice age in the Northern Hemisphere, foreshadowed by events during the Tertiary period, remains one of the most astonishing climatic events in the whole history of the earth, involving as it did a marked lowering of temperatures, and the repeated, relatively short, succession of glacial and interglacial epochs. In contrast the late Palaeozoic glaciations play only an insignificant and indirect rôle in the history of the Northern Hemisphere.

What the significance of the Eo-Cambrian glaciations was is difficult to say exactly, because far too little is known about them.

References

(Reference is in general not made to older work, for which there are detailed bibliographies in Schwarzbach[161]; and for the Quaternary in Charlesworth,[40] Klebelsberg,[95] Woldstedt[194] and Zeuner.[196]

1. Allard, H. A., in *Vernalization and Photoperiodism*, A. E. Murneek and R. O. Whyte, eds., *Chronica botanica Comp.*, Waltham (Mass.), 1948
2. Altehenger, A. *Eiszeitalter u. Gegenw.*, **9**, 104 (1958)
3. Anderson, J. G. C. *Quart. J. geol. Soc. Lond.*, **109**, 399 (1954)
4. Antevs, E. *J. Geol.*, **62**, 182 (1954)
5. Arellano, A. R. V. *C.R. Congr. Geol. Int. Algiers*, **7**, 53 (1953)
6. Askelsson, J. *Medd. dansk geol. Foren.*, **9**, 300 (1939)
7. Atwood, W. W. *Prof. Pap. U.S. geol. Surv.*, **95**B, 13 (1915)
8. Atwood, W. W. and Atwood, W. R. *J. Geol.*, **34**, 612 (1926)
9. Axelrod, D. J. *Publ. Carneg. Instn*, **590**, 215 (1950)
10. Axelrod, D. J. *Publ. Univ. Calif. geol. Sci.*, **33**, 1 (1956)
11. Axelrod, D. J. *Publ. Univ. Calif. geol. Sci.*, **34**, 91 (1958)
12. Bailey, E. B., Collet, L. W. and Field, R. M. *J. Geol.*, **36**, 577 (1928)
13. Bailey, J. M. and Sinnott, E. W. *Science*, **41**, 831 (1915)
14. Bain, G. W. *Amer. J. Sci.*, **256**, 596 (1958)
15. Bardarson, G. *K. danske vidensk. Selsk.*, **55**, 1 (1925)
16. Bardoschi, D. *Bull. Akad. Sci. U.R.S.S. (Geol. Ser.)*, **9**, 3 (1957) through *Zbl. Geol. Pal.*, **I** (1957)
17. Beljankin, D. S. and Petrow, W. P. *Bull. Acad. Sci. U.R.S.S. (Geol. Ser.)*, **2**, 33 (1950) through *Zbl. Geol. Pal.*, **I** (1951)
18. Bell, K. G. Dr.'s Thesis, M.I.T., Cambridge (Mass.), 1948
19. Berger, W. *Neues Jb. Geol.*, **2**, 471 (1952)
20. Berry, E. W. *Prof. Pap. U.S. geol. Surv.*, **91**, 1 (1916)
21. Berry, E. W. *Smithson. misc. Coll.*, **82**, 1 (1930)
22. Bersier, A. *Bull. Soc. vaud. Sci. nat.*, **59** (103), (1936)
23. Blackwelder, E. *Bull. geol. Soc. Amer.*, **37**, 615 (1926)
24. Blackwelder, E. *Science*, **76**, 212 (1932)
25. Blackwelder, E. *J. Geol.*, **40**, 289 (1932)
26. Blake, S. F. *Smithson. misc. Coll.*, **121**, 1, 1953
27. Blanc, A. C. *Geol. Meere*, **5**, 137 (1942)
28. Boettger, C. R. *Neues Jb. Geol.*, **100**, 247 (1954)
29. Bradley, W. H. *Prof. Pap. U.S. geol. Surv.*, **158** (1929)
30. Bramlette, M. N. and Bradley, W. H. *Prof. Pap. U.S. geol. Surv.*, **196**A, 1 (1940)
31. Broeker, W. S., Turekian, K. K. and Heezen, B. C. *Amer. J. Sci.*, **256**, 503 (1958)
32. Brooks, C. E. P. *Climate through the Ages*, 2nd edn. 1950. London: Benn
33. Bryan, M. S. *Danm. geol. Unders.* (II), **80**, 65 (1954)
34. Bucher, W. *Amer. J. Sci.*, **47**, 149 (1919)
35. Büdel, J. *Eiszeitalter u. Gegenw.*, **1**, 16 (1951)
36. Cailleux, A. *Bull. Carte géol. Fr.*, **240**, 1 (1954)
37. Chaney, R. W. *Publ. Carneg. Instn*, **349**, 1 (1925)
38. Chaney, R. W. *Bull. geol. Soc. Amer.*, **51**, 469 (1940)

39. Chaney, R. W. and Sanborn, E. I. *Publ. Carneg. Instn*, **439**, 1 (1933)
40. Charlesworth, J. K. *The Quaternary Era*, 2 vols. 1957. London: Arnold
41. Chevalier, J. P. *Bull. Soc. géol. Fr.*, (6) **6**, 127 (1956)
42. Coleman, A. P. *Ice Ages Recent and Ancient*. 1926. New York: Macmillan
43. Creer, K. M., Irving, E. and Runcorn, S. K. *Phil. Trans.*, *A*, **250**, 1 (1957)
44. Crouzel, F. *Bull. Carte géol. Fr.*, **248**, 1 (1957)
45. Crowell, J. C. *Bull. geol. Soc. Amer.*, **68**, 993 (1957)
46. Dangeard, L., Graindor, M. and Wegmann, E. *C.R. Acad. Sci.*, *Paris*, **230**, 979 (1950)
47. Davis, J. *Bull. Fla. geol. Surv.*, **30**, 1 (1946)
48. Deevey, E. S. *Amer. J. Sci.*, **249**, 257 (1951)
49. Deevey, E. S. and Flint, R. F. *Science*, **125**, 182 (1957)
50. Dillon, L. S. *Science*, **123**, 167 (1956)
51. Dorf, E. *Spec. Pap. geol. Soc. Amer.*, **62**, 575 (1955)
52. Dunbar, C. O. *Historical Geology*. 1949. New York: Wiley (2nd edn. 1960)
53. Dunham, K. C. *C.R. Congr. Geol. Int. Algiers*, **7**, 25 (1953)
54. Durham, J. W. *Bull. geol. Soc. Amer.*, **61**, 1243 (1950)
55. Eardley, A. J. *J. Geol.*, **56**, 409 (1948)
56. Emiliani, C. *J. Geol.*, **63**, 538 (1955)
57. Emiliani, C. *J. Geol.*, **64**, 281 (1956)
58. Eyles, V. A. *Mem. geol. Surv. N. Ireland*, 1952
59. Eythorsson, J. *Geogr. Ann.*, *Stockh.*, **31**, 36 (1949)
60. Farquhar, R. M. and Russell, R. D. *Spec. Publ. roy. Soc. Can.*, **2**, 28 (1957)
61. Fenton, C. L. and Fenton, M. A. *Mem. geol. Soc. Amer.*, **67**, 103 (1957)
62. Fiala, F. and Swoboda, J. *Sborn. geol. Ust. čsl.*, **22**, 257 (1956)
63. Firbas, F. *Spät- und nacheiszeitliche Waldgeschichte Mitteleuropas*. 1949. Jena: Fischer
64. Flett, J. S. *Int. Geol. Congr. XVII. Moscow-Leningrad, Abstr. Pap.*, 209 (1937)
65. Flint, R. F. *Arctic*, **5**, 135 (1952)
66. Flint, R. F. *Glacial and Pleistocene Geology*. 1957. New York: Wiley and Sons
67. Flint, R. F. and Gale, W. A. *Amer. J. Sci.*, **256**, 689 (1958)
68. Forman, Mc.L. and Schlanger, S. O. *J. Geol.*, **65**, 611 (1957)
69. Foyn, S. *Norsk geol. Tidsskr.*, **17**, 65 (1937)
70. Frenzel, B. *Erdkunde*, **9**, 40 (1955)
71. Frye, J. C. and Leonhard, A. B. *Amer. J. Sci.*, **255**, 1 (1957)
72. Gaertner, H. R. v. *Geol. Rdsch.*, **34**, 226 (1943)
73. Gerasimov, I. P. and Markov, K. K. *The glacial period in the U.S.S.R.* (Russian with Engl. Summary). 1939. Moscow
74. Godwin, H. *The History of the British Flora*. 1956. Cambridge University Press
75. Gordon, M., Tracey, J. I. and Ellis, M. W. *Prof. Pap. U.S. geol. Surv.*, **299**, 1 (1958)
76. Graindor, J. M. *Mém. Carte geol. France*, 1957
77. Gripp, K. *Mitt. geogr. Ges. Hamb.*, **36**, 159 (1924)
78. Gritschtschenko, M. N. and Gluschtschenko, E. I. *C.R. Acad. Sci. U.R.S.S.*, **106**, 1068 (1956) through *Zbl. Geol. Pal.*, **II** (1956)
79. Hall, W. E. *Bull. Amer. Ass. Petrol. Geol.*, **41**, 1633 (1957); **43**, 238 (1959)
80. Hantke, R. *Denkschr. schweiz. naturf. Ges.*, **80**, 31 (1954)
81. Hares, C. J. *Bull. geol. Soc. Amer.*, **37**, 174 (1926)
82. Harrassowitz, H. *Fortschr. Geol.* (IV), **14**, 253 (1926)
83. Heim, Arn. *Geol. Rdsch.*, **15**, 1 (1924)
84. Hill, D. *Geol. Rdsch.*, **47** (f. 1958), 590 (1959)

85. Humphrey, W. E., *Bull. geol. Soc. Amer.*, **66**, 1319 (1955)
86. Hunt, Ch. B. and Sokoleff, V. P. *Prof. Pap. U.S. geol. Surv.*, **221G**, 109 (1950)
87. Ives, R. L. *J. Geol.*, **56**, 79 (1948)
88. Jakubowskaja, T. A. *Acta Inst. bot. Acad. Sci. U.R.S.S.*, **11**, 7 (1955) through *Zbi. Geol. Pal.*, **II** (1957)
89. James, H. L. *Prof. Pap. U.S. geol. Surv.*, **314C**, 27 (1958)
90. Jonsson, J. *Geogr. Ann., Stockh.*, **36**, 146 (1954)
91. Jux, U. *Neues Jb. Geol.*, **110** (1960)
92. Kautsky, G. *Geol. Fören. Stockh. Förh.*, **71**, 595 (1949)
93. King, P. B. *Prof. Pap. U.S. geol. Surv.*, **187**, 1 (1938)
94. Kirk, E. *Amer. J. Sci.*, (4) **46**, 511 (1918)
95. Klebelsberg, R. v. *Handbuch der Gletscherkunde und Glazialgeologie*, 2 vols. 1948. Wien: Springer
96. Klotz, G. *Wiss. Z. Univ. Halle-Wittenberg*, **4**, 717 (1955)
97. Klotz, G. *Wiss. Z. Univ. Halle-Wittenberg*, **5**, 25 (1955)
98. Korn, H. *Neues Jb. Min. Geol. Paläont.*, **74A**, 50 (1938)
99. Kramer, W. B. *J. Geol.*, **41**, 590 (1933)
100. Kriwzow, A. I. *Inf. Sborn. Wses. nautsch. issl. geol. Inst.*, **40** (1955) through *Zbl. Geol. Pal.*, **II** (1957)
101. Krotow, B. P. and Sotowa, T. I. *C.R. Acad. Sci. U.R.S.S.*, **108**, 1144 (1956), through *Zbl. Geol. Pal.*, **II** (1957)
102. Kulling, O. *Geogr. Ann., Stockh.*, **161** (1934)
103. Kulling, O. *Sverig. geol. Unders. Afh.*, **503C**, 1 (1951)
104. Kurtz, V. E., McNair, A. H. and Wales, D. B. *Amer. J. Sci.*, **250**, 636 (1952)
105. La Forge, *Bull. U.S. geol. Surv.*, **839**, 1 (1932)
106. Lecompte, M. *Bull. Soc. géol. Fr.* (6), **7**, 1045 (1957)
107. Lotze, F. *Steinsalz und Kalisalze*, 2nd edn. 1957. Berlin: Borntraeger
108. Lowenstam, H. A. *J. Geol.*, **58**, 430 (1950)
109. Lowenstam, H. A. *Mem. geol. Soc. Amer.*, **67**, 215 (1957)
110. Lowenstam, H. A. and Epstein, S. *J. Geol.*, **62**, 207 (1954)
111. Lozek, V. *Rozpr. geol. Úst. čsl.*, **17**, 1 (1955)
112. Ludwig, G. *Jb. hallesch. Verb. Erf. mitteldtsch. Bodensch.*, **6**, 87 (1927)
113. Madler, K. *Abh. Senckenb. naturf. Ges.*, **446**, 1 (1939)
114. McKee, E. D. *Mem. geol. Soc. Amer.*, **61**, 1 (1954)
115. Miller, D. J. *J. Geol.*, **61**, 17 (1953)
116. Mistardis, G. *C.R. Congr. Geol. Int., Algiers*, **7**, 43 (1953)
117. Moffitt, F. H. *Bull. U.S. geol. Surv.*, **989D**, 65 (1954)
118. Moore, G. W. *Amer. J. Sci.*, **254**, 746 (1956)
119. Moore, R. C. *Amer. J. Sci.*, (5) **27**, 432 (1934)
120. Mortensen, H. *Erdkunde*, **6**, 145 (1952)
121. Moskvitin, A. I. *Fsw. Akad. nauk. S.S.S.R.*, Ser. geol. 22, **4**, 3 (1957)
122. Muller, S. W. *Amer. J. Sci.*, **31**, 202 (1936)
123. Murray, R. C. *Bull. geol. Soc. Amer.*, **66**, 341 (1955)
124. Naidin, D. P., Teis, R. W. and Tschupachin, M. S. *Geochimija*, **23** (1956) through *Zbl. Geol. Pal.*, **I** (1958)
125. Nejstadt, M. I. *The Floral History of the U.S.S.R. during the Holocene.* 1954. Moscow (see also Klotz[96])
126. Newell, D. N. *Bull. geol. Soc. Amer.*, **68**, 1569 (1957)
127. Newell, N. D. et al. *The Permian Reef Complex of the Guadaloupe Mountains Region.* 1953. San Francisco: Freeman
128. Opdyke, N. D. and Runcorn, S. K. *Endeavour*, **18**, 26 (1959)

129. Osborne, F., Fitz. *Nat. canad.*, **83**, 157 (1956)
130. Penck, A. and Bruckner, E. *Die Alpen im Eiszeitalter*, 3 vols. 1901–1909. Leipzig: Tauchnitz
131. Pepper, J. F., de Witt, W. and Demarest, D. F. *Prof. Pap. U.S. geol. Surv.*, **259**, 1 (1954)
132. Pfannenstiel, M. *Geol. Rdsch.*, **34**, 342 (1944)
133. Phleger, F. B. and Hamilton, W. A. *Bull. geol. Soc. Amer.*, **57**, 951 (1946)
134. Plumley, W. J. and Graves, R. W. Jr. *J. Geol.*, **61**, 1 (1953)
135. Pokrowskaja, I. P. *Bot. Shurn.*, **39**, 241 (1954), through *Zbl. Geol.*, **II** (1956) and Klotz [96]
136. Poole, F. G. *Bull. geol. Soc. Amer.*, **68**, 1870 (1957)
137. Poser, H. *Erdkunde*, **2**, 53 (1948)
138. Potzger, J. E. and Tharp, B. C. *Ecology*, **28**, 274 (1947)
139. Poulsen, Ch. *Congr. Geol. Int.*, 20, *Mexico, Sympos. Cambr.* **I**, 59 (1956)
140. Reid, E. M. *Proc. roy. Soc.*, **118**B, 197 (1935)
141. Reid, E. M. and Chandler, M. E. J. *The London Clay Flora*. 1933. London: British Museum
142. Reineck, H. E. *Neues Jb. Geol.*, **101**, 75 (1955)
143. Richter-Bernburg, G. *Jb. Reichsst. Bodenforsch.*, **61**, 283 (1941)
144. Richter-Bernburg, G. *Z. dtsch. geol. Ges.*, **105**, 593 (1955)
145. Ruedemann, R., in *Geology of North America*, edited by R. Ruedemann and R. Balk. 1939. Berlin: Borntraeger
146. Ruhe, R. V. *Amer. J. Sci.*, **250**, 46 (1952)
147. Ruhe, R. V., Gomez, R. S. and Gady, J. G. *Bull. geol. Soc. Amer.*, **69**, 1638 (1958)
148. Runcorn, S. K. *Handbuch der Physik*, **XLVII**, p. 470. 1956. Heidelberg–Berlin–Gottingen: Springer
149. Runcorn, S. K. *Amer. J. Sci.*, **257**, 235 (1959)
150. Rutte, E. *Neues Jb. Geol.*, **106**, 52 (1958)
151. Sanborn, E. I. *Publ. Carneg. Instn*, **465**, 1 (1937)
152. Sayles, R. W. *Bull. Mus. comp. Zool. Harv.*, **56**, 141 (1914)
153. Sayles, R. W. *Mem. Mus. comp. Zool. Harv.*, **47**, 1 (1919)
154. Sayles, R. W. *Proc. Amer. Acad. Arts Sci.*, **66**, 381 (1931)
155. Schafer, J. P. *J. Geol.*, **57**, 154 (1949)
156. Schindewolf, O. H. *Akad. Wiss. Lit. Mainz. Abh. Math.-Nat. Kl.*, **1**, 1 (1951)
157. Schott, W. *Geol. Rdsch.*, **29**, 322 (1938)
158. Schove, D. J., Nairn, A. E. M. and Opdyke, N. D. *Geogr. Ann., Stockh.*, **40**, 216 (1958)
159. Schwarzbach, M. *Naturwissenschaften*, **33**, 355 (1946)
160. Schwarzbach, M. *Naturwissenschaften*, **36**, 229 (1949)
161. Schwarzbach, M. *Das Klima der Vorzeit*. 1950. 2nd ed., 1961. Stuttgart: Enke
162. Schwarzbach, M. *Geol. Rdsch.*, **40**, 128 (1952)
163. Schwarzbach, M. *Naturwissenschaften*, **40**, 452 (1953)
164. Schwarzbach, M. *Neues Jb. Geol.*, 97 (1955)
165. Schwarzbach, M. *Sonderveröff. Geol. Inst. Univ. Koln.*, **3**, 1 (1958)
166. Schwarzbach, M. and Pflug, H. D. *Neues Jb. Geol.*, **104**, 279 (1956)
167. Scott, H. W. *J. Geol.*, **46**, 628 (1938)
168. Sears, P. B. and Clisby, K. H. *Bull. geol. Soc. Amer.*, **66**, 521 (1955)
169. Sharp, R. P. *J. Geol.*, **56**, 1 (1948)
170. Shepard, F. P. *J. Geol.*, **30**, 77 (1922)
171. Shotton, F. W. *Lpool. Manch. Geol. J.*, **1**, V. 450 (1956)
172. Smith, E. S. C. *Amer. J. Sci.*, (5) **15**, 61 (1928)

173. Stehli, F. C. *Amer. J. Sci.*, **255**, 607 (1957); **256**, 600 (1958); **257**, 239 (1959)
174. Sutton, J. and Watson, J. *Geol. Mag.*, **91**, 391 (1954)
175. Szafer, W. *Prace Inst. Geol.*, **11**, 1 (1954)
176. Teichert, C. *Bull. Amer. Ass. Petrol. Geol.*, **42**, 1064 (1958)
177. Thenius, E. *Neues Jb. Geol.*, 273 (1951)
178. Thenius, E. *Paläont. Z.*, **29**, 21 (1955)
179. Thorarinsson, S. *Geogr. Ann., Stockh.*, **26**, 1 (1944)
180. Tichwinskaja, E. I. *Trudy Wses. Sow. Schemy Strat. mesoz. Otl. Russl*, **162** (1956), through *Zbl. Geol. Pal.* **II** (1957)
181. Tricart, J. *Mém. Carte géol. Fr.*, 1956
182. Troelsen, J. C. *Congr. Geol. Int., 20 Mexico, Sympos. Cambr.* **I**, 71 (1956)
183. Troll, C. *Geol. Rdsch.*, **34**, 545 (1944)
184. Ullrich, H. *Geol.*, **5**, 360 (1956)
185. Urey, H. C., Lowenstam, H. A., Epstein, S. and McKinney, C. R. *Bull. geol. Soc. Amer.*, **62**, 399 (1951)
186. Valeton, I. *Geol. Jb.*, **73**, 149 (1957)
187. Van der Vlerk, I. M. and Florschutz, F. *Verh. Akad. Wet. Amst.* (1), **20**, 1 (1953)
188. Van Houten, F. B. *Bull. Amer. Ass. Petrol. Geol.*, **32**, 2083 (1948)
189. Venzo, S. *Atti Soc. ital. Sci. nat.*, **94** (II), 155 (1955)
190. Verzilin, N. N. *Věstn. Leningrad. Univ., Ser. Geol. Geogr.*, **11**, 81 (1956), through *Zbl. Geol. Pal.* **II** (1954)
191. Vznuzdaev, S. T. *C.R. Acad. Sci. U.R.S.S.*, (2) **90**, 635 (1953), through *Zbl. Geol. Pal.* **II** (1954)
192. Weller, J. M. *Mem. geol. Soc. Amer.*, **67**, 325 (1957)
193. Wiseman, J. D. H. *Proc. roy. Soc.*, **222**A, 296 (1954)
194. Woldstedt, P. *Das Eiszeitalter*, 2nd edn., Vol. II. 1958. Stuttgart: Enke
195. Zagwijn, W. H. *Geol. en Mijnb.*, **19**, 233 (1957)
196. Zeuner, F. E. *The Pleistocene Period*, 2nd edn. 1959. London: Hutchinson

XII

The Climatic History of the Far East

TEIICHI KOBAYASHI and TOKIO SHIKAMA *

I. Introduction

The size and diversity, both physical and political, of Eastern Asia makes the attempt to collect and collate evidence on past climates very difficult. To this, the imperfectly known geology of large areas which prevails even today must be added. For these reasons, it is simplest to consider climatic changes over broad intervals of time rather than during definite geological periods. The facts summarized here can therefore only be regarded as the first tentative step in Asian palaeoclimatology. It is hoped that none of the salient results from the continent and festoon islands have been overlooked, although much more yet remains to be studied.

II. Pre-Cambrian Climates

The Mach'ollyong or Matenrei System, the oldest Pre-Cambrian rocks of north Korea, displays a grand cycle of sedimentation,[12] including in the middle 6000 m of carbonate rocks. These thick limestones and dolomites must be warm, shallow water sediments. The Liaoho System of south Manchuria and the lower Wutai in north China have been correlated with the Matenrei System. In Manchuria, the succeeding Anshan series contains banded iron ores which are probably shallow water deposits formed in a typical monsoon climate.[45] This formation is intruded by the Kungchangling granite, whose age is given as 770×10^6 years.[58] The granite is overlain by

* Pre-Tertiary history is written by T. Kobayashi and post-Mesozoic history by T. Shikama.

the Shihho Series in which dreikanters are found in the basal red sandstone.[44] The Hoshan red sandstones of the Shansi basin and its surrounds, with sun-cracks and ripple marks, also suggest an arid climate.[22] In the Heinan geosyncline, which stretched from east to west through the Liaotung penin-sula in the Proterozoic, the Shogen cycle of sediments accumulated. Of a total thickness of 7000 to 10 000 m some 2500 to 3000 m is represented by limestone.[30]

The famous Nantou tillite near the Ichang gorge, central China, first supposed to be early Cambrian[70] can now be shown to be of Sinian age. Glacial deposits of this age can be traced into the lower Yangtse Valley where well-developed glacial deposits are also found in north-west Kiangsu and north-eastern Anhui.[24] There is also evidence of glaciation in the Ch'eng-chang series of east Yunnan,[69] and the Hirodo conglomeratic phyllite in the upper Shogen of north Korea may also be a floating ice deposit.[31] Pro-terozoic glacial deposits occur in the east Tienshan[38] Sayan, Kuznetsk Alatau, and the western border of the Siberian platform, where they are found in the upper Yenisei and Kutenbuluk formations.[61]

III. Palaeozoic Climates

III.1 *The Climate of the Early Palaeozoic*

The presence of gypsum, anhydrite and salt in the regressive facies of the Cambrian on the Siberian platform is considered proof of a warm or even hot climate.[67] In eastern Asia the main part of the Cambro-Ordovician formation is represented by a great limestone series, although red beds

Fig. 1. Map showing the Devonian equator (after Ma[25]).

predominate near the base; and this is again suggestive of a warm to hot climate. Salt pseudomorphs, which occur in the red formations in various regions from Tatung on the Sino-Mongolian border to south Manchuria, probably indicate a chain of lagoons along the northern shore of the Hwangho basin under a warm and arid climate.[65] In west Shansi gypsum is intercalated at some places near the top of the limestone.

Collenia appears in the Mach'ollyong and it commonly forms reefs in the Shogen system. Archaeocyathid limestone occurs in the Lower Cambrian of the middle Yangtse Valley and throughout the Lower and Middle Cambrian of the Siberian platform.[66] In eastern Asia stromatoporoids are locally abundant in the Middle Ordovician limestones. Coralline limestones are widely distributed in the Silurian and later Palaeozoic formations. Surveys on the growth rates of corals from Ordovician to lower Carboniferous[25-29] reveal that most corals in eastern Asia and Siberia show rapid growth without evidence of seasonal change, and on the evidence of corals the position of the Devonian equator (Fig. 1) is suggested.

III.2 *The Climate of the Late Palaeozoic*

Krystofovich[21] recognized three phytogeographical zones in the late Palaeozoic period. The tropical belt with luxuriant forests stretched in the Westphalian from North America and through Europe to Indonesia. The northern and southern temperate zones were marked by the Angara and Gondwana floras, respectively, in which trees with annual rings prospered.

In the so-called Hwangho basin which comprises Korea, north China and south Manchuria, the Cambro-Ordovician Chosen group is para-uncon-

Table I. The Heian Group in the Hwangho Basin

Age	Korea	Manchuria	N. China
Aniso-Skytic	Greenstone		Shihchifeng
Tartarian Kazanian	Kobosan	Tsaichia	Shihhotzu
Kungurian		Lioutang	Shansi
Artinskian	Jido		
Sakmarian		Huangchi	Taiyuan
Uralian	Koten		
Moscovian		Penchi	Penchi

formably overlain by the Heian group. There is a very significant change in flora and lithology through this group. In Korea red shales are common in the Koten series, the Jido is dark coloured and the Kobosan light or vari-coloured, while a green colour is prevalent in the Greenstone series (Table I). The upper Jido contains the main coal measures, though some occur in the lower Jido. Coal seams decrease in number and quality through the Kobosan and are absent in the Greenstone series. Similar changes are seen in south Manchuria and north China, although the Huangchi and Taiyuan are important coal-bearing formations. Black shales are common in the Penchi of north China, while a red colour is predominant in the Shihchifeng series in Shansi.

Aluminous shales are distributed in several horizons of Middle Permian and older strata; in pre-Kobosan times they are the product of kaolinization, while in the Kobosan they are the result of lateritization.[46] The abundant thick leaves of the Kobosan flora presumably represent a xerophytic adaptation. The Jido climate was therefore warm and humid while Kobosan sediments were deposited in a fairly arid, warm, non-seasonal climate. The green colour of the Greenstone series depends on chloritization in conditions of still higher aridity. Local differences in rock colour and lithology suggest climatic differences within the Hwangho basin.[17]

IV. Mesozoic Climates

In general throughout eastern Asia, after the only known glaciation in Pre-Cambrian times, the evidence is of a climate fluctuating between warm and hot. From the Permian onwards, however, the difference between the arid inland and humid coastal regions becomes greater and climatic conditions become more and more localized. The geographical differentiation and climatic localization are intimately related to the Akiyoshi and Sakawa orogenies through which the edifice of eastern Asia was constructed.

IV.1 *Mesozoic Lithology*

In eastern Asia limestone is not so well developed in the Mesozoic as in the Palaeozoic and older formations. This difference does not indicate the lowering of water temperatures but rather a change in crustal movement from epeirogenic to orogenic. As a result, topographic relief was increased and terrigenous sediments became prevalent. With the advance of orogeny through the Permo-Triassic Akiyoshi and Jurasso-Cretaceous Sakawa cycles, a red or variegated rock facies developed step by step from the continental interior to the festoon islands.[15] It is paralic in places, but the major part is non-marine or terrestrial. It fills the red basin of Szechuan. The so-called Indosinias in south-eastern Asia yields fossils from Westphalian to Palaeogene in age.[49] The Kyöngsang formation in South Korea and the Inkstone series in west Japan are Cretaceous sediments in the hinter basin of the Sakawa folded mountains and contain a great deal of volcanic material in the latter part of the orogenic cycle. False bedding, sun-cracks and rain prints are common in these non-marine formations, and salt and gypsum are deposited in arid continental basins.[1]

IV.2 *Mesozoic Land Floras*

The Mesozoic floras in Japan are grouped according to age into the Ladinic to Liassic Mine *Dictyophyllum* suite, the Toyora *Onychiopsis* suite from

Dogger to Neocomian and the Gyliak angiospermous suite of the middle and late Cretaceous period.[14] A tropical climate is indicated by the *Marattiaceae, Matoniaceae* and *Dipteridaceae*, in the Mine suite. Although some of these families remain in the Toyora, the *Schizaeaceae, Gleicheniaceae, Cyatheaceae* and *Polypodiaceae* are dominant in the Toyora and Gyliak suites. This change in floral aspect suggests that the Mesozoic climate became somewhat cooler towards the end,[40] and in the Senonian xerophilous *Cycadeoidea* occur from Kyushu to Sakhalin.[5]

Dipteris and *Onychium* are at present distributed in the western Pacific islands and the south-eastern monsoon region of the Asiatic continent.

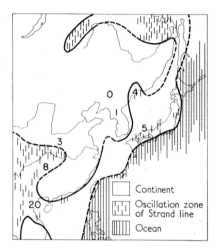

Fig. 2. Palaeogeographic map of Eastern Asia in the late Triassic and early Jurassic periods showing the distribution of fossil Dipteridaceae. The numbers indicate the percentage of species in the fossil flora of the region.

Temperatures of more than 25° and 20°C, respectively, are required for these plants to flourish. Remarkably enough, the percentage of fossil *Dipteridaceae* in Mine flora decreases not only towards the north but also towards the interior of the continent. It is also noteworthy that *Onychiopsis*, which is abundant in the Toyora suite in Japan, becomes uncommon in Manchuria and rare in north China. In this context the absence of growth rings in a Neocomian conifer from Yuasa in the Kii peninsula is significant, for most of the others so far reported from the Mesozoic of eastern Asia do show annual rings.[16]

IV.3 *Mesozoic Land Faunas*

In the non-marine formations of much of eastern Asia, plants are rare or absent because the sediments were derived from arid or semi-arid terrains. On the other hand, copious faunas of Estherians, insects, reptiles and so forth do occur.

The Mesozoic Estherians of eastern Asia can be divided into four groups forming two suits as follows:

S. Sakawa suite $\begin{cases} S_2 & \text{Sungari group, late Cretaceous} \\ S_1 & \text{Kyöngsang group, early Cretaceous} \end{cases}$

A. Akiyoshi suite $\begin{cases} A_2 & \text{Jehol group, Dogger to Malm} \\ A_1 & \text{Daido group, Ladinic to Liassic} \end{cases}$

The Daido group contains 6 genera and 16 distinct species, including some aberrant ones, with small forms very common. They are mostly distributed along the continental margin from Transbaikalia through Korea to Indochina and while species are numerous, many are indigenous to each basin. The Jehol group is, on the contrary, represented by large Estherians in 2 genera, 8 species and 3 varieties in which no aberrant form is found. They appear to have been widely distributed in large inland basins.

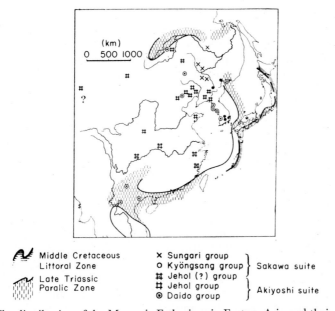

Fig. 3. The distribution of the Mesozoic Estherians in Eastern Asia and their relation to palaeogeography.

The Kyöngsang group contains 7 genera, 13 species and 5 varieties which are mostly distributed in basins near the continental margin. Like the Daido group there is morphological diversity and a number of aberrant forms. In the Sungari group there are 3 genera, 8 species, and aberrant forms are absent. Like the Jehol group they occur in a large basin extending from Central Manchuria to the upper Amur valley. In average size the Estherians in the Sungari Series are smaller than those in the Kyöngsang group but still larger than fossils in the Daido group. The Estherians of the

U

Daido and Kyöngsang are thus similar in their diversity of form, and in their occurrence in peri-continental, limno-paralic zones. The Jehol and Sungari groups are similar in the absence of aberrant forms and in their wide distribution in large intra-continental basins. These facts are intimately related to the Akiyoshi and Sakawa orogenic cycles. The earlier groups are synorogenic faunas in the intra- and peri-orogenic zones. The isolation of the basins within the Akiyoshi and Sakawa mountains may be the reason for the appearance of many indigenous species including the aberrant forms.

The Jehol Estherians are found in large basins in the interior of the continent embraced by folded mountains. The moderately sized Cretaceous Tsushima basin between Korea and Japan, in which many Kyöngsang Estherians occur, lies behind the Sakawa mountains. It was uplifted by the late orogenic invasion of the Chugaku granite. In a larger basin which appeared in the interior the Sungari Estherians flourished.

Inland basins with a hot season temperature of 20° to 30°C provide the optimum conditions for living Estherians. In view of the large size—some Jehol forms are larger than the largest living forms—the climate of the inland basins at the time is considered to have been best suited to these creatures. The diminution in the upper groups, however, does not necessarily mean a lowering of temperature, for the Sungari forms are distributed in higher latitudes[18] than the Kyöngsang forms.

IV.4 *Meszoic Marine Faunas*

In Japan coraline limestones are absent from the Upper Permian to the Dogger, and their maximum development was attained in the Upper Jurassic Torinosu series and declined during the Cretaceous.[72] The appearance of a few boreal ammonites such as the Carnic *Palaeophorus*, Liassic *Amaltheus* and Callovian *Seymourites* in the Mesozoic faunas of Japan is either local or temporary. In the maritime province of U.S.S.R., *Aucella* is the leading member of the Lower Cretaceous fauna,[66] but the genus has never been found in Japan. In Uhlig's Jurassic palaeogeography, Japan is located in the marginal neritic region of the boreal province. The Torinosu fauna, however, indicates a close connection with the Tethyan or Mediterranean fauna.[13] The Torinosu limestone lenses are built up with stromatoporoids, corals, calcareous algae, etc., and are traceable from South Kyushu to Central Hokkaido. This 1000-km chain of reef limestones along the Pacific coast may be comparable to the Great Barrier Reef of Australia.

V. Tertiary to Recent Climates

V.1 *Lithological Evidence*

Important Cenozoic red formations include the Amakusa in Japan of Paleocene to earliest Eocene age, the Eocene terrestrial beds of South China and the Pontian *Hipparion* red clay in North China. The Tunghu (Hunan),

Szechuan (upper Yangtse) and Nanhsiung (Kwangtung and Kwangsi) red sandstones have intercalated gypsum layers, but are unfossiliferous. These red and reddish sediments suggest a climate with a marked dry season. The erosion occasioned by Pleistocene (Chingshui) epeirogenic movements produced the Malan loess in North China, Kanto brown earths in Japan and reddish terrace deposits in the Mariana and Ryukyu islands.[52, 55] The change from reddish (Choukoutienian) to yellow sediments (Malan–Liaho) is thought to be climatic in origin. Strong prevailing winds are indispensable for the transport of loessic material. In the Würmian, South China and Japan were covered by loamy material; the Tsingling range formed the divide between the loessic and loamy regions. Lateritic sediments of Choukoutienian age occur in Anhwei, Kwangtung and Kwangsi, and according to Teilhard[62] uplift of China caused a southward retreat of the lateritic zone with the concomitant expansion of the desert area and continentality during the Pleistocene.

The existence of the Lushan glaciation, and its age, is still a moot point, but in any case, the boulder clay underlying the lateritic sediments is older than Middle Pleistocene.[23] Teilhard recognized four pluvial periods in China: the Paote (Pliocene), Sanmen (Villafranchian), Choukoutien (Middle Pleistocene), Trinil and Malan (Riss–Würm double glaciation stage of Barbour, see Shikama[55]). De Terra[3] correlated Sanmenian to Günzian, Choukoutienian to Mindelian, and the Choukoutien fluvial bed of locality No. 3 to Rissian and finally Malan to Würmian. Teilhard,[63] however, only recognized three fluvio-glacial stages in the Pleistocene of China instead of De Terra's four.[3] The occurrence of Mousterian cultures in the Malan loess of North China,[54] and Moustero–Aurignacian cultures in the Manchurian loess, however, favours the Riss–Würm correlation of the Malan pluvial period. The older beds of the Kanto brown earth around Tokyo can be correlated with the Malan loess, while the younger are correlated with the Manchurian loess. The spelean deposits of Kuzuü, 90 km north of Tokyo, consist of brecciated clay due to rain-wash and solifluction.[53] Wind-worn pebbles and dreikanters suggest strong storm winds in a peri-glacial region. The boulder debris bed in the Great Khingan shows the southern limit of permafrost.[10]

Actual evidence of glaciation is found in the moraines and glaciated topography of the high mountains of central and eastern Asia and north-western Siberia: in eastern Tibet, Sikang, north-west Yunnan, Tsinling (cirques at 4200 m), Tienshan, Altai, Yablonoy, Stanovoy, Dzhug-Dzhur, Verkhoyansk, Anadyr, Koryak, Kamchatka,[6] Setsurei of North Korea (cirques at 2400 m[48]), Khangai of Outer Mongolia (cirques at 2400 m), Morrison range of Formosa (cirques at 3 400 m), Hidaka of Hokkaido (cirques at 1400–1600 m[8]) and Hida, Kiso Akaishi Ranges of Honshu (cirques at 2300–2800 m). The snow line in the Kurile islands, according to Imamura,[11] was 150 m lower than at present. The glaciation of Hidaka, Hida and Kiso has been classified into four stages according to the altitude of cirques and moraines; the oldest is thought to be Rissian, while the remainder are Würmian. The latter stages are roughly coeval with the glaciations of Tali, Yunnan and Formosa.[71]

V.2 *Tertiary to Recent Floras*

Despite minor fluctuations, a general change from a warm humid to a cool arid climate can be traced in the Cenozoic of Eastern Asia by the increased number of grasses and serrated leaved plants. The early Eocene flora of Takashima in Kyushu is a subtropical swamp vegetation with *Sabalites*, *Ficus*, *Sterculia* and *Cinnamomum*,[73] allied to floras found in Indochina (Nagio), Burma, and Assam.[2] Late Eocene plants from the Ishikari coalfield (Central Hokkaido) and Early Oligocene plants from the Joban coalfield (Honshu) constitute a temperate lowland or lagoon flora. Similar floras are also known from Naibuchi and Dui in Sakhalin, Possiet Bay, Ussuri, Korf Gulf (Kamchatka), Commander Islands and the Anadir river in east Siberia. The leading members of the flora are also found in the Kenai flora of Alaska. The Late Eocene flora of Fushun, Manchuria is intermediate between a temperate and subtropical vegetation. Cool temperate floras are found on the Tas-Takh lake, New Siberian Islands and Tschirmyi. If these floras are of about the same age, a climatic zonation is indicated in which the boundary between the subtropical and temperate zones runs from the Tsinling range to central Japan, while the division between the temperate and cool temperate zones is drawn from the Sungari valley through central Manchuria and the Sikhota Alin range[2] to South Kamchatka.

Both highland and lowland floras can be found in Japan from the Burdigalian to the Vindobonian. The Aniai upland flora is of temperate type, while the lowland Daijima flora is representative of a subtropical humid climate containing elements of the *Liquidambar–Comptoniphyllum* flora of the lowlands of Formosa, Fukien and Chekiang. If this lowland flora is Middle Miocene in age and if the Aniai flora is Early Miocene the climatic change from temperate to subtropical must have been established at the beginning of the Miocene.[59] Another change from subtropical to temperate can be detected in the Miocene flora of the Kobe group in West Japan, where subtropical elements account for one third of the total species in the lower part but only one sixth in the upper part.[51] The decrease of subtropical elements and the increase of the temperate-cool ones towards the end of the Miocene has also been demonstrated in the Aizu basin.[55]

A rainy climate, foggy in summer and mild in winter, is suggested by the Pliocene *Pinus trifolia* flora[33] of Japan. This flora comprises 76 families and 83 species, 28 of which are endemic species, while South Chinese and North American members co-exist. The Pliocene flora of Taiku, Shansi[2] shows a semi-arid climate existed there. The Villafranchian flora is represented in Japan by the *Metasequoia japonica–Juglans megacinerea* flora with which *Parastegdon* is associated. It indicates an arid continental climate with mean temperatures about 5°C lower than at the present day.[32] This flora is found in the Akashi and lower Osaka groups, while in the upper Osaka group *Trapa macropoda*, *Euryale* and *Paliurus*, suggest a slightly warmer climate.

Most of the Late Pleistocene floras of Japan have cold elements. The Noheji beds of Aomori and the Manchidani bed of Nishinomiya, for example, yield *Menyanthes trifoliata* and other lowland plants,[34] and the highland flora of the Shiobara fossil lake indicates an annual temperature at least 5° to 5·5°C lower than at present.[4] Pollen analysis of peat in the Kushiro group of Hokkaido proves that *Picea*, *Abies*, *Betula* and *Larix* were dominant, as in the forests of north Sakhalin.[46] The flora from the basal

Table II. Curve Illustrating the Pattern of Climatic Change in the Cenozoic of the Far East

Age	Japanese Stage	Warm	Temperate	Cold	Flora	Vertebrate Fauna
Holocene	K					
Pleistocene L M E	J3 / J1-2 / I3 / I2 / I1				Rukutama Manchidani , Honshu / Upper Osaka / Akashi	Malan Manchurian / Choukoutien Sino- / Nihowan Malayan
Pliocene L E	H2 / H1				Taiku, Shansi / Tajimi, Honshu	Paote Siva-Malayan
Miocene L	G				Kôbe, Honshu	
Miocene M	F2-3				Daijima, Honshu	Hiramaki, Honshu
Miocene M	F1				Aniai, Honshu	
Miocene E	E					
Oligocene L	D				Shiramizu, Joban	Hsanda Gol, Mongolia
Oligocene M E	C				Harutori, Kushiro / Horomui, Ishikari	Ulan Gochu, Mongolia
Eocene L	B				Fushun, Manchuria / Yubari, Ishikari	Irdin Manha, Mongolia
Eocene M E	A				Takashim, Kyushu	
Paleocene L	A0					Gashato, Mongolia

part of the Kanto brown earth near Tokyo, which is probably Rissian in age, is further evidence of a cold climate.[9] The latest Pleistocene flora of Rukutama, Sakhalin, with *Betula* as a leading member, suggests the present climate of the Great Khingan.[74] In the Würmian, Sakhalin was part of the Asiatic continent, and the Shisuka flora in the southern part of the island grew in a humid oceanic climate.[74]

The Egota conifer bed, containing the *Larix* flora, cuts the younger loam in Tokyo which is flourishing 1500 to 2500 m above sea-level in Central Japan. It is still a matter of dispute whether this bed is of latest Pleistocene or earliest Holocene. However it does suggest a climate 6° to 8°C cooler

Table III. Correlation of the Quaternary of the Far East

Legend:

- G. Group
- B. Bed(s)
- l. Loam
- li. Limestone
- * Culture
- ● Warm fossils
- ○ Cold fossils

Chronological Unit	Stage of Japan (Marine)	Stage of Japan (Land)	Climate in Japan	Glaciation (Europe)	Glaciation (East Asia)	North China	Mariana–Ryukyu–Formosa	Cave	Japan (Land)	Japan (Marine)
Holocene — K b	Yurakuchoan (Shitamachian)	Anrakuian	Decreasing Warmer (III)	Subatlantic, Subboreal		Black earth *	Recent li.		Neolithic peat *	Numa B.
Holocene — K a	Numian (Shitamachian)		Humid Warmer (II)	Atlantic, Boreal, Preboreal					Oxided zone ○; Conifer B. ○	
Upper Pleistocene — J₃ b	Upper Yamatean — Takinogawian	Egotian; Tachikawian	Semiarid −6~8°C Cooler (II-I, I)	Würm	W₄ Hida Gl. / Hidaka Gl.; W₃ H2c HK4; W₂ H2b HK3; W₁ H2a HK2 (Tali Glaciation)	Sjara-Osso-Gol Manchurian loess *, sands *; Upper Kuhsiangtun B. *; Lower Kuhsiangtun-tun B. *	Tanabaco li.	Sa-Me Cave	Tachikawa l. *; Musashino l. *; Younger l.; Egota B.	Narita B. ○; Semata B. ○
Upper Pleistocene — J₃ a			Arid Cooler				Chacha li.	Akiyoshi brown clay	Yamate gravel	Zizodō B. ●
Upper Pleistocene — J₂ b	Takinogawian (Upper Yamatean)	Upper Kuzuuan	Humid Warmer	W/R	HK1	Malan loess	Red Clay *		Shimosueyoshi l.; Maruchi-dani B.; Tama l.	Kasamori B. ○
Upper Pleistocene — J₂ a			Semiarid −9°C Cooler	Riss	H1		Plateau gravel (Malan (Liaoho) Stage)	Upper Kuzuū B. ○	Older loam	Naganuma B. ●
Upper Pleistocene — J₁	Manzakian (Sematian)		−5~5.5°C Cooler	R/M	Continental uplift, High mountain emergence	Reddish clay (Upper Sanmenian)	Terrace B.; Crustal movement	Middle Kuzuū B.	Byobugaura B. ○; Hodogaya Gravel	Sanuki B. ○
Middle Pleistocene — I₂ c	Makutian	Middle Kuzuuan	Humid Warmer	Mindel		Chingshui erosion				
Middle Pleistocene — I₂ b	Sanukian	Lower Kuzuuan	Cooler	M/G	Fluvioglacial	Choukoutien B.	Ryukyu limestone	Lower Kuzuū B. ●	Yamashitacho B. ○	Nagahama B.
Middle Pleistocene — I₂ a									Upper Osaka G.	Kakinokidai B.
Lower Pleistocene — I₁	Kanōzanian		Temperate	Günz		Huangshui erosion	Shokkozan B.			Kokumoto B. ○
Lower Pleistocene — H₁ b	Akashian		Continental Arid Cooler −5°C	Donau	?Lushan Glaciation	Nihowan (Lower Sanmenian)			Akashi B.	
Lower Pleistocene — H₁ a						Taiku				
Pliocene — H₂	Umegasean								A-Ge G.	Umegase B. ○ ●

than at the present time.[37]   Four stages are distinguishable in the Oze peat
in the mountains of central Japan (see Table III) where RI corresponds
to the *Betula–Pinus* climate and probably to Egotian.[36]

During the cold periods the boreal flora and fauna migrated southwards,
and in the succeeding period of climatic amelioration either retreated northwards or into highland regions where they became isolated relicts.   The

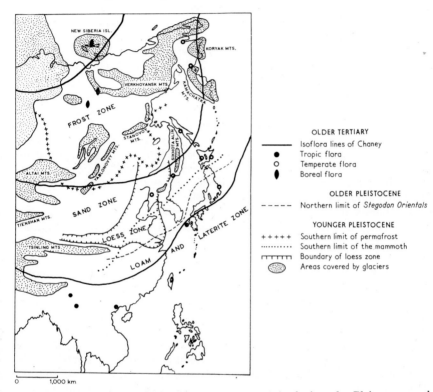

Fig. 4. Composite palaeoclimatic map of Eastern Asia during the Pleistocene and
Older Tertiary.

Japanese alpine plants are boreal relicts related to the Arcto–Altai flora
rather than to the Chinese forms.   They migrated to Japan via Sakhalin and
the Kuriles, and were associated with *Mammuthus* and *Anourosorex*; the latter
is now restricted to the high mountains of Szechwan and Formosa.   *Parnassius*
is found on Mt. Daisetsu (2000 m) in Hokkaido, the Kaima plateau in
North Korea and the Great Khingan range.[52]

V.3 *Tertiary to Recent Land Faunas*

The Eocene mammalian fauna in Mongolia was linked by the Bering land
bridge with that of North America in most of the Cenozoic era.   *Colodon*,

Cristidentinus, Desmatotherium and *Amynodon* were widespread in Japan, Korea, Shantung, Honan, Shansi, Burma and Borneo.[7] *Amynodon,* related to *Hippopotamus* in habit, may be an inhabitant of a humid climate. The Middle Miocene (Hiramakian) fauna in Japan which contains *Bunolophodon, Stegolophodon* and *Aceratheruim* is associated with the Daijima flora. These forms also occur in the Indian fauna, while *Desmostylus* and *Cornwallius* are Miocene emigrants from the eastern Pacific coast.

The Pontian or Paotean *Hipparion* fauna in north China characterized by *Hipparion, Tetralophodon* and *Chilotherium*, is a steppe fauna related to those of Tsaidam–Tung Gur of central Asia, northern Persia and eastern Europe.[62] Java lies at the south-eastern end of the Asiatic province where during Pliocene times a Siva-Malayan and, during the Pleistocene, a Sino-Malayan fauna,[19] thrived. This Pliocene Tji-Djulang fauna is coeval with the Tatrot fauna of the Siwalik series of India, both containing *Archidiskodon* and *Hippopotamus.* The later animal, however, does not occur in China.

The Lower Pleistocene (Villafranchian) Akashian fauna of Japan is related to the lower Sanmen fauna of north China by cervids, and to the Djetis fauna of Java through the occurrence of *Stegodon.*[50]

In Middle Pleistocene (Choukoutienian) times the Sino-Malayan fauna migrated along the eastern border of Cathaysia.

The Sanukian-Choukoutienian fauna with *Stegodon orientalis* and *Dicerorhinus* is widely distributed in Japan, Formosa and south China (Wanghsien, Szechuan). In north China this stage is represented by *Palaeoloxodon* which flourished in Japan until the end of the Upper Pleistocene. At the end of the Upper Pleistocene (Würmian) the Japanese fauna contained *Palaeoloxodon aomoriensis, Bison* and megacerid, and is related to the Manchurian loessic fauna. The Upper Pleistocene, upper Kuzuü fauna of Japan containing *Palaeoloxodon, Sinomegaceroides, Cervus (Deperetia), Moschus* and *Putorius,* belongs to the Rissian or Riss–Würmian, and with 59 per cent of the total fauna being Amur elements a cooler climate[53] is indicated. At this time *Sorex shinto* lived as far south as Yamaguchi (34°N) while its present limit is Aomori (41°N). The southern boundary of mammoth distribution ran from southern Hokkaido through Talien to Szechuan. The late palaeolithic culture of Japan found in the Kanto brown earth and related beds is seemingly associated with these mammoth faunas, as in the Kuhsiangtun beds of Harbin, Manchuria.

V.4 *Tertiary to Recent Marine Faunas*

The marine fauna of Japan is composed of the cold Oyashio elements, warm Kurashio and indigenous elements. The first group is related to the fauna of western North America, whereas the second belongs to the Indo-Pacific fauna. The cold Oyashio and the warm Kuroshio currents join off the Pacific coast of Japan between 35°N and 38°N. During the Tertiary the effects of these currents can be detected, the Kuroshio appearing to have flowed as far north as Hokkaido. Thus the Ariake (Lower Eocene), Nogatu (Late Eocene) and Ashiya (Late Oligocene) faunas containing *Strombidae,*

Volutidae and *Aturia* are of Kuroshio type.[35] *Nummulites* occur in the Paleo-cene–Lower Eocene of Kyushu and foramenifera are abundant in the Eocene limestones of the Philippines, Formosa, the Ryukyu and Bonin islands. The Asagian or lowest Miocene sea was cold and its fauna is related to the Vaqueros in California. The Middle Miocene seas which flooded over Japan, however, were tropical or subtropical; for the Yatsuo fauna includes molluscs of mangrove swamp type,[42, 64] and algal limestones of this age also contain foramenifera and corals. In Late Miocene times the cool temperate fauna reinvaded the area, and the subtropical fauna retreated to the south.

The Pliocene Kuroshio fauna is known in Honshu (Kakegawa) south of 35°N, in Kyushu (Tsuma) and in the Ryukyu islands (Shimaziri), while the Oyashio fauna is found north of 35°N in Hokkaido (Takikawa) and Sakhalin. Some fluctuation of water temperature is indicated by the Pleistocene benthonic fossils of the Kanto region.[39] In Saipan, reef building was repeated seven times, in Late Oligocene, Middle Miocene, Early Pliocene, Günz–Mindelian, Würmian, Early Holocene and Recent times. Reef control by the multiple glaciations is insignificant, but reef destruction is remarkable in Würmian times.[60]

References

1. Brown, J. C. *Rec. geol. Surv. India*, **73**, 514 (1938)
2. Chaney, R. *Bull. geol. Soc. China*, **14**, 349 (1935)
3. De Terra, H. *Publ. Inst. Geol. Biol.*, **6**, 1 (1946)
4. Endo, S. *Johns Hopk. Univ. Stud. Geol.*, **11**, 251 (1934)
5. Endo, S. *J. geol. Soc. Japan*, **62**, 391 (1956)
6. Flint, R. F. *Glacial and Pleistocene Geology.* 1957. New York: Wiley
7. Halle, T. G. *C.R. Congr. Strat. geol. Carbon. Heerlen*, 237 (1935)
8. Hashimoto, S. and Kumano, S. *J. geol. Soc. Japan*, **61**, 208 (1955)
9. Hatori, K. and Juen, S. *J. geol. Soc. Japan*, **64**, 232 (1958)
10. Huzita, K. *Min. Geol.*, **1**, 107 (1947)
11. Imamura, G. *Glacial Age and Glaciers of the Japanese Alps.* 1940. Tokyo: Iwanami
12. Kinosaki, Y. *Geological Atlas of Chosen*, nos. 14, 18 (1932, 1938)
13. Kobayashi, T. *Jap. J. Geol. Geogr.*, **12**, 69 (1935)
14. Kobayashi, T. *Jap. J. Geol. Geog.*, **16**, 75 (1938)
15. Kobayashi, T. *J. Fac. Sci. Tokyo Univ.*, **7**, 219 (1941)
16. Kobayashi, T. *Jap. J. Geol. Geogr.*, **18**, 157 (1942)
17. Kobayashi, T. *C.R. 3e Congr. Strat. géol. Carbon. Heerlen*, 337 (1951)
18. Kobayashi, T. *J. Fac. Sci. Tokyo Univ.*, **9**, 1 (1954)
19. Koenigswald, G. *Peking. nat. Hist. Bull.*, **13**, 293 (1938–9)
20. Krystofovich, A. N. *Amer. J. Sci.*, **5**, 200 (1923)
21. Krystofovich, A. N. *XVII Internat. Geol. Congr. Moscow*, 208 (1937)
22. Lee, J. S. *XVII Internat. Geol. Congr. Moscow*, 213 (1937)
23. Lee, J. S. *The Geology of China.* 1939. London: Murby
24. Lee, T. Y. *Bull. geol. Soc. China*, **16**, 131 (1936)
25. Ma, T. Y. H. *J. geol. Soc. Japan*, **43**, 340 (1936)
26. Ma, T. Y. H. *Research on Past Climate and Continental Drift, Taipei*, **7**, 1 (1955)
27. Ma, T. Y. H. *Research on Past Climate and Continental Drift, Taipei*, **9**, 1 (1956)

306   TEIICHI KOBAYASHI AND TOKIO SHIKAMA

28. Ma, T. Y. H. *Research on Past Climate and Continental Drift, Taipei,* **10**, 1 (1956)
29. Ma, T. Y. H. *Research on Past Climate and Continental Drift, Taipei,* **11**, 1 (1956)
30. Matsushita, S. *Jap. J. Geol. Congr.,* **18**, 1 (1941)
31. Matsushita, S. *Mem. Coll. Sci. Kyoto,* **19**, 37 (1947)
32. Miki, S. *Jap. J. Bot.,* **9**, 213 (1938)
33. Miki, S. *Min. Geol.,* **2**, 105 (1948)
34. Miki, S., Huzita, K. and Kokawa, S. *Proc. imp. Acad. Japan,* **33**, 41 (1957)
35. Mizuno, A. *Bull. geol. Surv. Japan,* **7**, 25 (1956)
36. Nakamura, J. *Res. Rep. Kochi Univ.,* **1**, 1 (1952)
37. Naora, N. *Mem. School Sci. Engng Waseda Univ.,* **22**, 11 (1958)
38. Norin, E. *Sino-Swedish Expedition,* **III**, 1 (1937)
39. Ogose, S. *Lexicon of Stratigraphic Names of Japan, Cenozoic Erathem.* 1953
40. Oishi, S. *J. Fac. Sci. Hokkaido Univ.,* **5**, 123 (1940)
41. Otuka, Y. *Jubl. Publ. Prof. Yabe 60th Birth.,* 481 (1939)
42. Oyama, K. *Rep. geol. Surv. Japan,* **131–132**, 1 (1950)
43. P'an, C. H. *Palaeont. sinica,* **4A**, 1 (1936)
44. Saito, R. *Bull. geol. Instn. Manch.,* no. 97, 47 (1939)
45. Sakamoto, T. *Amer. J. Sci.,* **248**, 499 (1950)
46. Sakamoto, T. *J. geol. Soc. Japan,* **56**, 59 (1950)
47. Sasa, Y. *Jubl. Publ. Comm. Prof. Yabe 60th Birth.,* 56 (1939)
48. Sasa, Y. and Tanaka, K. *J. Fac. Sci. Hokkaido Univ.,* **4**, 193 (1938)
49. Saurin, E. *Lexique Stratigraphique International,* **III**, 1 (1956)
50. Shikama, T. *J. geol. Soc. Japan,* **43**, 557 (1936)
51. Shikama, T. *J. geol. Soc. Japan,* **45**, 621 (1938)
52. Shikama, T. *Bull. cent. nat. Mus. Manchoukuo,* **6**, 9 (1943)
53. Shikama, T. *Sci. Rep. Tohoku Imp. Univ.,* **23**, 1 (1947)
54. Shikama, T. *Min. Geol.,* **3**, 1 (1950)
55. Shikama, T. *Sci. Rep. Yokohama nat. Univ.,* **1**, 29 (1952)
56. Suzuki, K. *Symposia Japan Cenozoic,* 34 (1958)
57. Takai, F. *Jap. J. Geol. Geogr.,* **22**, 167 (1952)
58. Takubo, J. and Minato, T. *Sci. Rep. Kyoto Univ.,* **2**, 23 (1943)
59. Tanai, T. *Rep. geol. Surv. Japan,* **163**, 1 (1955)
60. Tayama, R. *Bull. Trop. Indust. Inst. Palau,* **1**, 1 (1938)
61. Tchurakov, A. N. *XVII Internat. Geol. Congr. Moscow,* 212 (1937)
62. Teilhard, P. *Publ. Inst. Geol. Biol. Peking,* **7**, 1 (1941)
63. Teilhard, P. and Leroy, P. *Publ. Inst. Geol. Biol. Peking,* **8**, 1 (1942)
64. Tsuda, K. *J. Paleont.,* **30**, 974 (1956)
65. Ueda, F. *J. Toyo Univ.,* **12**, 151 (1958)
66. Vershachagin, V. N. *Soviet Geol., Moscow,* **55** (1957)
67. Vologdin, A. G. *XVII Internat. Geol. Congr. Moscow,* 213 (1937)
68. Vologdin, A. G. *Ann. Centre d'Etude et de Documentation Paléont.,* **23**, 83 (1957)
69. Wang, C. S. *Bull. geol. Soc. China,* **22**, 1 (1942)
70. Willis, B. and Blackwelder, E. *Research in China,* pts. 1–2, 1907
71. Wissmann, H. *Z. Ges. Erdk. Berl.,* **241**, 1 (1937)
72. Yabe, H. and Sugiyama, T. *J. Paleont.,* **9**, 183 (1935)
73. Yabe, H. and Endo, S. *VIth Pac. Sci. Congr., Ocean. Mar. Geol.,* 631 (1940)
74. Yamasaki, T. and Sasa, Y. *Nippon Gakuzyutu Kyo-Kai Hokoku,* **13**, 346 (1938)

XIII

The Palaeoclimatology of Gondwanaland during the Palaeozoic and Mesozoic Eras

L. C. KING

I. The Concept of Gondwanaland

The task of surveying the palaeoclimatic history of the continents of the southern hemisphere during the Palaeozoic and Mesozoic is feasible only when some connecting pattern or theme exists. This connecting pattern, the master print by means of which palaeoclimatic information from the scattered continents can be harmonized into a single broad scheme, is the concept of Gondwanaland, subject to continental drift. When the present continents of the Southern Hemisphere are reunited into one super-continent the data form a consistent pattern, and climatic belts can be traced across it in broad latitudinal zones.

All evidence from sedimentary rocks relating to past climates indicates three things: (a) that since post-Archean time at least all varieties of climate at present existing upon the earth have been abundantly and recurrently represented; (b) that within the limitations of palaeontologic dating different climatic regimens have been manifest in different regions at one and the same time, perhaps with some system of global zoning; and (c) at no time has the world climate so departed from the range of climates now current as to constitute an entirely strange environment, significantly hotter or colder than can be matched at present. (d) These conclusions from the physical nature of sedimentary rocks are supported by the continuous existence of organic life, with a restricted tolerance to temperature range, for at least the past 1000 million years.

Typically, in South Africa where Cambrian and Ordovician systems have not been identified, the Silurian rocks of the Table Mountain series in Cape Province begin with maroon shales with sun-cracked surfaces indicative of a warm temperate environment. The succeeding pale sandstones and blue-green Upper shales (the latter with a local tillite horizon in the extreme south-west) imply a local fall of temperature, though in the Transvaal a thousand miles to the north the correlative Waterberg formation * remains bright red throughout. The Devonian Bokkeveld series, marine and continental, is of dark shales and false-bedded, somewhat feldspathic, sandstones, without limestone, indicative of a cool climate which was maintained during accumulation of the white Witteberg quartzites. The succeeding Witteberg shales (formerly called the lower Dwyka shales) are very dark, thin-bedded and unfossiliferous, and may well have accumulated in a cold inland sea.

A climatic nadir was reached during the late Carboniferous when the Dwyka tillite was deposited under marine conditions in the south but upon a land surface north of latitude $32\frac{1}{2}°$S. The continental ice sheets of this period extended far and wide, and local valley glaciation occurred as far north in Africa as the present equator. Rare fossils from the tillite are fronds of *Gangamopteris*, recalling the rain forests that now flourish close to the termini of the Fox and Franz Josef glaciers in New Zealand.

Thereafter, the refrigeration passed and the upper Dwyka shales are again dark, relatively unfossiliferous, coldwater shales. At the very top of the Dwyka series the 'Chert Band', possibly a diatomaceous ooze, contains *Glossopteris* and the curious little reptile *Mesosaurus*. Succeeding formations record progressive amelioration of climate.

Accumulation of the Ecca series occupied early and middle Permian time. Its sandstones, arkoses and shales are grey, brown and black in hue, and the middle (coal measure) sandstones contain much fresh feldspar. The facies is typically cold temperate. The *Glossopteris* flora, which seems to have lived in a high-latitude environment like that of the modern southern beech (*Notofagus*), was sufficiently abundant to make coal beds. The only other fossils are a few fish scales. In South-West Africa a change of facies brings in the 'Red Ecca', indicative of warmer conditions.

The general entry of vari-coloured shales, with yellow and light grey sandstones lacking fresh feldspar, initiates the Beaufort series and records a spread of warm temperate conditions over southern Africa. Under the benign climate entered and flourished the rich Karroo reptilian fauna (late Permian–Triassic). There is no trace of a break, stratigraphically or palaeontologically, between the Palaeozoic and Mesozoic eras such as characterized the northern hemisphere. Such differentiation is meaningless in the Karroo sequence.

The Stormberg series followed after a brief time interval. Its Triassic Red

* The original correlation of the Table Mountain and Waterberg series by Hatch and Corstorphine, though rejected by du Toit, has been reinstated by King.[11]

Beds and yellow, aeolian Cave Sandstone record a true desert environment with debris washed and blown hither and thither during accumulation. Fossils are naturally scarce, mainly plants with rare dinosaurs and fresh-water fish. The Stormberg series extends from the Cape Province as far north as the Congo Basin.

In South Africa Karroo-type sedimentation was terminated by outwelling of the Rhaetic Drakensberg basalts; but northward in the Belgian Congo sedimentation continued into the Jurassic, as the Lualaba series which contains fossil fish.

A similar broad and simple climatic cycle is found for the same time span in all the more southerly remnants of Gondwanaland, as du Toit[5] clearly demonstrated. Such consistent evidence from regions so widely scattered is of primary importance to palaeoclimatologists.

But though these major similarities are uniquely convincing, sundry differences of climatic interpretation between the several theatres of Gondwanaland are no less important. By virtue of its size Gondwanaland must have extended beyond any single climatic girdle, and so the facies of each continental rock system must alter from place to place in conformity with different latitudes and distinct, coexisting climatic environments. The Karroo rocks of the Congo Basin, for instance, indicate generally warmer conditions than the Karroo rocks of Cape Province.

While it is true that any large land mass to some extent generates its own climate, especially in the interior (as in Asia), comparative records over very large areas may yet demonstrate the existence of climatic girdles during the geological past, and furthermore whether such climatic girdles correspond with the frigid, cold temperate, warm temperate and tropical girdles of the present day. The huge landspread of Gondwana, indeed, does exhibit palaeoclimatic zoning appropriate to two or three of these girdles at any given time (see Section IIA). This is important following Sir George Simpson's recent conclusion that even during an ice age polar ice-caps would not extend beyond latitude 55°.

If, as is suspected, drift of Gondwanaland took place as a unit during the Palaeozoic era and carried the super-continent progressively through different climatic girdles, then not only should local changes of climatic environment be apparent but such changes should vary coherently from one locality to another. While most of such changes would doubtless be sympathetic, particular importance attaches to changes induced when drift took part of the super-continent across the equator or through the polar regions so that antipathetic changes occurred simultaneously in regions on opposite sides of the tropical or frigid girdles. Such antipathetic changes[13] surely tell very heavily against theories of global climatic change in explanation of the Gondwana phenomena. Naturally, in the establishment of such contrasted variation, precise dating of geological events is of prime importance.

The concept of Gondwanaland might well have become untenable in this generation were it not for the remarkable hypothesis of Continental Drift advanced by Wegener in 1912.

Under Wegener's hypothesis Gondwanaland was achieved not by the invention of phantasmal past continents, but by reassembling the southern land masses, with India, into a single coherent super-continent in the manner of a jig-saw puzzle. Modern reconstructions of this kind, carried out upon globes and taking into consideration also the substance of the great suboceanic ridges[14] show how remarkably the outlines of the continents do fit, rendering in only one possible way a single land mass of simple ovoid outline that displays an almost continuous peripheral girdle of Kainozoic fold-mountain systems.[9] This is the modern conception of Gondwanaland as it existed during Palaeozoic and early Mesozoic time. Of course, refitting by

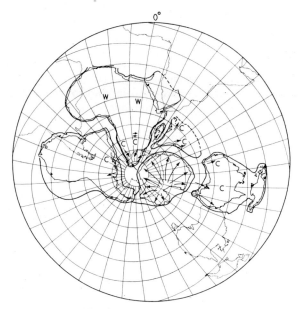

Fig. 1. Late Carboniferous.

C = cold; W = warm temperate; arrows show movement of ice sheets, with modern directions for Antarctica.

outlines brings into proximity parts of the continents that are now separated by broad oceanic basins, and if the hypothesis of continental drift is true, these juxtaposed regions should show conjugate geological systems and structures.

The test was made principally by du Toit[5] who, already possessed of an unrivalled knowledge of the geology of Southern Africa, visited South America, India and Australia wherein he found stratigraphic and structural relationships so closely alike that they could not possibly have originated in regions so widely separated as these are now. Continental drift provided the only valid answer. du Toit's synthesis has been upheld by other workers who have studied the same regions: I have done so myself (with the exception of

India) and have been compelled by the field evidence to accept the general thesis.

The converse also holds true: that the geological phenomena observed within any single theatre could not have developed within that area alone.[10] Thus, the Karroo system of late Palaeozoic and early Mesozoic rocks, wholly continental in facies and with a maximum thickness of 20 000 ft, spans the full width of South Africa from the east coast to the west, and could not possibly have been derived from within the sub-continent. Minor structures in the east, west and south also demonstrate that the source of the materials lay beyond the present shorelines, not in narrow mountain chains but in broad, plateau landscapes like the Africa of today. But there is no space for such terrains within the narrow continental shelf girdling the sub-continent.

Visible geological phenomena involving many thousands of feet of strata that crop out (often with a minimum of tectonic disturbance) over many thousands of square miles within the southern continents therefore establish the Reality of Gondwanaland under continental drift.

Though some critics have been reluctant to accept Drift because they could find no mechanical explanation for it, recently developed palaeomagnetic techniques independently establish relative movement between the southern continents, and reinforce the concept of Gondwanaland during the Palaeozoic era (Fig. 1).

Without the Gondwanaland concept, as will appear in the sequel, all palaeoclimatic interpretations for the southern hemisphere during Palaeozoic and Mesozoic time are meaningless. With the Gondwanaland concept all such interpretations fall into a synthesis of extreme simplicity, which is the subject of this chapter.

II. Palaeoclimatic Data from Gondwanaland

Three distinct categories are immediately apparent in palaeoclimatic data from Gondwanaland:

(1) Data from the early Palaeozoic era, though decisive in type, are sparse owing to later tectonic disturbance and to the immense blanket of later sedimentary rock systems belonging to the second category. On the evidence available, therefore, no complete picture of Gondwana palaeoclimatology can be given for the early Palaeozoic.

(2) Data from the continental Carboniferous–Triassic rock systems which crop out over vast areas are, on the contrary, the most complete in time and space from any rock formations on earth; and the conclusions to be drawn from them far transcend any other ancient demonstrations available to palaeoclimatologists.

(3) Data for the Jurassic period are meagre, and for the Cretaceous period a new order was introduced by the disruption of Gondwanaland and radial dispersion of the fragments towards their present positions on the terrestrial globe.

II.1 *Early Palaeozoic Palaeoclimatology of Gondwanaland*

The beginning of the Palaeozoic, in the classical sense, does not exist in Gondwanaland, for in India (Vindhyan), Australia (Adelaidean) and Africa (Transvaal and correlatives) are mighty rock sequences that begin as infra-Cambrian and pass up without marked unconformity into strata sometimes assignable on a palaeontological basis to the Cambrian itself. Our palaeo-climatic studies begin conveniently therefore at a time somewhat anterior to the Cambrian.

A. *Infra-Cambrian*

Remarkable developments of infra-Cambrian glacials, appearing in many parts of Gondwanaland, have been correlated by almost all stratigraphers concerned with rock systems of this age. Though there is no evidence of precise dating for these deposits, the general correlation upon facies is doubt-less correct. We review these formations.

In South America the Lavras series east of the Rio São Francisco contains extensive tillites and conglomerates with admixed soled and striated pebbles. Guimarães [7] has diagnosed an inland ice sheet though striated pavements are rare. Fluvio-glacial deposits of the same epoch have been reported from southern Brazil and Matto Grosso, and local geologists have thought the occurrence so widespread as to require a change of the region with respect to the South Pole.

Central and South Africa also display tillites, thick and thin, of an age that is generally assessed as 'late Pre-Cambrian'. The 'Grand Conglomerat' of the Mwashya series, 2000 to 3000 ft thick, is widespread in Katanga; and the 'Petit Conglomerat' at the base of the later middle Kundelungu system, though usually marine, is in places a true tillite.[1] In South Africa the Numees tillite, 600 ft thick, occurs with dark shales and limestones; and at higher stratigraphic levels the lesser Ongeluk-Griquatown tillite of the Transvaal system, 250 ft thick at a maximum, is both under- and overlain by shales, showing that the formation is not a ground moraine but accumu-lated in a body of water. Martin's correlation of the Damara system with the Transvaal places the Chuos tillite also in this group. But the Nabas beds overlying the Kuibis quartzite of the Nama system, and consisting of tillite 50 ft thick, are probably younger. Infra-Cambrian glaciation of the southern lobe of Africa may well have involved the spread of continental ice sheets covering twenty degrees or more of latititude.

The Adelaidean system of Australia likewise includes towards the top clear testimony of an ice age of great severity. The Sturtian tillites include six beds of true tillite varying from 30 to 500 ft in thickness and aggregating 1000 ft. With the interglacial beds the total thickness measures 1500 ft. Most of the deposit is terrestrial though some may have dropped from floating ice. Fluvio-glacial beds are disposed to the north of the morainal facies, suggest-ing that the source of the ice lay to the south (present orientation). Australian authors [3] have suggested correlation with the South African Numees tillite.

Even if all these occurrences of late Pre-Cambrian glacial rocks are not precisely contemporaneous they indicate for some parts of Gondwanaland a time when the climate was extreme. The climate may not have been frigid for the whole area at any one time, but certainly part of the super-continent experienced the passage of a frigid regime. These phenomena bear remarkable resemblance to those of the subsequent Palaeozoic refrigeration described in Section II.2.

B. *Cambrian and Ordovician*

Except where the encompassing geosynclinal sea lapped marginally across the continent, Cambrian and Ordovician formations are seldom identifiable in Gondwanaland because of lack of fossils. Even for the Silurian and Devonian periods palaeoclimatic interpretation is so hampered for lack of a detailed chronology that the construction of a climatic chart is impossible. Nevertheless, broad sympathetic trends of climatic change are perceptible. Thus Cambrian rocks are frequently bright coloured and have been cited as indicative of a warm climate, whereas Silurian formations tend to be pale and leached and sometimes contain evidence of minor glacial action. These characteristics are not, however, universal.

Harrington[8] has cited 1500 m of brightly coloured sandstones and shales in Northern Argentine as Cambrian in age. They are succeeded by Ordovician black and green shales carrying marine fossils with white quartzites and a local glacio-marine conglomerate. In Brazil, Guimarães[7] writes of a warm Cambrian climate but Ordovician formations are unknown.

Northern Africa has early Palaeozoic fossils which indicate that the marine transgressions there were warm;[2] but south of the Sahara all sequences are continental. If Cambrian strata are present they are probably red; part of the Kundelungu or Oendelungu system of the Congo and Angola, or, farther south to the Fish River, Swartmodder beds or the Matsap system. Nothing is proved.

The Cambrian of the Salt Range in India is dated by fossils. Above the salt and gypsum phase lie purple sandstones with sun-cracks and ripple marks that suggest correlation with the rufous Upper Vindhyans covering 40 000 square miles of the peninsula. Certainly a phase of strong iron oxidation, and probably low rainfall, marks the Cambrian of India. As in Central and Southern Africa there is no hint of Ordovician formations.

The Cambrian of south-eastern Australia, too, has its share of red beds beginning with the Purple Slates at the very base (Wilpena Pound). The Ordovician is largely of graptolithic slates (Victoria).

The prevailingly ruddy complexion of the Cambrian formations in Gondwanaland may indicate continental accumulation under a dry or strongly seasonal climate in landscapes devoid of vegetation; but there is no certainty of this. Only in the Salt Range are salt and gypsum deposits associated to support an interpretation of aridity, and these have sometimes been thought to be younger and emplaced by tectonics.

Certainly the Ordovician formations that follow are generally drab by

x

comparison, and the difference may be due to change towards a cooler regimen. More examples would be helpful.

C. *Silurian*

'Thick and very extensive basal Palaeozoic sandstones lying immediately on the crystalline complex in South America, are usually identified as Silurian' (Caster). And in general this holds for Africa south of the Sahara, also. There is indeed a great extent of arenaceous beds in the Amazon, Bolivia, western Argentina, the Cape Province and India (Muth quartzite) that are known to be of Silurian or early Devonian age, and that are bleached or white in aspect, suggesting that they accumulated in cool waters. This conclusion is borne out by restricted occurrences of water-laid tillite, both in Brazil and near Capetown.

Within the arcuate outcrop of the formations, African reddish sandstones of the Waterberg–Umkondo–Upper Kundelungu–Bukoban groups (the Kundelungu with fish scales) are possibly coeval,[11] and represent a warmer continental phase, extending from the Transvaal to Uganda. This gives a hint of palaeoclimatic zoning, possibly confirmed by the contrasted nature of the Silurian in south-eastern Australia where corals proliferated in the epicontinental seas. David[3] described the local Silurian climate as 'more genial than the present day'.

D. *Devonian*

Stratigraphic thermometry indicates a cool climate in the south-western and a warm climate in the northern and eastern areas (modern orientation) of Devonian Gondwanaland. The facies of the Andean pre-Cordillera includes thick dark green greywackes and uniformly black shales (Bolivia) with plant remains. Important for climatology is an intercalated glacio-marine conglomerate in the Argentine. This is not matched in Brazil or Paraguay, but the Silurian and Devonian (Furnas) sandstones are such as could well have accumulated in a cool climate. In the Falkland Islands and across the southern tip of Africa are dark (Bokkeveld) shales and sandstones with cold fauna in the lower and sparse plant remains in the upper part. They are succeeded by the White Witteberg quartzites and dark shales before the Dwyka ice time, so there are no doubts of the cold Devonian climate in this region.

By contrast, Northern Brazil and North Africa have characteristically warmer water marine faunas of 'northern hemisphere' type, as though these regions then lay in lower latitudes than those previously cited. Extra-Peninsular India shows a similar fauna which extended to Australia where corals flourished; and, according to David, arid conditions are suggested for the latter part of the period by an enormous development of red rocks.

The data for the early and middle Palaeozoic era suffice to indicate the existence of palaeoclimatic regions in general but are too sparse to afford a comprehensive view of the climatic regions of Gondwanaland for any precise time interval; or to render possible a coherent statement of successive climatic fluctuations within any specific area. In other words, they fail to define either the situation of the Gondwana reassembly on the globe in terms of latitude or successive changes with continental drift from one latitude to another. Such a demonstration becomes possible, however, for the periods that follow.

II.2 *Palaeoclimatology of Gondwanaland during the Period from Carboniferous to Triassic*

With the Carboniferous period, the plaguey uncertainties of early Palaeozoic stratigraphic dating disappear. Sufficiently close synchronization of formations can be established and the rock systems used as palaeoclimatic indicators have wide, and tectonically undisturbed, distribution over much of Gondwanaland. The data available to the palaeoclimatologist are, indeed, uniquely rich, detailed and varied: the finest that the whole scope of geology affords.

A. *Carboniferous*

Widespread in the Carboniferous and early Permian record for all the southern continents (except Antarctica from which insufficient data are yet available) are occurrences of tillites and varvites indicating a phase of very low temperature and extensive glaciation. While certain of these occurrences represent local glaciation of mountain and valley type (as in the Belgian Congo where the deposits are spread east and west from a north–south ridge), others record the former existence of ice sheets of continental dimensions. Source studies for the erratics carried by these ice sheets and the striae etched into the subglacial pavements, show many trends of ice movement, some away from local highlands and gathering grounds of Carboniferous time, others controlled by a larger pattern that exceeds the dimensions of any of the present continents. In South Africa, for instance, in addition to ice sheets passing into the southern quadrant from gathering grounds in the Transvaal and South-West Africa, mighty ice sheets bearing voluminous moraine passed on to Natal from the Indian Ocean area to the north-east; and the tillite of the southern Cape Province, exceeding 2000 ft in thickness, has been shown by Haughton to have been derived from the *south*.

When the known directions of ice movement are plotted for Gondwanaland (Fig. 1) they make a coherent pattern into which the modern directions of ice-radiation in Antarctica integrate. In a general way, facies of deposition follow the same pattern, with a proved absence of Carboniferous ground moraine (tillite) over part, at least, of Antarctica, where the main gathering ground of ice seems to have lain; with an inner girdle including the southern tip of Africa where tillites are thickest and varvites minor in the sequence; and with an outer girdle predominantly of marginal, often lacustrine, glacial deposits recording numerous local advances and retreats of the ice fronts, e.g. Brazil, India, Australia.

Gondwanaland at this epoch constitutes a palaeoclimatic entity with the South Pole situated not far from its present position in Antarctica. The orderly distribution of former glacial phenomena was apparently disrupted at a later date by fragmentation of Gondwanaland and dispersal of the fragments to their present positions on the globe, where the inter-relationships of the glacial deposits are now quite incomprehensible (e.g. Brazil and India, situated in the southern and northern tropics respectively). This unity of 'Permo–Carboniferous' glacial phenomena in the southern hemisphere was clearly established by du Toit[5] and has never received any satisfactory explanation other than under the Gondwanaland hypothesis. Now we must carry the matter further.

More precise dating of glacial deposits in the several regions reveals a much wider time range than is generally recognized. In western Argentina they are cited as early Carboniferous in age; in Brazil they are late Carboniferous but do not persist until the end because the succeeding coal measures are also included within that period; in South Africa refrigeration continued until the close of the Carboniferous; in India it survived into the early Permian; and in Australia tillites were deposited as late as the mid-Permian.[13] Thus Gondwana refrigeration was not a simple event that affected all regions simultaneously and in the same sense, but was a climatic state that passed slowly, through millions of years, across Gondwanaland from west to east. The refrigeration had passed in western Argentina and the climate had warmed considerably before ice sheets even began to accumulate in Australia! Simultaneous climatic changes thus took place *in the opposite sense* in western and eastern regions of Gondwanaland. This is the type of *contrasting* phenomena that only a land mass on the scale of Gondwanaland can demonstrate, and so important is it that attention must now be devoted to some local details of the Gondwana glaciation.

In South America, glacial outwash or discontinuous tillite appears between dark Devonian shales and late Carboniferous cold-water marine facies in borehole cores along the lower Tapajoz, a tributary of the Amazon almost on the present Equator. This is matched (Gondwanaland again) by a boulder bed in the Adjua shales at the base of the Sekondian system of Ghana where a few pelecypod fossils were classed by Morley Davies as possibly early Carboniferous. The Bermejo series of Bolivia affords glacial evidence that may be of the same age. The lowest tillite in Western Argentina, assessed by Caster as the most 'thoroughly glacial record of Argentina', underlies beds with the *Rhacopteris* flora, a position which assigns it definitely to the early Carboniferous. Nowhere else in Gondwanaland is such a relationship known. Consistently, therefore, the great glaciation seems to have commenced in western and north-western Gondwanaland.

Tillites near the Sierra de la Ventana of Buenos Aires, overlain by the Bonete series of molluscan and *Glossopteris* fossils, appear to be younger and to conform more in age with the extensive Itarare tillites of the Parana Basin in Brazil. These constitute the basal member of the Santa Catarina system (*cf.* Karroo system of South Africa) and compare with the South African Dwyka facies. The formation increases in thickness northwards from Uruguay to 1000 m in certain occurrences in São Paulo State, and like all South American occurrences includes much evidence of advance and retreat of ice fronts and fluvio-glacial outwash. Minor occurrences are known in Minas Gerais and Baia. The large area covered by tillite (4×10^6 km^2) and the abundance of well-soled and striated pebbles confirm this as a continental glaciation; with movement of the Brazilian ice sheets, according to Caster and Burlen, from south to north, and of the East Argentine glacials westwards from a source that lay outside South America to the east.

The glacials are succeeded by the Rio Bonito coal measures, with *Glossopteris*, and by the dark Irati shales, with *Mesosaurus* (end-Carboniferous), and so the end of the period was cold, but not frigid, in the Brazilian region.

The Andean region, except in the south, lay beyond reach of the ice sheets and preserves normal marine and continental formations. In northern Brazil, also, continental beds with late Carboniferous coals indicate a cool temperate climate beyond the frigid zone.

The Carboniferous rocks of South Africa begin with the Witteberg series of white, clean quartzites and dark, unfossiliferous shales indicative of cold, though not frigid, climatic controls. By the late Carboniferous thousands of square miles of country were shrouded beneath continental ice sheets[5, 6] which later left behind them a more permanent covering of (Dwyka) tillite ranging from 30 ft thickness in the southern Transvaal to 2500 ft in the southern Cape Province. Most of this is unbedded, but bedding is sometimes conspicuous towards the top or indicates a break of deposition within the body of the tillite. Striated tillite also appears in such situations, indicating renewed advance of ice over frozen tundra. Two to five such readvances are known in different parts of the Union. Other shaly laminae record the transient existence of lakes. Minor paper shales, or fluvio-glacial sands locally, conclude the Dwyka series of glacial and associated formations in the north; a considerable thickness of dark, unfossiliferous upper Dwyka shales follows the tillite in the south. The final member of the series is a chert-band containing *Mesosaurus* that affords an exact palaeontological horizon correlating with South America. South African coal measures (Ecca series), however, post-date this horizon in contrast to the Rio Bonito measures that precede it (Table I).

Tillite is not known from the northern Transvaal, which apparently functioned as a centre of ice dispersal, but Bond has recorded 100 ft of tillite with varved shales in southern tributaries of the Zambezi Valley, and similar varves are known across the valley in Northern Rhodesia. Bond judged that the deposits were local and did not imply the former existence there of a continental ice sheet. The same is true of further occurrences in the Lukuga Valley which forms the outlet from Lake Tanganyika. The original extent of the Lukuga tillite is uncertain, for much of it was removed by denudation before the succeeding dark shales were laid down, but similar beds with tillite occur as the Lutoe series of neighbouring Angola. In the abundance of varvites and frequent bedding of tillite, these Central African glacials resemble the Itarare series of Brazil more than they do the massive tillite of South Africa. With this their age, beginning before the late Carboniferous and ending before the close of the period, also seems to be in agreement.[13]

No report of Carboniferous glaciation has been received from East Africa, but in the Sakoa area of south-western Madagascar boulder beds which are followed by black shales and coal-bearing strata with *Glossopteris* are considered by Besairie to represent the glacial epoch.

North Africa as a whole lay beyond the frigid zone. In Carboniferous time a broad arch of elevated country apparently extended across tropical Africa from east to west. Debris from denudation of the arch was shed northwards across the Sudan and Libya where it accumulated as broad piedmonts fossilized now as the sandstones of the Nubian series. Shallow marine transgressions from the north have left intercalated marine strata with appropriate fossils. The general facies of these Nubian sandstones implies accumulation under warm temperate climatic environments. If, as has been suggested above (Fig. 1), the Carboniferous South Pole was situated near South Africa, then North Africa would lie about 25–30°S in a climatic girdle wholly appropriate to the Nubian formations, and the dark shales of the southern Congo, Angola and Southern Madagascar also fall appropriately in the cold temperate latitudes 60–65°S. Already the facts of stratigraphy seem to indicate, for South America and Africa, a palaeoclimatic zoning during the Carboniferous period that is essentially the same as the modern climatic girdles of the earth. But the positions of the continents are different, bound together in Gondwanaland.

In India the Talchir conglomerate, of glacial and fluvio-glacial origin,[6, 19] is found at the base of the Gondwana system (= Karroo) in all localities where it crops out from the Rajmahal Hills to the Godaveri River and from Raniganj to Nagpur. Later, the ice reached beyond the Punjab to the Salt Range and Kashmir. According to Fox, glaciers there deposited material directly into a shallow sea. Several local gathering grounds have been identified, chief of which are the Aravalli Hills and the Eastern Ghats.

The characteristic soled and striated pebbles, often far travelled, are embedded in a fine, silty matrix suggestive of deposition in lakes; striated pavements are uncommon, and the general impression is of marginal deposition from vast ice sheets lying to the south. In Orissa, at least, we meet the familiar problem that some of the ice must have come from beyond the present boundaries of the sub-continent. The direction of ice movement was from south to north (incomprehensible on the present situation of India), but tillites are absent from southern India, either because the moraine was exported from there or because they have been stripped following severe uplift of that region in late Mesozoic and Tertiary time.

Greenish 'needle shales' that follow the conglomerate resemble the upper Dwyka shales of South Africa, and also contain the earliest local specimens of *Glossopteris*. The Umaria marine bed which overlies the Talchir conglomerate in the north maintained connection with the Tethyan mediterranean of the Salt Range. It corresponds with the *Eurydesma* and *Conularia* stages of other parts of the Southern Hemisphere, the fauna being stunted by cold and possibly by dilution of the sea water.

The evidence on Carboniferous palaeoclimatology from India integrates it closely with Gondwanaland, of which it evidently formed a part of the northern margin. The tillites are less thick and massive than those of South Africa, which perhaps accumulated in a central continental basin like the ice-filled depressions that occupy the heart of Antarctica and Greenland at the present day.

Little positive evidence of Carboniferous glaciation is yet forthcoming from the Antarctic continent. Along the western flank of the Ross Sea inlet the Gondwana formations lie upon the older rock systems without the intervention of a tillite, or indeed of any conglomerate. Sedimentation appears to have begun during the Permian period. True, if the Antarctic continent functioned as the focus of radiation for the primary Gondwana ice-cap as the recorded directions of ice movement indicate (Fig. 1), then little deposition of tillite is to be expected over much of the region.

Recently (1957) I was privileged to see in the British Museum a remarkable conglomerate specimen brought back from Queen Maud Land by the Norwegian–British–Swedish expedition of 1948–50. In a sand-silt matrix are embedded worn pebbles of vein quartz, jasperoid and similar hard rocks such as strew the ground in Archean terrains undergoing pedimentation. I have long known boulders of such peculiar conglomerates in the Dwyka tillite of the Natal coastal region, where they had been brought on the ice sheet that swept in from the sea. There was no clue as to their source, but as Queen Maud Land is the terrain which lies nearest to Natal on the Gondwanaland reconstruction I had reasoned that, maybe, they came from there. Such conglomerates, found as glacial erratics, could be of any geological age; but the Natal erratics had been soled and striated before they were wholly indurated and thus were of an age immediately prior to the glaciation (though found especially at the higher horizons). The Antarctic specimen contains a pebble that is lithologically indistinguishable from the Table Mountain sandstone that underlies much of the tillite in Natal; not a very characteristic sandstone it is true, but thousands of similar pebbles bearing glacial soles and striae occur in the tillite of Natal. The conglomerate may thus be compared with the Dwyka tillite. This slender evidence is all that is currently available of the late Carboniferous glaciation from the Antarctic sector of Gondwanaland.

Every state of Australia retains evidence of glaciation during Carboniferous–Permian time. According to David,[3] the main ice sheets travelled northwards 'from high land lying to the south of Tasmania' (another Gondwanaland source-problem!); and there is a broad zoning of phenomena from Tasmania and the Inman Valley of South Australia, where the most striking pavements and *roche moutonnées* are found with erratics up to 23 ft in length, to Queensland and Central Australia, where on the Finke River sandy tillites and highly contorted fluvio-glacial beds mark the edge of the ice sheets. There was also local dispersal from a chain of freshly-created mountains along the eastern seaboard and, as the mountains were in part volcanic, quantities of ash are there mixed with the glacial beds of the upper Kuttung series. From the mountains piedmont glaciers extended into the sea, and the glacial sediments became mixed with marine facies of the sea that encompassed Gondwanaland.

Much fluctuation of the ice-fronts is evident and at Bacchus Marsh, Victoria, eleven advances are recorded in a total thickness of tillite, fluvio-glacial conglomerate, sandstone and shale amounting to 2000 ft. Varved shales are ubiquitous and local thicknesses of 200 ft must represent accumulation over thousands of years. Altogether the phenomena imply a situation in Gondwanaland marginal to the main central ice-caps, and recall conditions in India. The comparison with India is fully borne out by the glacial deposits of Western Australia where most of the occurrences are aqua-glacial and remote from the centres of glaciation. On the Irwin River, for instance, heaps of erratics in the upper glacial beds appear to have been dropped from icebergs. As in India, 'some of the advances took place during upper Carboniferous time, but they evidently persisted into the Permian' (David); unless indeed the Sakmarian deposits are rewashed Carboniferous glacials.

The nature of the glacial (and also the pre-glacial) beds of Australia is wholly consistent with the position of Australia in the Gondwanaland reassembly, and with the slow passage of that reassembly through the Antarctic frigid zone in such a manner that the actual pole at no time lay within the Australian land mass. Figs. 1 and 2 bring the concept out clearly; let the palaeoclimatologist pause to contemplate, in imagination, the huge Gondwana ice-cap, silent and dead save for the howl of the wind and the hiss of the wind-driven snow, as the lights of the *Aurora Australis* flicker and sway through the six-monthly night.

B. Early Permian

What conditions followed the melting of the icy carapace? Far and wide was left the mantle of till, lacustrine and fluvio-glacial deposition as a record of the frigid episode, but what followed?

Fortunately, in many regions post-glacial deposition continued in sinking basins in which accumulated dark, cold-water, usually non-marine shales, sometimes with grey sandstones and arkoses. Characteristic also are coal-seams of the *Glossopteris* flora which flourished then like the modern *Notofagus* (southern beech) flora of southern cold temperate latitudes which in New Zealand and Tierra del Fuego maintains itself in forests almost up to the ice fronts. Specimens of *Gangamopteris* have indeed been recovered from truly glacial deposits.

The distribution of these cold temperate sediments in the existing southern continents (with India) is nonsensical; but they appear rationally in relation to one another in the Gondwanaland reassembly, and group in latitudes appropriate to their palaeoclimatic facies (Fig. 2).

Like the tillites that precede them, the phenomena of the cold temperate phase do not appear simultaneously throughout Gondwanaland but successively from west to east following the retreat of the frigid phase in that direction. This relationship is brought out in Table I. So the cold temperate phase appeared in South America even before the Permian period, and is represented in Brazil by the Rio Bonito coal measures which precede the *Mesosaurus* zone. Cold conditions were sustained in Uruguay and Argentina, however, well into the Permian as shown by the black, argillaceous Irati series, and the widespread Argentinian Patquia formation that even includes rewashed glacial material.

Climatic zoning is indicated by a change of facies in Baia, the Matto Grosso and the Andean zone of Argentina where *red* shales appear. These formations (Estancia beds, Aquidauana facies) imply a situation in an arid, and possibly desert, belt; indeed upon the reconstruction they all appear between latitudes 25° and 35°S. Still farther north, in the northern states of Brazil, swamps were generated in subsiding basins, and these were occupied by a 'northern' *Psaronius* flora indicative of a warm, perhaps tropical, climate. Upon the reconstruction, and with the continued movement of Gondwanaland, this is thoroughly understandable. The climatic zoning exhibited by the early Permian formations of South America is an important contribution that needs to be followed up by examination of other sectors of Gondwanaland in order to test the accuracy of the reconstruction and its siting in this epoch.

The characteristic early Permian deposits of Africa, from the Cape as far north as the southern border of Congo Belge, Tanganyika and Madagascar, are the cold temperate shales and sandstones of the lower and middle Ecca series with coal-seams of the *Glossopteris* flora. The Ecca beds are remarkably consistent in type, except that in South-West Africa they change to the 'Red Ecca' like the Estancia beds of Brazil (Fig. 2). This red facies is devoid of useful coal.

In Africa north of the broad Nigeria–Lake Rudolf arch, the piedmont accumulation of Nubian sandstone continued in a prevailingly dry climate. Except for marine inundations in the north the sandstones are wholly continental in type.

The rock collections from Queen Maud Land in east Antarctica made by Root[17] and Reece include representatives of an almost horizontally disposed sequence of continental rocks overlying a presumably archean basement, and evidently corresponding with the Gondwana–Karroo system of the southern hemisphere. Indeed, many grey and brown sandstones and shales from these collections in the British Museum may be assigned with little doubt to the Ecca facies. The constituents are less well sorted by grain sizes than in the South African series but this is readily understandable if, as for the glacials, the source of some of the South African materials lay in the direction of Queen Maud Land.

In the opposite direction, these Antarctic formations may correlate with the sediments, totalling 2000 to 5000 ft in thickness and overlying ancient basement in the Ross Sea sector. These arkoses, shales and sandstones, with lignites and rare, thin limestones are characteristically of shallow-water continental environment. Leaves of *Glossopteris* specify a probable Permian age for the Beacon Sandstone, while *Rhexoxylon* indicates that the youngest beds are Triassic. Deposition probably began in the early Permian, upon a surface innocent of glacial deposits. Except that they clearly fall within the ambit of the Gondwana system, too little is established concerning these beds to afford reliable palaeoclimatic interpretation.

In India, after the Talchir glacial episode, a brief, though distinct, interlude supervenes before accumulation of the Barakar stages of pebbly grits, sandstones and shales containing much carbonaceous matter as streaks, lenticles and beds of coal. These coals appear earlier in India than in South Africa (equivalent to the lower instead of the middle Ecca), relatively soon after the disappearance of the glacial conditions. This accords with the

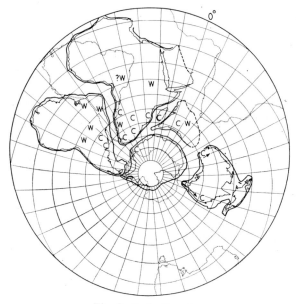

Fig. 2. Early Permian.
C = cold; W = warm temperate; T = tropical.

position of India 10 degrees farther north upon the reconstruction of Gondwanaland, and also with the marginal rather than central nature of the glaciation. Later, when South Africa accumulated its middle Ecca coals under cold temperate conditions, the 'Barren measures' of sandstone and low-grade, ferruginous shales in India indicate a distinctly warmer climate; so that India makes valuable contributions to palaeoclimatic zoning of the early Permian.

Though continental glaciation had vanished from most of Gondwanaland before the early Permian, in Western Australia renewed advance then pushed ice fronts north of the Fitzroy River into 'forests of well grown trees whose distinct annual growth rings told of sharply marked seasonal changes. . . . Similar types flourished in the Lower Coal Measure swamps of northern Queensland, but in the colder south the trees were of stunted growth.'

Much of Western Australia was covered by a shallow sea into which melting icebergs unloaded erratics throughout much of the early Permian. In the cold water benthos was scanty.

Eastern Australia was heavily glaciated throughout most of the early Permian, and erratics continued to be dropped even during accumulation of the first (Greta) or lower coal measures. Similar coals rest in a depression of the Darling Plateau 100 miles south of Perth in the Collie coalfield; but the major coals of Australia did not accumulate until the late Permian. The main phase of coal formation in Gondwanaland therefore ranges in age from late Carboniferous in Brazil, through early Permian in Africa and India to late Permian in eastern Australia which, like the glacials that precede in every case, is consistent with a travel of Gondwanaland through a succession of palaeoclimatic girdles.

C. Late Permian

No marked physiographical changes occurred in Gondwanaland between the early and late stages of the Permian, so that there is often no significant break between the two formations; but in all theatres the late Permian formations provide evidence of calefaction as Gondwanaland withdrew from the vicinity of the southern frigid zone into warmer environments. New floras and faunas, including numerous reptiles and amphibia, also confirm the increased caloric. India and the Belgian Congo, indeed, record semi-tropical conditions, but eastern Australia remained cold until the end of the period, testifying the continuance of palaeoclimatic girdles as before.

In South America the best known late Permian formation is the Estrada Nova series. These argillaceous members, greenish in fresh exposures, resemble lithologically the lower Beaufort series of South Africa, but Caster[2] considers them to be somewhat older, and also includes the Rio do Rasto group within the late Permian as its plant fossils indicate contemporaneity with the lower Beaufort. These formations belong to a warm temperate environment, and abundant sapropel is indicated by oil seeps in the Estrada Nova series.

Sapropelic torbanites appear also in the uppermost horizons of the middle Ecca series of South Africa, and thin, shaly, 'drift' coals occur in the upper Ecca scattered over a wide area of the Rhodesias, but the facies is of a cool temperate environment corresponding to 10° more of southern latitude than for the Estrada Nova series of Brazil.

But the drift of Gondwana from the pole apparently covered these 10 degrees before very long, because the lower Beaufort series of South Africa assumes the warm temperate facies of the Estrada Nova, a conclusion that is confirmed by the rich and varied reptilian fauna that has been recovered from the Beaufort, and the substitution of the *Glossopteris* flora by the *Taeniopteris* flora.

Farther north, in the Belgian Congo, the sediments of this epoch are conglomeratic and coarse, vari-coloured and reddish towards the top as though they had accumulated under desert conditions within the torrid zone. At a slightly more southern latitude, formations in southern Tanganyika and Madagascar have yielded reptilian and amphibian fossils of Karroo types.

In India the Raniganj and Panchet stages are assigned to the late Permian. These are as distinct from each other as the upper Ecca and lower Beaufort series of South Africa and, indeed, there is a slight break between for the Panchet sometimes overlaps on to the Barakars. The former has coals of the *Glossopteris* flora, whereas this flora is being supplanted by *Taeniopteris* and its allies in the Panchet. The greenish brown and buff sandstones of the Panchet also carry fossil labyrinthodonts and *Dicynodon* that reveal its essential contemporaneity with the lower Beaufort.

Quite clearly, the end Permian deposits of Brazil, South-Central Africa and India are all of warm temperate to torrid environment with a transition in that sense from south to north. Such palaeoclimatic zoning is appropriate to a change in position of the reassembly on the globe from the position in Fig. 2 towards that in Fig. 3. On the same orientation, North Africa including the high Atlas, and the meseta of Morocco and Algeria falls into the latitude 20–30°N. Here Krenkel[15] records late Permian red sediments with warm or tropical flora of northern aspect (*Equisitites, Pecopteris, Gingko* and *Walchia*) that are again entirely appropriate.

In Antarctica no formations have been precisely dated as late Permian but some of the Beacon sandstone formation is probably of this age as it spans upwards into the Triassic. The sandstones and shales carry *Glossopteris*.

The principal late Permian formations of Australia crop out in the east where the climate continued to be very cold. In Tasmania, grey shales with erratics dropped into them overlie the glacials of the early Permian: the facies is Ecca and even when sandstone appears at the end of the period it is still of cold, Ecca type quite unlike the warm temperate, contemporaneous Beaufort sandstones of South Africa. Calefaction was retarded until the middle Triassic when the Langloh sandstone with its weathered feldspars records conditions probably warmer than now.

On the mainland tectonic basins near the coast were kept full of sediment and the lagoonal vegetation built the rich coal seams of the Tomago and Newcastle stages. An abundant sapropel furnished oil shales, but the flora and fauna clearly indicate a cool climate.[3] Later, the climate warmed up rapidly and forests of stately trees replaced the swamp floras.

In the interior, a thin continental sequence with coal seams (*Glossopteris* and *Noegerrathopsis* like the Indian flora) is known in Central Queensland, otherwise the next occurrences are in the North-west Basin where estuarine and associated marine beds include abundant floras and faunas possibly indicating a warmer environment than in eastern Australia.

All the facts from Australia accord with a transition during the late Permian from the siting of Gondwanaland in Fig. 2 (early Permian) towards that of Fig. 3 (late Triassic). Such a transition covers: (1) the very cold climate of the mid-Permian and the continuance of cold conditions in Tasmania until the end of the period, (2) the warming up of Queensland and New South Wales more rapidly than the other parts of Gondwanaland, and

(3) the indications of distinctly warmer conditions in Western Australia as compared with New South Wales towards the end of the period, though in early Permian times there was no marked difference.

D. *Triassic*

'Except locally and peripherally, Gondwanaland experienced no tectogenesis in the period following the late Palaeozoic ice age. By the Triassic period, relief seems to have been relatively slight . . . subject only to broad epeirogenic movement creating axial upwarpings that, under denudation, shed quantities of land waste into intervening basins which thereby became

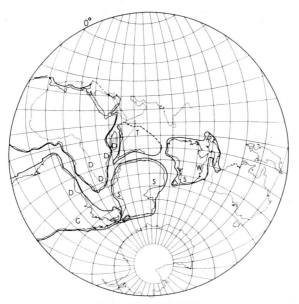

Fig. 3. Late Triassic.

D = desert;   T = tropical;   S = seasonal;   W = warm   temperate;   G = cool temperate.

wholly or partially filled up with shallow water or sub-aerial sediments. Thus some regions show continuing sedimentation across the Palaeozoic–Mesozoic boundary, others show an hiatus. On the whole, the early Triassic afforded widespread non-deposition and even denudation over the western half of Gondwanaland; but deposition, under desert or tropical conditions, supervened generally in the latter half of the period.' The Permian *Glossopteris* flora had vanished and was replaced in the often featureless Triassic landscape by the Mesozoic 'weeds' *Cladophlebis*, *Dicroidium* and their allied flora, and reptiles abounded under the prevailing warm temperatures. Their fossils are widespread. Much less evidence of climatic zoning is forthcoming from Triassic stratigraphy, and daily weather forecasts for the period were probably monotonous: 'Warm to hot with bright sunshine; rain not expected.' Seasonal changes are evident, however, in the south.

Following the early Triassic hiatus, continental red beds (Santa Maria formation) containing fossil reptiles of the dicynodont, cynodont, archosaurian and saurischian groups accumulated in southern Brazil, and were succeeded first by the red beds of the Piramboia formation laid down to a thickness of 0–300 ft in ephemeral desert lakes, and finally by the aeolian desert sandstones of the Botucatu series (600 ft thick) which covered an enormous extent of country by the close of the Triassic period. de Almeida describes this as one of the greatest deserts in recorded earth history, and it locates southern Brazil at that epoch with certainty about the southern tropic. Extensive Triassic accumulation in Argentina is somewhat masked by volcanic debris but indicates a cooler, though not cold, climate. Its flora has been compared closely by Frenguelli with that of the somewhat similar Narrabeen series of eastern Australia, at that time on a similar latitude.

As in Brazil sedimentation failed over much of South-Central Africa during the early Triassic and there are few equivalents of the upper Beaufort series in the Transvaal or the Rhodesias. These beds in the Cape, however, contain numerous reptiles and on lithological grounds may be assigned to a warm environment. Late Triassic (Stormberg) formations are widespread in all territories of South and East Africa except the Congo, and all are consistently of wind-blown, desert sandstone type like the Botucatu formation of southern Brazil, thus enlarging enormously the 'great desert' phase of de Almeida. In the Union of South Africa the corresponding 'Cave' sandstone, 300 ft thick, is a fine-grained, loessic phase that rests on red beds with dinosaur fossils.

Similar late Triassic formations with reptilian fossils testify an arid environment near the coast of Tanganyika and Moçambique, and many thousands of feet of cross-bedded sandstone with silicified wood in the Isalo series of Madagascar reveal the same conditions there through late Triassic and early Jurassic time. The scale of de Almeida's 'great desert' becomes truly astonishing.

In North Africa (Morocco and Tunis), red sandstones of Bunter lithologic type with salt and gypsum deposits fall appropriately on the reconstruction into the northern desert belt at 30°N (Fig. 3). In between the two desiccated belts, a broad swathe of northern Brazil and North Africa that might be expected to reveal tropical conditions apparently underwent denudation and so affords no useful data.

The stratigraphic history of India for the Triassic accords closely with that already established for Brazil and Africa (Central and East). The smooth erosional planation of early to mid Triassic time appears on the same horizon in India, as the hiatus between the Panchet and Mahadevi series. The latter series, moreover, is coeval with the late Triassic Botucatu and Stormberg series. Its lower (Pachmari) stage of red and buff sandstones with red haematitic clays undoubtedly corresponds with the desert phase elsewhere. The upper (Maleria) stage represents a humid tropical environment in which flourish labyrinthodont amphibians with rhynchocephalian and saurischian reptiles of late Triassic age. At this stage of the reconstruction the region lay beneath the Triassic equator.

Within Australia, Triassic strata are known only in the east: most of the continent remained under denudation throughout the period. The Hawkesbury sandstone and Wianamatta shales of New South Wales are of temperate, palaeoclimatic facies though not without a cold winter season recorded by seasonal growth rings to the trees.[3] In Queensland the flora was abundant, with large fossil insects. Arid cycles of some duration are also recorded by red beds but the regime was not comparable with the great desert of the Brazil–African region. Recent studies indicate for Tasmania that the early Triassic Knocklofty formation was laid down in shallow lakes that dried up in the dry season. A pronounced wet season maintained abundant flora, however. Towards the end of the period the climate became both hotter and wetter.

Noteworthy in all these records from the eastern seaboard of Australia is the emphasis that has been laid on the occurrence of a wet season and the consequently heavy flora. These distinctive conditions might well have been induced by the situation of this eastern part of Gondwanaland within a trade wind belt which shifted annually north and south. The latitude and aspect on the reconstruction (Fig. 3) are appropriate.

II.3 *Late Mesozoic Palaeoclimatology of Gondwanaland*

A. *Jurassic*

Few sedimentary formations of continental type are known in Gondwanaland for the Jurassic period, and those are generally unfossiliferous so that their age has to be inferred by reference to other stratigraphic units. Instead, as in the early Triassic a phase of broad planation (the 'Gondwana' landsurface) was current over much of the super-continent. Data for palaeoclimatic interpretation are, in consequence, scanty and a coherent picture is difficult to construct.

No deposits of definitely Jurassic age are known from eastern Brazil, though the red Uberaba series of Triangulo Miniero and the Cayua red sands of São Paulo may be eo-Jurassic. There is no reason to suppose, on the contrary, that climate changed during the Jurassic from the arid, warm to hot regime that prevailed during both the preceding and succeeding periods of the Mesozoic.

Much the same is true of the Union of South Africa and the Rhodesias; but in the Congo and neighbouring Angola (where Triassic formations are absent) sedimentation was resumed upon a wide scale (the Lualaba series) in late Jurassic time. The fresh and brackish water shales and sandstones are said to contain fish allied to marine types then living off East Africa in a new gulf extending slowly southward along the eastern seaboard of Africa. A considerable indentation had existed here since the Permian, as shown by the occurrence of fossiliferous marine facies in Madagscar, but from the mid-Jurassic the gulf became much larger, so that by the earliest Cretaceous it extended southward to the eastern Cape Province and Gondwanaland was largely, if not completely, severed into eastern and western halves.

The chief Jurassic beds of Gondwana type in India are light-coloured clays and massive soft sandstones of the Jabalpur series. Plant fossils are plentiful though rather imprecise for dating. Equivalent beds in Kathiawar are regarded as mid or late Jurassic. A warm climate is indicated.

The continental Gondwana of the east coast pass laterally into marine facies with fossils of late Jurassic or early Cretaceous age indicating that a new arm of the sea also outlined the eastern coast of the Indian peninsula at

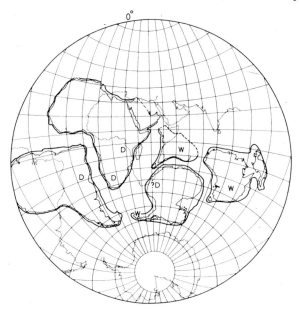

Fig. 4. Late Jurassic–Earliest Cretaceous.

D = desert; W = warm temperate.

this time. Freed from Gondwana, the flight of India to its collision with Asia was ready to begin.

Of East Antarctica, at that time adjacent to India, no Jurassic record is known. In West Antarctica, warmth-loving types of fossil plants and animals have been recovered from Grahamland showing that conditions were vastly different from now. On the reconstruction (Fig. 4) the region falls in latitude 55°S but perhaps it was reached by a warm current (ancestral to the Moçambique current) passing down the newly-opened rift to the east of Africa.

The Great Artesian Basin of Australia has Jurassic Gondwana deposits. There, in vast expanses of fresh-water lakes, soft calcareous sandstones and clays rather like the Jabalpur of India accumulated to a thickness of 3000 ft or more. The flora, in the swampy terrain, was locally sufficient to make thin coal seams, but reptiles were scarce.

Table 1. Correlation of Late Palaeozoic and Mesozoic Facies in Gondwanaland.

	Southern Brazil and Uruguay	Southern Africa	Peninsular India	Antarctica	Eastern Australia
		Fragmentation of Gondwanaland into modern continental masses			
Early Cretaceous					
Late Jurassic	? Red sands of the interior	Lualaba series of Congo. Marine series in East Africa	Jabalpur (continental) Marine beds of Cutch		Freshwater beds of Artesian Basin (sauropods and dinosaurs) Denudation
Jurassic	'Gondwana'	Cyclic	Continental		
Rhaetic	São Bento basalts	Drakensberg basalts and dolerites	Rajmahal basalts	South Victoria Land dolerites	Tasmanian dolerites
Late Triassic	Botucatu red desert	Stormberg series ending in 'Cave sandstone' desert (Cape Province folding)	Mahadevi series (tropical environment with saurischia)	Unknown	Wianamatta } Cool temperate environment
Mid-Triassic	(Buenos Aires folding) Santa Maria (reptiles)	Upper Beaufort } reptiles; Middle Beaufort } tiles	Hiatus		Hawkesbury Narrabeen
Early Triassic	Grupo Rio do Rasto	Lower Beaufort (green mudstones with Dicynodon, Taeniopteris)	Panchet Series (Dicynodon, Thinnfeldia)	Upper Beacon Sandstone	
Late Permian	Estrada Nova Series (green mudstones); Estancia Beds (partly red)	Upper Ecca shales (red in South-West Africa). Middle Ecca coal measures	Raniganj (coals) Ferruginous shales	Coal Beds; Lower Beacon Sandstone	Upper coal measures
Early Permian	Irati dark cold-water shales; Mesosaurus	Lower Ecca cold-water shales (rare Glossopteris)	Barakar Series with coal		Upper Marine Series (with tillites)
Late Carboniferous	Rio Bonito coal measures; Itarare series including glacials; Glacials in Western Argentina	Dwyka tillite with over- and under-lying fine dark cold-water shales	Talchir glacial and fluvio-glacial	Tillite not yet known	Greta Coal. Lower Marine series (with multiple coals); Late Carboniferous glacials and associated beds of South-Eastern Australia
Early Carboniferous					

(Diagonal climate labels across the table: HOT / TEMPERATE / COLD GLACIAL)

Y

Nowhere in Gondwanaland are Jurassic sediments known that indicate other than a warm, or even tropical environment, such as is consistent with the siting of the reconstruction in Fig. 4.

B. *Cretaceous*

With the Cretaceous period, exciting events came with a rush, more splits opened up and by the middle of the period all the modern continental outlines were established and washed by the ocean.

It is fascinating to follow, by marine formations, the penetration of the Indian and Atlantic oceanic gulfs along the new coasts, but the deposits and their fossils tell us little of Cretaceous climatology other than that the oceans seem to have been warm. But zoological realms existed. For instance, the Mediterranean Cretaceous molluscan fauna of West Africa and Angola never mixed round the Cape with the Indo-Pacific molluscan faunas of East Africa and Uitenhage, and the same distinction persists today.

Deposition upon the continents was more widespread during the Cretaceous than it had been during the Jurassic. It was similar in type, however, and from Brazil, Central and North Africa, and India at least warm dry climates are uniformly indicated. There is no adequate evidence of marked climatic girdles.

Australia, especially for the early Cretaceous, has been cited as perhaps experiencing a lowering of temperature, but by the end of the period the climate seems to have been as warm as it is now. Parkin has corrected David's inference of glaciation by showing that the supposedly glacial beds are Permian glacials rewashed in the Cretaceous sea; but some lowering of temperature, as distinct from the rest of Gondwanaland, may well have occurred by eastward drift of Australia on a great circle route taking it temporarily through more southerly latitudes.

Anyway, however curious the details of disruption, Gondwanaland by the mid Cretaceous had ceased to exist.

III. Conclusion

A wide variety of palaeoclimatic data based upon the physical characteristics and fossil content of rock series, and involving (1) synchronous but different climatic environments, (2) coherent transitions from one set of environments to another with time, and (3) changes in the opposite sense in different regions, have been harmoniously and simply synthesized over a vast lapse of geological time by the Gondwanaland concept combined with continental drift.

But any readers who may have been misled by the judicious sitings of the Gondwanaland reconstruction in suitable latitudes to admire the author's ingenuity in synthesizing the data are due to be disabused. The reconstruction and the sitings were achieved without reference to these data and were indeed in the author's possession two years before the palaeoclimatic data were assembled as a test of a hypothesis already established.

The diagrams were made[14] in explanation of the pattern of great sub-oceanic ridges which indeed fill the spaces between the continents on the reconstruction.

That so many and varied facts of palaeoclimatology fit the reconstruction so simply and so well is indeed satisfactory, rendering high the probability that both the reconstructions and the basic palaeoclimatic assumption of climatic girdles, existing in the Palaeozoic and Mesozoic essentially as in modern times, are correct. *Nothing* need be altered except the positions of the southern continents long avouched by austral stratigraphy and familiar to geologists who have researched there.

Well may palaeoclimatologists unite in tribute to Alexander Logie du Toit, who began this approach to their subject a full quarter of a century ago.

References

1. Cahen, L. *Geologie du Congo Belge.* 1954. Liege
2. Caster, K. E. *Bull. Amer. Mus. nat. Hist.*, **99**, 105 (1952)
3. David, T. W. E. *Geology of the Commonwealth of Australia.* 1950. London: Arnold
4. De Oliveira, A. I. and Leonardos, O. H. *Geologia do Brasil*, Serv. Inform. Agric., Ser. Didactica (1943)
5. Du Toit, A. L. *Our Wandering Continents.* 1957. Edinburgh: Oliver and Boyd
6. Du Toit, A. L. *Geology of South Africa*, 3rd edn. 1954. Edinburgh: Oliver and Boyd
7. Guimarães, D. *Dept. Nac. da Prod. Min.*, Bol. 88, (1951)
8. Harrington, H. J. *Mem. geol. Soc. Amer.*, **65**, 129 (1956)
9. Holmes, A. *J. Wash. Acad. Sci.*, **23**, 169 (1933)
10. King, L. C. *Bull. Amer. Ass. Petrol. Geol.*, **37**, 2163 (1953)
11. King, L. C. *Ann. Natal Mus.*, **12**, 383 (1953)
12. King, L. C. *Quart. J. geol. Soc. Lond.*, **112**, 445 (1957)
13. King, L. C. *Quart. J. geol. Soc. Lond.*, **114**, 47 (1958)
14. King, L. C. *Continental Drift, A Symposium.* 1958. University of Tasmania, Hobart
15. Krenkel, E. *Geologie Afrikas.* 1925. Berlin: Borntraeger
16. Krishnan, M. S. *Geology of India and Burma.* 1949. Madras
17. Root, E. F. *Saert. Norsk. geol. tids.*, **32**, 18 (1953)
18. Simpson, G. C. *Quart. J. R. met. Soc.*, **83**, 459 (1957)
19. Wadia, D. N. *Geology of India.* 1939. London: Macmillan

XIV
The Climates of Gondwanaland in Kainozoic Times

E. D. Gill

I. Introduction

Climatically the present is not the key to the past, in the sense that existing climate is atypical of the Kainozoic, the present climatic pattern being one that came with the Quaternary and quite different from that of the previous 60 or 70 million years. The most fundamental change in climate is temperature, and major rises and falls in mean temperature can be deciphered from the geological record by the study of fossils, the biological method or by the assay of isotopes, the physical method. Assay of isotopes can also provide the time calibration by which to measure the rate of these changes. The biological method is undergoing considerable refinement as biological science develops through the growth of palaeoecology. The physical method, still in its infancy, can be more accurate than the biological, and great developments therein may be anticipated.

Fundamentally, it may be argued whether, because a certain genus is now limited to warm waters, it has always been stenothermic. However, although some forms may have changed their character in this way, it is unlikely that all will have done so, and such sources of error should be avoided when all the biological, geological and geophysical evidence is taken into account.

As far as the writer is aware, this is the first attempt to provide an account of the Kainozoic palaeoclimatology of the Gondwana countries although much has been written on the palaeoclimatology of earlier periods. In the preceding chapter it was found convenient to adopt a Gondwanaland reconstruction in order to describe pre-Tertiary climates. As will be seen from this chapter, such a grouping is meaningless and it is simpler to consider the Gondwana 'fragments' separately and discuss the climatic variations of each region individually. There is a paucity of evidence of the kind desired, so that time will inevitably reveal many imperfections in this interpretation. The treatment of each area is naturally somewhat variable depending largely on the information available. The discussion of the climate of Australia does, however, show that with increasing knowledge a consistent pattern can be discerned.

II. Australia

During the Tertiary, the whole of Australia had a tropical to subtropical climate, according to time and latitude. Conditions of humidity were also very different from the present. Australia's extensive arid zone[67] appears to be a development of the past million years or so. For the Kainozoic geological history of Australia, Singleton[98] and David[29] may be consulted, while Hills[68] gives a treatment of the tectonic pattern.

Gross geography profoundly affects climate, but the palaeoclimatology of Australia has not yet been studied sufficiently to confidently link orogenic change with climatic evolution. Indeed most of Australia has retained a rather flat and featureless terrain during the Kainozoic, so that there are vast expanses over the Australian Shield characterized by duricrust formation.[112] The eastern border of the continent, however, has been mobile, and the present picture is that movement during the Kainozoic has had two maxima, in the early and late Kainozoic respectively, and that these movements have been accompanied by the copious floods of lavas known as the Older Basalts and Newer Basalts.[59]

II.1 *Temperature Changes*

A. *Marine Faunas*

Changes in world climate during the Kainozoic resulted in the narrowing or widening of the tropical belt. Temperate zones are therefore the best in which to trace the changes that have taken place. The most southerly Tertiary marine faunas in Australia occur in limestones in northern Tasmania at about latitude 41°S.[3] These beds are of Oligocene and Miocene age, and contain organisms of tropical to subtropical aspect such as the foraminifera *Lepidocyclina* and *Carpentaria*,[58] the echinoderms *Phyllacanthus*, *Schizaster*, *Eucidaris* and *Lovenia*,[11,44] a number of corals,[31] the lamellibranchs *Cucullaea*, *Hinnites* and *Spondylus*, and gasteropods including numerous cowries and volutes, and shells of the *Columbarium*, *Murex* and *Astralium* groups. Lime-stones of this age on Cape Barren Island in Bass Strait contain the warmer water forms *Amphistegina* and *Operculina*,[23] while on King Island club-shaped spines of *Eucidaris* have been collected.[24]

Farther north again, in Victoria, the marine faunas of this age are similar to the Tasmanian ones, but possess still further evidence of warmer waters in forams such as *Cycloclypeus*,[21] and the increased numbers of species of cones, volutes, cowries and muricids, including giant forms of the first three. Tropical shells such as *Xenophora* also occur. It is of some interest that certain genera of tropical mollusca, present in Victoria during the warm mid-Tertiary period, continue there now as very rare forms. Thus, *Xenophora* is found in the Oligocene and Miocene strata, but is not known thereafter as a fossil. However, occasionally *Xenophora peroniana* is dredged at 60–100 fathoms off the coast of Victoria and New South Wales. Other examples of Tertiary relics are the very rare species *Pterospira roadknightae* found at 20–80 fathoms off southern Australia, and *Hypocassis fimbriata* at 1–10 fathoms off Portland in Western Victoria and off the South Australian coast.[83] *Pterospira hannafordi* is common enough in Miocene strata to be used as an index fossil,[98] but the living *P. roadknightae* is rare. Evidence for palaeoclimatic change in this case is in the history of the genus and the relative abundances of species and individuals.

In Victoria there are marine faunas older than the oldest Tasmanian ones, for in the Otway district there are strata of Paleocene to Eocene age. These faunas are not as well known as the Oligocene and Miocene ones, but it is clear that waters a little warmer than at the present day are involved, although there is not the prolification of warm-water types found in the Middle Tertiary beds. There are corals, and molluscs of the *Murex* and *Fusus* types, but many of the typical warmer water forms that occur later are absent at this stratigraphic level in this latitude. Available evidence from marine faunas thus indicates over-all rising temperatures in the first half of Tertiary time leading to tropical mid-Tertiary conditions.

Farther north again are the Tertiary faunas of the Adelaide area in South Australia, round about latitude 35°S. Reynolds,[95] Glaessner[60] and Lud-brook[80] have described these sediments and their faunas. Ludbrook[81] and Carter[10] provide an account of the Tertiary beds in the Murray Basin, part of which is in South Australia and part in Victoria. The living marine fauna in the Adelaide area is a slightly warmer one than that in the Melbourne area, having for example the foram *Fabularia*[15] and the gasteropod *Ninella torquata*. It is not surprising, therefore, to find the mid-Tertiary tropical forms lingering a little longer in the Adelaide area than they do in southern Victoria and Tasmania. In the Willunga Basin, strata of Eocene to Oligo-cene age occur, but no Miocene. However, the Pliocene beds include the warm-water giant form *Marginopora vertebralis*. The Oaklands Limestone, known only in bores in the Adelaide Basin, is of Miocene age, and of this Crespin[25] writes: 'The foraminiferal assemblage in the Oaklands Limestone indicates a change, not only in depth of the water, but also in temperature, from the environment under which the beds of the Blanche Point Limestone and Aldinga Limestone were deposited. The change was to warm, sub-tropical moderately shallow clear water conditions. The assemblage in this formation is marked by the presence of the warm-water Indo-Pacific form *Austrotrillina howchini*, in association with the sub-tropical to tropical *Marginopora vertebralis*. *Marginopora* thrives in Recent seas in warm shallow water in the vicinity of coral reefs and at depths of not more than 100 fathoms. Other sub-tropical genera are *Gypsina, Planorbulinella, Calcarina, Crespinella, Carpentaria, Operculina* and *Amphistegina*.'

Crespin [26] has also reported on the foraminifera of the limestones of the Nullabor Plain. They include a number of tropical genera. Farther north, the Tertiary marine beds lie in the present tropical zone and show warm water faunas consistently through Kainozoic time.

The rise in temperature to mid-Tertiary, rather tropical conditions was followed by a fall to the Pleistocene. This drop in temperature is apparent in the Cheltenhamian Stage (uppermost Miocene).[98,56] Warmer waters are indicated by the large numbers of sharks, the prolific occurrence of the echinoderm *Lovenia* and the presence of mollusca such as *Cucullaea*. On the other hand, the tropical mollusca listed for the Lower and Middle Miocene have been strongly reduced in numbers both of species and individuals, even when allowance is made for difference in facies. It is only when the Kalimnan Stage (Lower Pliocene) is reached that marine faunas comparable with the present are to be observed. Nevertheless, in the type area there are still definite warmer water elements such as the wealth of the gasteropod *Tylospira*, and the echinoderm *Arachnoides*. Parr [88] has drawn attention to foraminiferal evidence for warmer waters. At the close of the Pliocene in southern Australia was deposited the Maretimo Member of the Whaler's Bluff Formation; [6] between the Maretimo and the Werrikoo Member the Plio-Pleistocene boundary has been drawn.[57]

Marine faunas also reflect the rapid changes of climate that characterized the Quaternary. Emerged marine shell beds rising to about 25 ft above the present low-tide level are widespread around Australia. In southern Australia they contain foraminifera[14] and mollusca, indicating temperatures higher than the present.[27,43,55,105] Sediments of the earlier part of the Flandrian Transgression, as seen in the Yarra delta at Melbourne, Victoria, do not have the warmer water mollusc *Anadara*, but it becomes exceedingly plentiful and of large size in the top part of the deposit which extends above present high-tide level. *Anadara* is common between tide-marks farther north (e.g. at Sydney and Brisbane), but is at the limit of its present range in Port Phillip, Victoria. It occurs only as a couple of small populations which, instead of living between tide-marks, as is usual, are found at low-tide level and below. The *Anadara* bed rising above present high-tide level is mid-Holocene in age, as is shown by geological observations and radiocarbon dating.[55]

The evidence of the marine faunas suggests a higher temperature in those areas of Australia now in the temperate zone during the earlier half of the

Tertiary Era, apparently resulting from a widening of the tropical belt. From tropical conditions in the mid-Tertiary, temperatures dropped until the Quaternary, which was characterized by rapid changes of temperature between much colder and a little warmer than the present. These are broad generalizations, and there must have been many local variations, and also oscillations superimposed on the main curve.

B. *Terrestrial Faunas*

Little is known as yet about the terrestrial faunas of Australia during Tertiary time, but of recent years a number of Tertiary marsupials has been found,[56,104] and others have been discovered but not yet described. The palaeoclimatic significance of the Tertiary marsupials is not yet understood, but it may be noted that a cuscus has been recorded from Upper Pliocene beds near Hamilton, Victoria.[56] This possum now lives only in the Cape York Peninsula and in New Guinea. Tertiary fish, chelonians and reptiles have also been recorded.

Fig. 1. Distribution of living and fossil crocodiles in Australia.

The distribution of crocodiles has significance in the study of palaeo-temperatures. Colbert[96] states that: 'The large crocodilians and turtles, and the largest lizards and snakes, find the optimum conditions for life and growth in a band round the equatorial part of the earth and bounded north and south more or less by the 30th parallels of latitude.' Two species of crocodiles are found living in Australia at the present time—the small (about 4 ft), harmless, slender-snouted fresh-water *Crocodilus johnstoni* Krefft,[79] and the large (about 16 ft), man-eating, broad-snouted, estuarine to marine

Crocodilus porosus Schneider.[113] Crocodiles are rarely found farther south than Rockhampton on the east coast of Australia, and the Ord River on the west coast (see Fig. 1). Crocodiles date from the Cretaceous Period, and it is to be expected that they have been in Australia since that time. Although the palaeontological record is very incomplete, enough information is available to show changes in the distribution of crocodilians in the past. Fossil crocodiles have been recorded in the area of present distribution,[36, 77] but in the warmer interglacial periods of the Pleistocene they extended farther south in the coastal areas, and farther south in Central Australia when pluvial conditions obtained. Thus they are known from localities in southern Queensland (e.g. the Darling Downs), from the Diamantina River in Central Australia (National Museum of Victoria collection), from the Lake Eyre district [30] and from the Fitzroy and Gascoyne Rivers in Western Australia.[61, 62] Judging by the fossil lists, the Western Australian localities are Pleistocene. Hale and Tindale [63] have recorded an aboriginal petroglyph of a crocodile which was found 25 miles south-east of Yunta railway station on the Adelaide–Broken Hill line. As it provides presumptive evidence of the presence of crocodiles in the area, the southern limit of crocodiles in the Quaternary is drawn through this point in Fig. 1. Dr. B. Daily has kindly informed me that four successive faunas are present in the Lake Eyre district of Central Australia, the oldest being the *Perikoala* fauna of Stirton.[103] In all four faunas, crocodilian remains have been found, so crocodiles have been present in the area in both Tertiary and Quaternary times. During the Tertiary Era, crocodilians were to be found as far south as Victoria, where tropical conditions obtained.[37] In the Clunes district about 85 miles north-west of Melbourne, Victoria, part of the tibia of a crocodilian about the size of *Crocodilus porosus* was found in the main shaft of the Spring Hill Central Leads Co.'s gold mine at a depth of 295 ft.[35] At the time, the Geological Survey ascribed to this fossil a Pliocene age, but a Miocene age is quite possible.

Previously unrecorded is part of a large crocodilian found *in situ* in the Tertiary rock of the shore platform, on the north-east side of Rocky Point, near Bell's Headland, between Torquay and Point Addis, Victoria (for map see reference 90). The age of the fossil is Janjukian (Oligocene). Dr. Edwin H. Colbert of the American Museum of Natural History has identified the fossil as part of the right ramus of the lower jaw of a crocodilian. This is the oldest crocodilian so far recorded in Australia, and proves that this group has had a long history on this sub-continent. The Torquay crocodilian was a large animal, and was found in marine beds, so possibly it was analogous in size and habits to the present *Crocodilus porosus*.

Reviewing the evidence from the fossil crocodilians, it can be seen that the area of their distribution has progressively contracted from the mid-Tertiary till the present (Fig. 1). This is but a general picture, and it will be improved in detail as more fossils are found, and the dating of the beds in which they occur more adequately determined.

C. *Terrestrial Floras*

The unique flora of Australia is characterized by the genera *Eucalyptus* and *Acacia*, there being some hundreds of species of each. This flora is essentially Quaternary, for during the Tertiary Era Australia was characterized by forests of beech, conifers and broad-leaved trees whose distribution depended on the ecological conditions. The climate was warmer and more humid. At Hamilton in Victoria, Upper Pliocene beds retain a record of the transition from the Tertiary conifer forest to the *Eucalyptus–Acacia* forest of the Quaternary.[56]

Illustrative of the change in temperature in Australia during Kainozoic time is the history of the Araucaraciae.[17] The natural distribution of *Araucaria* at present extends from the mountain forests of New Guinea, where the average temperature for the coldest month is 64°F, to the coastal rain forests of Queensland and northern New South Wales. At its most southerly extension,[4] the average temperature of the coldest month is 54·2°F. During the Tertiary, however, *Araucaria* grew in the vicinity of Hobart, Tasmania (latitude nearly 43°S), and it is commonly found in the brown coal at Yallourn, Victoria.[17]

The present distribution of the Queensland Kauri *Agathis* is limited to that northern state, but in the Quaternary it existed in northern New South Wales, as is shown by a large humified stump of *Agathis* in coastal sandrock near Evans Head, N.S.W.[2,82] During Tertiary times, *Agathis* was much more widespread in Australia than it is now, having been identified in Queensland, N.S.W., Victoria, South Australia, and possibly Western Australia.

D. *Pedology*

In that soils are the product of certain climatic conditions acting on a given terrain, they can be palaeoclimatic indicators. Thus, 'the equatorial forest is the milieu of soil laterization'. Laterite and bauxite soils are found all over Australia, including Tasmania, indicating the presence of climatic conditions very different from those now obtaining in the temperate zone of the continent. Owen[87] comments that: 'The prevalence of laterite and bauxite within the tropics suggests that tropical conditions of weathering are necessary for its formation. Undoubtedly high mean temperatures, copious rainfall, and abundant supply of organic acids from vegetable debris are very important conditions necessary for the development of laterite with sufficient rapidity to ensure its preservation, and its presence well outside the tropics, e.g. Tasmania, Oregon, Northern Ireland, suggest that warm conditions and dense vegetation may have existed in early Tertiary time at higher latitudes than at the present day.' A well-developed deposit of bauxite exists at Ouse in southern Tasmania, approximately 42° 30″S. Tropical to subtropical conditions spread over Australia during the Tertiary and rain forests were widespread. These conditions contracted northwards beginning in the Upper Miocene and continuing through the Pliocene. It would appear that during the Lower Pliocene a belt of monsoonal type conditions (alternating wet and dry seasons) passed over the country, producing widespread laterites. In Southern Australia, the bauxites are generally Lower Tertiary while the laterites are Upper Tertiary. In the Launceston Basin, Northern Tasmania, bauxites have been developed on the Mesozoic dolerite [87] and are overlain by Eocene sediments. The high-level surface of the Tertiary sediments shows evidence of laterization.

E. *Lithology*

Widespread Quaternary wind-blown deposits or *parna* [9] have been reported in south-east Australia. They have their origin in times of higher temperature and/or lower rainfall when considerable desiccation took place resulting in movement of the fine fractions of the soils by winds. Periods of desiccation occurred in the Pleistocene, and there was one during the post-glacial thermal maximum when the beds of existing lakes became dry, and sediments from them were blown into dunes. [54, 66, 102]

Till and other rocks of glacial origin that occur on the highest part of the Great Dividing Range and in Western Tasmania [7, 74] prove periods of Pleistocene lower temperatures.

F. *Oxygen Isotope Analyses*

Cainozoic marine fossils, from many localities in southern Victoria within one degree of latitude, have been assayed for oxygen isotopes in order to determine the changes in mean temperature for that period. The fossils had

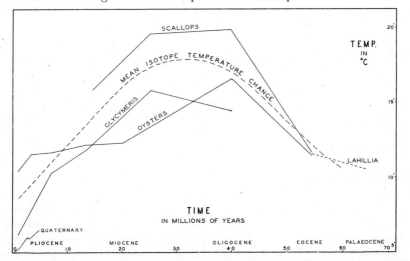

Fig. 2. Oxygen isotope palaeotemperature measurements on Tertiary marine shells from Victoria, Australia.

perforce to be from shelf sediments, and it was found that there is variation from genus to genus, as might be expected by reason of the different ecological locations and different habits of the animals concerned. Fig. 2 summarizes the results obtained.[37] It shows a rise in temperature over the first half of the Tertiary Era, and a decline in the second half. This is in keeping with the biological evidence already outlined.

II.2 *Humidity*

Australia has not always been the dry country that so much of it is today. In the past, the humid areas have been far more extensive. On the other hand, there have been relatively brief periods in the Quaternary when the climate as a whole has been drier than now.

A. *Terrestrial Floras*

The Southern Beech (*Nothofagus*) requires a humid environment, and its typical habitat is well-drained slopes in a high rainfall area. It lives at the present time in New Guinea and certain limited high rainfall areas of all the eastern States of Australia. The Yallourn brown coal of Oligocene age consists largely of coniferous plant remains,[89] yet beech pollen is very abundant, suggesting that the brown coal was formed from the coniferous forest of the swamplands, but that beech forests clothed the surrounding hills.[16] *Nothofagus* was much more widely distributed than now during the Tertiary in Australia, and also at times in the Quaternary its range was widened, indicating an increase in humidity. Clifford and Cookson[13] have described a fossil Oligocene moss from Yallourn. Under both the Older and Newer Basalts (lower and upper Kainozoic respectively) remains of broad-leaved plants are common, indicative of widespread humid conditions in the Tertiary. From Allandale in Victoria, Professor E. S. Hills and associated authors have recorded a piece of Tertiary resin weighing 34 lb and containing a Kauri pine (*Agathis*) leaf (still green, although the chlorophyll was yellowish), a millipede, a mite, a spider, some beetles and some ants. The imprint of the bole of the tree from which the resin came was still preserved, showing it to be a large and well-grown one. The millipedes indicate a damp environment, and the families represented by the other fossils are those belonging to a wooded, moist environment.

B. *Terrestrial Faunas*

Fossil fish and crocodiles of Pliocene and Quaternary age have been found in Central Australia in areas where lakes and rivers are now ephemeral. Their presence is evidence of more pluvial conditions in the past. In Miocene, Pliocene and Pleistocene times, herds of breeding giant marsupials inhabited Australia.[56,103,104] The distribution of these animals is evidence of a marked change in the pluvialty of certain areas. Such herds could not survive now in areas such as Lake Callabonna in Central Australia and Balladonia Soak in Western Australia. The broad-toothed rat once had a much wider distribution, and change in rainfall appears to account for the change in range. Certain insects and birds that require humid conditions now occupy areas as far separated as the Mt. Lofty Ranges of South Australia and the Grampian Mountains of Victoria, but in the past they must have occupied all the country in between. The snail fauna, likewise, is indicative of changes in humidity. For example, in the Pleistocene aeolianite of Warrnambool, Western Victoria, helicid snails proper to dry conditions occur in the dune rock, while fossil snails requiring damp conditions are preserved in the intercalated fossil soils.

C. *Pedology*

Whitehouse[107-109] has described widespread laterites in Queensland extending down into the far south-west of that state towards Lake Eyre. Upper Kainozoic geological history is considerably concerned with the breakdown of this lateritic profile, and the redistribution of the materials under drier conditions. The formation of laterite must have taken place in a climate with alternating wet and dry seasons. The post-lateritic alluvia extend much farther than any floods now reach, indicating that the present is more arid than the immediate past. Whitehouse states that 'from late Pleistocene times there has been a marked decline in the river flow'.

The widespread lateritic 'duricrust'[112] of Western Australia, Northern Territory, and South Australia is apparently a function of those same conditions that formed the laterite described by Whitehouse in Queensland. Laterites are also found in New South Wales, Victoria and Tasmania. They bear evidence in waterless places of a considerable seasonal rainfall that deeply leached and altered the country rock.

D. *Lithology*

Heavy fluviatile gravels and conglomerates of Kainozoic age bear evidence of bounteous and fast-moving waters in Tertiary times. In Quaternary deposits, river terraces built high above the present flood levels from the same thalweg, emerged lake terraces, and widespread lacustrine deposits beyond present lakes all bear witness to more pluvial conditions in the past. On the other hand, wind-blown sediments, gypseous and saline deposits, alternating with the above, indicate times even drier than the present.

II.3 *Winds*

Another aspect of past climates that can be read from the geological record is the direction and strength of the winds. Fossil coastal dunes and inland dunes are common. Calcareous dunes have been lithified to form aeolianites, while other dunes have been compacted and protected by vegetative and soil cover. Recent volcanic ash spreads conform to the present wind directions, while older spreads may provide evidence of a different direction of the prevailing winds.[49] In Western Victoria, both ash spreads and lake shore dunes show that during the Holocene prevailing winds blew from the west and north-west instead of from the south-west as at present.

II.4 *Summary*

The evidence as currently understood points to climates during the Kainozoic quite different from the present day. In general, temperatures increased during the early Tertiary reaching a maximum in mid-Tertiary times when warm tropical to subtropical conditions covered Australia. This is seen in the spread of marine and terrestrial faunas, while the growth of rain forests and the development of bauxites is witness to higher humidity.

The history of the later Tertiary is one of a temperature decline and increasing aridity, to a minimum temperature in Quaternary times. This would explain the northward retreat of the tropical faunal and floral elements. The development of laterites even suggests monsoonal conditions in Pliocene times. The Quaternary was characterized by the comparatively rapid alternation of periods wetter and drier than the present day.

III. New Zealand

The climatic history of New Zealand in Tertiary times and since closely parallels that of Australia. There is ample evidence of mid-Tertiary tropical and subtropical climates with a change to temperate conditions at the end of the Tertiary. Palaeotemperature curves have been drawn, the latest being those of Squires[100] (see Fig. 3). Fleming[46,47] has outlined the evidence from the marine molluscan faunas, Fell[44,45] has treated the echinoderms, and

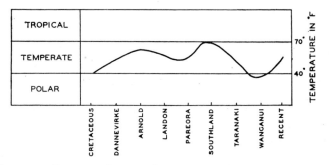

Fig. 3. Cretaceous–Recent palaeotemperature curve for New Zealand. Redrawn from Squires.[101]

Squires[100,101] the corals, while Hornibrook[70,71] has dealt with the marine microfossils, and Couper[19] the spores and pollen. Harris[65] states that 'a return to warmer conditions appears to have been general during the Miocene and our mid-Tertiary flora may have developed many tropical features. It is perhaps to the Miocene that our fossil coconuts belong and also the southern occurrence of the kauris.'

Although the general palaeoclimatic history of the Kainozoic Era in New Zealand parallels that of Australia, the geological, and to a certain extent the ecological, setting was different. The Kainozoic deposits of Australia (apart from New Guinea) consist of shelf-type deposits. They are comparatively thin and commonly calcareous. The only formations of appreciable thickness are those developed in basins, such as the Mt. Gambier Sunkland on the border of South Australia and Victoria. Australian Kainozoic strata have not been deformed very much; many are still horizontal, and any folding is open. On the other hand the Papuan Geosyncline [29] of the New Guinea area possesses Kainozoic strata tens of thousands of feet thick, and recent uplift has resulted in the deep dissection of these beds. The setting in New Zealand is similar, and indeed some regard it as an extension of the same general structure. The Kainozoic strata are miles thick, permitting a finer time subdivision of the fossil succession than has been achieved in Australia; Cotton[18] reviewed 23 stages of the Paleocene to Pleistocene geological history of that country. Recent uplift, which is still in progress, has resulted in the deep dissection of these rocks so that magnificent natural sections are available for scientific study. The Kainozoic rocks have been strongly folded and faulted, so much so that in Fiordland a marine Pliocene silty sandstone stands vertically.[106] In view of the different ecological settings of the Tertiary sediments of the Australian mainland and New Zealand (the former thin shelf sediments; the latter very thick geosynclinal sediments), it is not surprising that although they have many faunal and floral elements in common, they have their own indigenous genera.

Fleming[48] has reviewed the relationships through time of the Australian–New Zealand area. He pictures New Zealand and Australia in the Lower Cretaceous as a connected land mass (although Australia is fractionated by epeiric seas) lying outside the equatorial region characterized by coral reefs; then in the Upper Cretaceous New Zealand was isolated, continuing thereafter to the present time as a constantly changing archipelago. Throughout Kainozoic time, the existence of New Zealand as a comparatively small land mass in a wide ocean has modified its climate. New Zealand is situated 'near the centre of the greatest area of sea in the world'. New Zealand has also had its climate affected by the coming and going of mountain chains. In the Paleocene the former mountains were reduced to plains, then in the Pliocene the building of the present chain was begun, although chiefly a Quaternary movement. The creation of these high areas, and the active vulcanism that attended the uplift, have modified the climate. Furthermore, the considerable north–south length of the country has meant a considerable range of climatic conditions due to latitude.

A significant change in the surface oceanic waters occurs across a boundary known as the Subtropical Convergence (Fig. 4). The whole of Australia lies north of this Convergence, while New Zealand straddles it. Thus the Aupourian faunal province of New Zealand is subtropical, while the Cookian province is an area of mixed water across the Convergence, and the southern Forsterian province is sub-antarctic. 'For example,' writes Fleming,[48] 'Aupourian molluscs, starfish and sea-urchins include more Australian forms which have been able to colonize by larval drift in the Tasman current, than the two southern provinces.' Analysis of fossil faunas suggests that palaeo-climatic changes in the Australasian area have been accompanied by a significant migration of the Subtropical Convergence.

Fleming, by the study of the mollusca, and Couper and McQueen[20] by study of the floras, have been able to fix the Pliocene–Pleistocene boundary

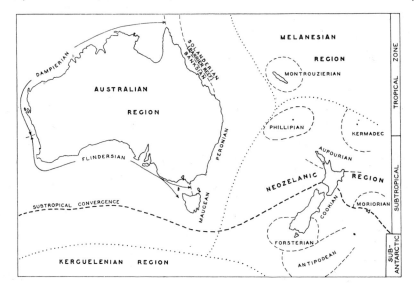

Fig. 4. Faunal provinces of Australasia in relation to the subtropical convergence. Redrawn after Fleming.[48]

in New Zealand, using palaeoclimatic criteria. Numerous papers by Brodie, Brothers, Collins, Cotton, Fleming, Gage, Searle, Stevens, Suggate, Te Punga, Wellman and others attest the climatic changes of the Pleistocene Period. Raeside[91] has described evidence of some recent changes, while Holloway[69] has shown how the forests bear signs of climatic fluctuations at present in progress.

IV. India, Ceylon, Pakistan and Burma*

These countries lie between latitudes 6° and 37°N approximately, and so by position are tropical to subtropical in geographical zone. During Kainozoic time the differences in climate created by vast tectonic move-ments have been greater in the Himalayan region than changes due to world climate. Southern India and Ceylon have been tropical throughout, while northern India, Pakistan and Burma have been strongly affected since early Tertiary times by tectonic movements. The general geological story[94] is that in early Tertiary time the northern part of this region was covered by a

* The author is indebted to the Director, Geological Survey of India, for pro-viding a bibliography of Kainozoic palaeoclimatology for India.

sea which was part of the great Eurasian sea-way called the Tethys, while the southern part was largely a terrain of ancient rocks, over a considerable area of which the widespread Deccan basaltic lavas were exuded. Fig. 5 shows the extent of the outcrops of the Tertiary sea sediments in northern India and Pakistan. These marine rocks include warm water Foraminifera such as *Nummulites, Lepidocyclina, Cycloclypeus, Amphistegina* and *Heterostegina*.[86] The Tertiary Tethys held tropical waters. A considerable succession of coral faunas in north-west India, beginning with the Cretaceous and rising through the Lower Tertiary, has been described. The echinoderms and molluscs likewise present evidence of warm seas. There are endemic forms in all these

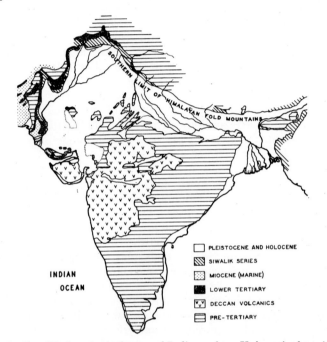

Fig. 5. Simplified geological map of India to show Kainozoic deposits

groups of organisms, but also many biological affinities with Europe and Australia. Apparently much migration took place in the Tethys during the time of more widespread tropical conditions.

By reason of its immense dimensions, the great orogenic belt of the Himalayas is as significant for palaeoclimatology as it is for present world geography and climatology. 'At the end of the Eocene,' writes Reed,[94] 'the first of the Tertiary crustal movements took place which resulted in the upheaval of the Himalayas. The considerable folding and disturbance which then occurred reduced the area of the Tethys and shallowed the sea over large tracts, and in places completely excluded it, so as to lead to the formation of fresh-water instead of marine deposits, as in the case of the

z

Sirmur and Murree beds.' 'Towards the close of the Middle Miocene there was a second great mountain-building disturbance affecting the north of India and Central Asia. This broke up the Tethys Ocean, and reduced it in places either to the condition of isolated lagoons or completely elevated its floor into dry land. The earlier rocks were folded and eroded before the deposition of the succeeding beds, which rest unconformably upon them.' 'No typical marine Pliocene beds are known in India, and the great bulk of the Upper Miocene and Pliocene deposits are of fluviatile or terrestrial origin; they constitute the great Siwalik System in the Himalayas, and the similar series with local names in Assam and Burma.' (See Fig. 5).

The Siwalik beds include the bones of numerous mammals, including some remarkable extinct giant forms such as *Dinotherium*. Breeding herds of these elephantine animals imply certain conditions of temperature and humidity, for they require very large quantities of herbaceous food. Horses, elephants, camels and crocodiles are also found in the Siwaliks of India–Pakistan and the equivalent beds of Burma. At certain horizons fossil wood is very abundant, and silicified tree trunks of large size occur, bearing evidence of conditions pluvial enough to grow large trees, and sometimes forests.[92, 99] The sediments in many places are indicative of strongly flowing streams. In the past, as at present, there must have been a wide range of ecological conditions in the Himalayan region, and as knowledge becomes available these will be defined.

Through Kainozoic time much igneous activity has accompanied the uplift of the Himalayan fold mountains, and this must have affected the climate, although in a limited degree. The chief volcanic gas is steam, most of which is precipitated as rain in the area concerned. The carbon dioxide and volcanic ash of eruptions also affect the climatic conditions.

The area covered by the Siwalik beds, plus the vast alluvial plain across the front of the Himalayas where the rivers Ganges, Brahmaputra and Indus flow, constitute a gigantic 'foredeep' of the mountain system over 1500 miles wide. Into this trough have been poured the erosion products of the rising mountain chain for millions of years. The series of sediments involved is miles thick *in toto*, and the ecological analysis of these sediments and their fossils will throw much light on the palaeoclimatology of that interesting area. The picture can only be seen in broadest outline at present. The building of the Himalayas still goes on, and a comparison between the foredeep sediments and those being deposited now shows that the pluvial conditions of the Tertiary were not greatly different from those obtaining at present. In Burma, there is a foredeep at right angles to the Ganges valley, but the general geological history is similar.

In the Himalayan mountain chain, evidence has been found of colder Pleistocene periods, old glacial moraines being found as low as 7000 ft. In some areas, cold dry periods accompanied the retreat of the ice, leaving signs of desiccation of the terrain. Loess and aeolian sands of Quaternary age have been described from the north-west Punjab, the Salt Range, and other localities. Alternating beds of loess and conglomerate in the Salt Range are signs of alternating wet and dry conditions. De Terra and Hutchinson [34] have recorded evidence of very recent climatic changes as shown by certain Tibetan highland lakes. Paved paths and mani walls are now submerged or partly covered by lake waters.

Southern India and Ceylon contrast with the mobile Himalayan belt, for they are relatively stable, and throughout the Kainozoic have mostly maintained a low relief, the mountain area of Ceylon being the exception. A large area of the peninsula of India is covered by the Deccan volcanics, [86] while over the rest gneiss and granite outcrop with interpolations of Pre-Cambrian, Palaeozoic and Mesozoic rocks. Sahni's famous work on the silicified plants preserved between the flows of Deccan basalt has been reviewed by Halle [64] and Sitholey. [99] Delicately preserved in chert, Sahni found the remains of palms (including coconuts), conifers, angiosperms and some interesting water weeds. He envisaged the lava flows damming water courses into lakes and making rivers sluggish. In these, sediments with volcanic ash and plant remains accumulated until further flows obliterated the terrain, but colloidal silica from the lavas immediately silicified the plants preserving them in the finest detail. Some plants are indicative of brackish water, probably estuarine conditions. Sahni was able to show that the floras were not Cretaceous, as thought at the time, but Eocene. The 'intertrappean series' also includes molluscs, crustaceans, frogs and fishes. [99] The flora and fauna in general reflect a warm and somewhat pluvial climate. Mahabale [84] has discussed ferns and palms as palaeoclimatic indicators with special reference to India.

The deep ferruginous soil known as laterite was named by Buchanan [8] in 1807 from its occurrence in Southern India. Laterite is widely spread on the surface of the Peninsula, and is of palaeoclimatic significance. The deep (50–200 ft) leaching that characterizes it is a function of warm copious waters plus acids from decomposing vegetable matter. The equally characteristic horizon of iron oxide is a function of seasonal wetting and drying (oscillation of the water table) assisted by bacterial activity. A monsoonal type of climate is thus indicated. The literature describes a 'high level laterite' and a 'low level laterite', the former apparently being the soil *in situ*, and the latter 'chiefly of a detrital nature'. In that there is so much lateritic detritus, it is inferred that the laterite is not a current pedological product, but belongs to a period now past. Laterite is also widespread in Ceylon, which was only recently separated from the Peninsula. Most of Ceylon consists of ancient rocks, but Miocene marine beds with a tropical fauna give witness to tropical temperatures at that time. Deraniyagala [33] has described marked climatic changes in Ceylon during the Pleistocene Period. He states that the faunas indicate a cool phase and an arid phase.

V. South Africa

Africa is an ancient continent, even to the geologist, and much of it has been a land surface throughout the Kainozoic. The Tertiary marine deposits of South Africa are limited therefore to areas at or near the coast. Beds of

Eocene to Miocene age occur in south-east Somaliland, Kenya, Tanganyika, Mozambique (formerly Portuguese East Africa), the Union of South Africa, south-west Africa and Angola on the west coast. These deposits lie between the Equator and latitude 35°S. The faunas are tropical to subtropical, containing foraminifers such as *Nummulites*, *Lepidocyclina*, *Amphistegina* and *Operculina*; lamellibranchs such as *Cucullaea* and *Spondylus*; gasteropods such as *Ficus*, *Tonna* and *Strombus*; corals such as *Flabellum distinctum*; and echinoderms such as *Linthia*. All of these are warm-water forms. *Nummulites* is an Eocene and tropical form, and beds containing it extend as far south as Beira in Mozambique (20°S). Recently King[39] has described an early Miocene (Burdigalian) marine fauna from the Umfolozi River in Zululand (28·5°S). It has a tropical aspect in that it contains the giant shark *Carcharodon megalodon* and the invertebrates *Cucullaea*, *Strombus*, *Tonna*, *Amphistegina* and *Flabellum distinctum*. It is more difficult to trace the Tertiary changes in the tropical and subtropical countries than in the temperate ones where the changes were greater, but the fossils as listed for mid-Tertiary faunas in South Africa suggest an extension south of the tropic zone at that time. From the Pliocene and Pleistocene beds temperature indicators found in the mid-Tertiary strata are missing.

Non-marine sediments of Eocene to Miocene age are known from Somaliland, Kenya, Nyasaland, the Union of South Africa and south-west Africa. Anhydrites in Somaliland indicate that the climate of this tropical area was as hot as it is now. Interdigitated marine layers show that the salts were derived from the sea. Miocene fresh-water and terrestrial beds in Kenya contain the Proboscidean *Dinotherium* (already noted in the section on India), which would require large quantities of vegetation for food, and crocodiles. Calcified tree trunks have also been recorded. *Dinotherium* bones are found in torrent gravels, another sign of pluvialty. Several interesting genera of primates also occur.[75] Thus there is evidence in the areas concerned of sufficient humidity to provide large trees, support giant herbivores and cause rivers (at least seasonal) large enough to deposit torrent gravels. To the west of Lake Rudolf in Kenya, plant and animal remains (including mastodont elephants) of Lower Miocene age have been described. Thick-bedded sandstones and conglomerates occupying an old but minor rift valley in Nyasaland are regarded as being of Miocene age. Such sediments infer strongly moving water to transport them. Mid-Tertiary fluviatile strata near Bogenfels in south-west Africa contain bones representing a rich mammalian fauna indicative of a steppe climate.

Pliocene beds are not clearly distinguished in many cases from the Quaternary beds, but marine Pliocene is reported from Mombasa in Kenya and Zanzibar in Tanganyika. Inland in this region, lacustrine beds of this age are found containing fossil elephants, hippopotami and antelopes, suggesting an ecology similar to that existing in some areas there today. Lacustrine beds in the Lake Edward basin, west of Lake Victoria on the border of the Belgian Congo, show that the climate became increasingly arid during their deposition, 'for towards the top of the series are gypsiferous clays and deposits of kunkar (limestone concretions in clays and sands) and frequent bands of ironstone, sometimes oolitic'. The fauna includes mammalia, crocodiles, turtles, fish and mollusca.[94]

Reference has been made earlier to laterite and its palaeoclimatic significance. This type of soil (sometimes called ferricrete) is found in many places in southern Africa, e.g. Nyasaland, Rhodesia, the Union of South Africa and to a small extent in south-west Africa. The age of these soils is variously given as Pliocene to Holocene, and indeed soils of these varying ages may well occur. They constitute evidence of a monsoon-like climate, and so indicate for the past a different climate from the present in some places.

Pleistocene deposits consist of emerged marine shell beds and a varied array of non-marine sediments. 'Beginning at the Orange River at Kheis, spreading over the Kalahari and adjoining parts of S.W. Africa and Southern Rhodesia and thence far into Angola and Northern Rhodesia, extends this almost uninterrupted mantle of transported red to grey sand' called the Kalahari Sand.[39] Although covering so vast an area, this sand is consistently fine in grain size. It is concluded that the sand is aeolian, probably blown from the south-west where extensive dunes exist at present. The age of the Kalahari Sand is Pleistocene, for Palaeolithic artefacts have been found under it, while at Taungs the ape-like *Australopithecus* 'seemingly marks the early stages of this sand-incursion'. The Kalahari Sand reflects a period of arid conditions when the surface of the terrain was completely unstable. Professor R. F. Flint states that: 'Evidence of former Pleistocene climates in the southern half of Africa consists mainly of features that are no longer forming actively in some particular area, but that are forming elsewhere under different climatic conditions. . . . Other lines of evidence are biogeographic. . . . Most of the evidence pertains to changes in rainfall, but some of it suggests former climates cooler than those of today, by as much as 5°C.' 'The existing glaciers on Mts. Kenya, Ruwenzori and Kilimanjaro were preceded by others of much greater extent, as is proved by the distribution of moraines and other glacial features.'

There is thus abundant evidence of climatic change in southern Africa during Kainozoic time, but as in all the countries reviewed in this chapter, much more evidence is required before a reliable and connected account can be given.

IV. South America

Marine and non-marine sediments of Kainozoic age are widespread in South America. Among the Tertiary fossils collected by Darwin [28] at Port Desire and Santa Cruz was the warm water mollusc *Cucullaea*. Santa Cruz is on latitude 50°S, much further south than Australia and New Zealand. Darwin noted this, and remembered that there was evidence of a warmer Tertiary climate in Europe, but he knew of no such evidence from places like Australia. He therefore concluded that the temperature rise was a local and not a universal phenomenon. With the further evidence now available it is known that the latter is the correct interpretation. The Miocene and early Pliocene beds of Chile contain such tropical molluscs as *Ficus* and *Cucullaea*, and 'invite comparison with the Miocene faunas of Australia and New Zealand'.[86]

There is evidence that the equatorial region of South America had a tropical climate throughout the Kainozoic. Bosworth[5] reported *Nummulites* and *Lepidocyclina* from the Eocene of Peru, while Sheppard[97] described *Lepidocyclina* from the Eocene, Oligocene and Miocene of Ecuador and *Nummulites* from the Eocene. The Upper Socorro Sandstone (Eocene) of Ecuador contains the fruits of tropical palms. Liddle[76] reports warm water faunas throughout the full succession of Tertiary marine beds in Venezuela. From Para, in Brazil, De Oliveira and Leonardos[32] list *Eutrochus*, *Strombus* and *Xenophora* from the Miocene, and a flora with broad-leaved plants such as *Bombax*, *Trichilia*, *Ficus* and *Pisonia* from the Pliocene.

The upthrust of the great Andean Cordillera profoundly influenced the Kainozoic climates of South America, especially the western side of the continent. Movements continued at varying tempos throughout the Kainozoic, but the main orogeny appears to have occurred in Miocene times. During the Quaternary, also, strong movements have taken place.

The Pleistocene Period in South America was characterized by climatic changes that parallel those elsewhere in the world.[1,12] Glaciers ranged from Cape Horn to Sierra Nevada de Santa Marta (11°N), being found in Peru, Bolivia, Chile, Columbia and Ecuador, where they extended 600–800 m below their present limits. Fjords now filled with water were then being formed by rivers of ice. Peri-glacial loess underlies the pampas through 20° of latitude from Bolivia to Patagonia.[12] These Quaternary changes of climate have altered the distribution of plants and animals.

VII. Antarctica

The Antarctic promontory of Graham Land may be considered an extension of the southern end of South America. In certain islands of Graham Land early Tertiary marine mollusca are found that are readily comparable with those recorded from Patagonia. Wilckens[110,111] has described such faunas from Seymour Island (64°17″S, 56°45″W) and Cockburn Island (64°12″S, 56°50″W). The Seymour Island fauna contains two species of the warmer water shell *Cucullaea*, and other forms such as *Crassatellites*, *Donax* and *Panopaea*, which are significant for such southerly latitudes. Thus in what is now a land of ice and snow, warm-water seas existed in early Tertiary time. Wright and Priestley[114] record a Pliocene fauna from Cockburn Island which suggests 'a slightly warmer sea than that in the same latitude at the present time' (p. 435). Some factor other than the widening of the tropical belt would appear to be operative during the Tertiary to explain the Graham Land faunas. Two suggestions are made. One is that a warm water current swept down the east side of southern South America to Graham Land, thus making the sea temperature higher than normal for that latitude. It should be remembered that this was before the main Andean uplift movements. Secondly, the students of polar wandering aver that at this time the South Pole was on the edge of the Antarctic continent opposite Graham Land, i.e. Graham Land was much further from the South Pole than it is now.

References

1. Auer, V. *Ann. Acad. Sci. fenn.*, A (III), **45, 50** (1956, 1958)
2. Bamber, K. and McGarity, J. W. *Proc. Linn. Soc. N.S.W.*, **81**, 59 (1956)
3. Banks, M. R. *Geol. Surv. Tas.*, *Min. Res.*, **10**, 39 (1957)
4. Baur, G. N. *Aust. J. Bot.*, **5**, 190 (1957)
5. Bosworth, T. O. *Geology of the Tertiary and Quaternary Periods in the N.W. Part of Peru.* 1922. London: Macmillan
6. Boutakoff, N. and Sprigg, R. C. *Min. geol. J.*, **5** (2), 2 (1953)
7. Browne, W. R. *J. Glaciol.*, **3**, 111 (1957)
8. Buchanan, F. *A Journey from Madras through the countries of Mysore, Canara, and Malabar, etc.* 1807. London. In Owen[87]
9. Butler, B. E. and Hutton, J. T. *Aust. J. agric. Res.*, **7**, 536 (1956)
10. Carter, A. N. *Geol. Mag.*, **95**, 297 (1958)
11. Chapman, F. and Cudmore, F. A. *Mem. nat. Mus., Melb.*, **8**, 126 (1934)
12. Charlesworth, J. K. *The Quaternary Era, with special reference to its glaciation.* 1957. London: Arnold
13. Clifford, H. T. and Cookson, Isabel C. *Bryologist*, **56**, 53 (1953)
14. Collins, A. C. *Mem. nat. Mus., Melb.*, **18**, 93 (1953)
15. Collins, A. C. *Contr. Cushman Fdn.*, **7**, 105 (1956)
16. Cookson, Isabel C. *Aust. J. Sci.*, **7**, 149 (1945)
17. Cookson, Isabel C. and Duigan, Suzanne L. *Aust. J. sci. Res.*, **4B**, 415 (1951)
18. Cotton, C. A. *Trans. roy. Soc. N.Z.*, **82**, 1071 (1955)
19. Couper, R. A. *Bull. geol. Surv. N.Z.*, **22** (1953)
20. Couper, R. A. and McQueen, D. R. *N.Z. J. Sci. Tech.*, **35**, 398 (1954)
21. Crespin, Irene. *Proc. roy. Soc. Vict.*, **53**, 301 (1941)
22. Crespin, Irene. *Proc. roy. Soc. Vict.*, **55**, 157 (1943)
23. Crespin, Irene. *Pap. roy. Soc. Tasm.*, 13 (1945)
24. Crespin, Irene. *Pap. roy. Soc. Tasm.*, 15 (1945)
25. Crespin, Irene. *Rep. Bur. Miner. Resour. Aust.*, **12** (1954)
26. Crespin, Irene. *Rep. Bur. Miner. Resour. Aust.*, **25**, 26 (1956)
27. Crocker, R. L. *Trans. roy. Soc. S. Aust.*, **65**, 103 (1941)
28. Darwin, C. *Geological Observations on South America.* 1891. London: Ward, Lock
29. David, T. W. E., in *The Geology of the Commonwealth of Australia*, ed. W. R. Browne. London: Arnold. III vols. 1950
30. Debney, G. L. *Trans. roy. Soc. S. Aust.*, **4**, 145 (1882)
31. Dennant, J. and Kitson, A. E. *Rec. geol. Surv. Vict.*, **1** (1903)
32. De Oliveira, A. I. and Leonardos, O. H. *Geologia de Brasil.* 1943. Rio de Janeiro: Servico de Informacao Agricola, Ministerio da Agricultura
33. Deraniyagala, P. E. P. *The Pleistocene of Ceylon.* 1958. Ceylon National Museums Publication
34. De Terra, H. and Hutchinson, G. Evelyn. *Geogr. J.*, **84**, 311 (1934)
35. De Vis, C. W. *Mon. Progr. Rep. geol. Surv. Vict.*, Nov.–Dec., 1899, 58 (1899)

36. De Vis, C. W. *Ann. Qd. Mus.*, **7**, 3 (1907)
37. Dorman, F. H. and Gill, E. D. *Proc. roy. Soc. Vict.*, **71**, 73 (1959)
38. Duigan, Suzanne L. *Proc. roy. Soc. Vict.*, **63**, 41 (1951)
39. Du Toit, A. *The Geology of South Africa*, 3rd edn. 1954. New York: Hafner
40. Emiliani, C. *Science*, **119**, 853 (1954)
41. Emiliani, C. *J. Geol.*, **64**, 281 (1956)
42. Emiliani, C. *Science*, **125**, 383 (1957)
43. Fairbridge, R. W. *Proc. Pan-Indian Ocean Sci. Congr.*, Perth 1954, Sect. F, 64 (1954)
44. Fell, H. B. *Bull. geol. Surv. N.Z.*, **23** (1954)
45. Fell, H. B. *Proc. XIV Internat. Congr. Zool. Copenhagen*, **1953**, 103 (1956)
46. Fleming, C. A. *Proc. 7th Pacific Sci. Congr.*, **3**, 309 (1952)
47. Fleming, C. A. *N.Z. J. Sci. Tech.*, **34B**, 444 (1953)
48. Fleming, C. A., 'Trans-Tasman Relationship in Natural History', in *Science in New Zealand*. Wellington: A.N.Z.A.A.S.
49. Gill, E. D. *Proc. roy. Soc. Vict.*, **60**, 189 (1950)
50. Gill, E. D. *Aust. J. Sci.*, **15**, 47 (1952)
51. Gill, E. D. *Victorian Nat.*, **70**, 72 (1953)
52. Gill, E. D. *Aust. J. Sci.*, **17**, 204 (1955)
53. Gill, E. D. *Aust. J. Sci.*, **18**, 49 (1955)
54. Gill, E. D. *Mem. nat. Mus. Melb.*, **18**, 25 (1953)
55. Gill, E. D. *Quaternaria*, **3**, 133 (1956)
56. Gill, E. D. *Mem. nat. Mus. Vict.*, **21**, 135 (1957)
57. Gill, E. D. *Aust J. Sci.*, **20**, 86 (1957)
58. Gill, E. D. and Banks, M. R. *Rec. Q. Vict. Mus.*, n.s. 6 (1956)
59. Gill, E. D. and Sharp, K. R. *J. geol. Soc. Aust.*, **4**, 21 (1957)
60. Glaessner, M. F. *J. roy. Soc. N.S.W.*, **87**, 31 (1953)
61. Glauert, L. *J. roy. Soc. W. Aust.*, **7**, 85 (1921)
62. Glauert, L. *Bull. geol. Surv. W. Aust.*, **88**, 36 (1925)
63. Hale, H. M. and Tindale, N. B. *S. Aust. Nat.*, **10**, 30 (1929)
64. Halle, T. G. *Palaeobotanist*, **1**, 22 (1952)
65. Harris, W. F. *Tuatara*, **3**, 53 (1950)
66. Hills, E. S. *Aust. Geogr.*, **3** (7) (1940)
67. Hills, E. S. *Desert Res., Spec. Publ. 2, Res. Counc. Israel*, 355 (1953)
68. Hills, E. S. *Geotekt. Symp. Ehren. Hans Stille*, Deutsch. Geol. Ges., Stuttgart (1956)
69. Holloway, J. T. *Trans. roy. Soc. N.Z.*, **82**, 329 (1954)
70. Hornibrook, N. de B. *Bull. geol Surv. N.Z.*, **18** (1953)
71. Hornibrook, N. de B. *Micropaleontology*, **4**, 25 (1958)
72. Howchin, W. *The Building of Australia and the Succession of Life*. 1925–1930. Adelaide: British Science Guild (S.A. Branch)
73. Howchin, W. *Trans. roy. Soc. S. Aust.*, **55**, 113 (1931); **57**, 1 (1932)
74. Jennings, J. N. and Banks, M. R. *J. Glaciol.*, **3**, 298 (1958)
75. Le Gros Clark, W. E. *History of the Primates*. 1953. London: British Museum Publications
76. Liddle, R. A. *The Geology of Venezuela and Trinidad*. 1946. Ithaca, N.Y.: Paleontological Research Institution
77. Longman, H. A. *Mem. Qd. Mus.*, **8**, 16 (1924)
78. Longman, H. A. *Mem. Qd. Mus.*, **8**, 103 (1925)
79. Longman, H. A. *Mem. Qd. Mus.*, **8**, 95 (1925)
80. Ludbrook, N. H. *Trans. roy. Soc. S. Aust.*, **77**, 42 (1954); **78**, 18 (1955); **79**, 1 (1956); **80**, 17 (1957); **81**, 43 (1958)
81. Ludbrook, N. H. *J. roy. Soc. N.S.W.*, **90**, 174 (1957)

82. McGarity, J. W. *Proc. Linn. Soc. N.S.W.*, **81**, 52 (1956)
83. Macpherson, J. Hope and Chapple, E. H. *Mem. nat. Mus. Melb.*, **17**, 107 (1951)
84. Mahabale, T. S. *Palaeobotanist*, **3**, 33 (1954)
85. Mountford, C. P. *Trans. roy. Soc. S. Aust.*, **53**, 245 (1929)
86. Neaverson, E. *Stratigraphical Palaeontology*, 2nd edn. 1955. Oxford: University Press
87. Owen, H. B. *Bull. Bur. Min. Resour. Aust.*, **24** (1954)
88. Parr, W. J. *Min. geol. J.*, **1**, 65 (1939)
89. Patton, R. T. *Proc. roy. Soc. Vict.*, **70**, 129 (1958)
90. Raggatt, H. G. and Crespin, Irene. *Proc. roy. Soc. Vict.*, **67**, 73 (1955)
91. Raeside, J. D. *Trans. roy. Soc. N.Z.*, **77**, 153 (1948)
92. Ramanujam, C. G. K. *Palaeobotanist*, **3**, 40 (1954)
93. Rao, L. Rama. *Half-yrly J. Mysore Univ.*, **10**, 25 (1950)
94. Reed, F. R. C. *The Geology of the British Empire*, 2nd edn. 1949. London: Arnold
95. Reynolds, M. A. *Trans. roy. Soc. S. Aust.*, **76**, 114 (1953)
96. Shapley, H. ed. *Climatic Change*. 1953. Cambridge, Mass.: Harvard University Press
97. Sheppard, G. *The Geology of S.W. Ecuador*. 1937. London: Murby
98. Singleton, F. A. *Proc. roy. Soc. Vict.*, **53**, 1 (1941)
99. Sitholey, R. V. *Palaeobotanist*, **3**, 55 (1954)
100. Squires, D. F. *Trans. N.Y. Acad. Sci.*, **18**, 415 (1956)
101. Squires, D. F. *Bull. geol. Surv. N.Z.*, **29** (1958)
102. Stephens, C. G. and Crocker, R. L. *Trans. roy. Soc. S. Aust.*, **70**, 302 (1946)
103. Stirton, R. A. *Rec. S. Aust. Mus.*, **13**, 71 (1957)
104. Stirton, R. A. *Mem. nat. Mus. Vict.*, **21**, 121 (1957)
105. Tindale, N. B. *Rec. S. Aust. Mus.*, **8**, 619 (1947)
106. Wellman, H. W. *N.Z. J. Sci. Tech.*, **35**B, 378 (1954)
107. Whitehouse, F. W. *Univ. Qd. Papers, Geol.*, **2** (1) (1940)
108. Whitehouse, F. W. *Univ. Qd. Papers, Geol.*, n.s., **34** (1948)
109. Whitehouse, F. W. *Univ. Qd. Papers, Geol.*, **53** (1954)
110. Wilckens, O., 'Die Mollusken der antarktischen Tertiärformation', in *Wiss. Ergebn. schwed. Südpolar Exped.*, **3**, (1901–3)
111. Wilckens, O., 'Die Tertiäre Fauna der Cockburn-Insel (Westantarktika)', in *Further Zool. Res. Swed. Antarct. Exp.*, **1** (5) (1924)
112. Woolnough, W. G. *J. roy. Soc. N.S.W.*, **61**, 17 (1927)
113. Worrell, E. *Proc. roy. zool. Soc. N.S.W.*, *1951–2*, 18 (1952)
114. Wright, C. S. and Priestley, R. E. *British (Terra Nova) Antarctic Expedition 1910–13. Glaciology.* 1922. London: Scott Antarctic Fund

Author Index

355

Subject Index

A A